ROCKS Rails & Trails

Paul Karl Link and
E. Chilton Phoenix

Second Edition November, 1996
Idaho Museum of Natural History

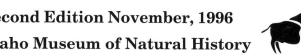

Copyright and Sources of Photographs

Front Cover

(clockwise from right)

Kathy Priddy walking the Oregon Trail near Chesterfield, (September, 1986).

Union Pacific mainline, Pocatello. View looks southeast toward Portneuf Narrows. Pocatello warehouse district and Red Hill are across the tracks, (January, 1991).

The Portneuf Range and Inkom, looking southeast, (May, 1990). Mount Bonneville and Pebble Creek Ski Area in upper left. Basalt of Portneuf Valley in middle distance.

(background photo)
Inverted topography at the north end of Marsh Valley, looking south from above Inkom, (June, 1990). The Portneuf River on the left and Marsh Creek on the right are pushed to the sides of the valley by the basalt of Portneuf Valley in the middle of the view.

Back Cover

Satellite image of southeastern Idaho. For full description see page 3.

Permission

Acknowledgment of permission to use copyrighted figures and poetry:
Blue Scarab Press, c/o Harald Wyndham, p. 88, 93, 172.
The Chesterfield Foundation Inc., p. 74, 89.
Idaho State Historical Society, p. 50, 51, 84.
Mabey, Don R. p. 83.
Princeton University Press, p. 10.
University of Chicago Libraries, p. 60, 61, 118.
University Press of Idaho and Leigh Gittins, p. 50, 51.

Source and acknowledgment for use of photographs and diagrams:
Bannock County Historical Society, p. vi, 49, 56 (bottom), 57, 58, 61, 62, 71, 108 (right), 116 (lower right), 117, 118, 119, 120, 121, 122, 123, 124, 125, 126, 128, 129, 132, 134, 135, 136, 137, 153, 154, 155, 174, 175, 177, 182, 183, 192, 193.
Community Library, Ketchum Idaho, p. 171, 172, 173.
Cuoio, Fred 129, 138
Eli M. Oboler Library, Idaho State University, p. 2, 37, 55 (top), 59 (top), 63, 81 (lower right), 92, 105, 106 (bottom), 113, 114, 116 (middle), 133, 141, 146, 162, 163, 170.
Horsely Memorial Library, Soda Springs and Dr. Evan Kackley, p. 81 (middle).
Idaho Department of Transportation, p. 119.
Idaho Museum of Natural History and Smithsonian Institution, p. 37 (left and center), 38, 55 (bottom), 56 (top).
J.R. Simplot Co., p. 142, 143.
Madden, Doug p. 194.
Troyer, Dianna, p. 175.
Union Pacific Railroad, p. 52, 62, 64, 65, 67, 78, 108, 161, 165.
U.S. Bureau of Reclamation, p. 73.

All other photographs and diagrams were taken or prepared by P.K. Link.

Published 1996 by the

Idaho Museum of Natural History
Campus Box 8096
Idaho State University
Pocatello, Idaho 83209
Phone (208) 236-3168

Allen K. Jackson, Director

The Idaho Museum of Natural History, founded in 1934, offers exhibits, lectures, outreach to schools and maintains permanent collections in anthropology, biology, geology and paleontology. As an academic department of the university the museum offers academic courses and wilderness field studies, sponsors research, and publishes a bi-annual journal *Tebiwa* as well as *Occasional Papers*. The purpose of the museum is to enhance an understanding and delight in the natural and cultural history of the region.

Copyright ©
First Edition December, 1994
Second Edition November, 1996
by
Paul K. Link
and
E. Chilton Phoenix

ISBN# 0-9378346-0-2

Table of Contents

Aerial view looking east at the Portneuf Narrows, Gateway to the Pacific Northwest, (May, 1990).

Preface

Preface to First Edition

I am very honored to be able to offer my viewpoint regarding *"Rocks, Rails and Trails"*. This book is the natural progression of the class by the same name that Dr. Paul Link and Mr. Chilton Phoenix have been teaching through Idaho State University.

"Rocks, Rails and Trails" is a comprehensive guide to the history and geology of southeastern Idaho and gives one an appreciation of the tremendous forces of nature and the incredible perseverance of the human spirit which combined to create the wonderful place in which we live.

All to often, we get caught up in the day-to-day events of our modern world and forget about the land and the people who came before us. Paul and Chilton's book gives us the chance to rediscover and enjoy the history of the land and the people.

The compilations of historical photographs and personal accounts of the early inhabitants of our area brought together in this volume will excite and energize the reader to learn more about our physical and cultural environment.

You will also notice that the historic and geologic past is distinctly, and sometimes humorously, blended in with the issues and problems of our present-day lives. The authors gently point out that our problems and concerns, given the context of geologic time and prior human history, are a lot easier to solve than we may think.

I highly recommend that *"Rocks, Rails and Trails"* be given an honored place in your personal library. It is a fascinating book to read and will be a handy reference for the future. My thanks to Dr. Paul Link and Mr. Chilton Phoenix for compiling this outstanding work on Idaho geology and history.

> Peter Angstadt
> Mayor, City of Pocatello
> June 20, 1994

Preface to Second Edition

The first edition of *Rocks, Rails and Trails* sold out of its 1500-copy press run in 15 months, by March, 1996. It was the fastest-selling book in the history of ISU Press. As interest in Idaho history and the Oregon Trail grows, so does demand for this book. This second edition contains numerous minor changes which we hope will correct (almost) all the errors of fact and syntax in the first edition. We hope the second edition will stand for some years as a source of fact, reminiscence and pleasure related to southeastern Idaho.

We thank the many individuals who sent us corrections, in particular Fred Dykes (who provided 99 annotated comments), Marilyn Smith, Mary Dunham, and Dr. Alan Frantz. The Kackley Endowment again paid for typesetting costs. It was determined that marketing the book was more appropriate to the mission of the Idaho Museum of Natural History than to ISU Press. We are grateful to Dr. Allen Jackson, Museum Director, for his enthusiastic acceptance of this project, and to ISU President Dr. Richard Bowen for financial support of the second printing. Typesetting was by Brian Hawk, AutoCAD drafting by Jose Bunzow and Michelle Byrd, photographic assistance by Dave Myers, Susan Duncan and Julie Hillebrant.

"Potato-sized" basalt boulders being removed from site of new First Security Bank building, South Main Street, downtown Pocatello, (June, 1994). The boulders, both about 8 feet in diameter, were carried by the Lake Bonneville Flood from the Portneuf Narrows area.

Portneuf Narrows, south of Pocatello, (March, 1939). Photograph by Cook Photo Laboratory looking east from the old Bannock Highway at Portneuf Narrows and Mount Bonneville in the center distance.

Eastern Idaho is a backwater; even as we approach the 21st century it is by-and-large undiscovered, underdeveloped, sparsely populated. This book is an attempt to celebrate this beautiful and fascinating corner of America, to describe, in words and pictures, its history and geology.

This book grows out of a class of the same name that we have taught since 1986 at Idaho State University. The central notion behind the class and thus the book, is that the geology and history of eastern Idaho are closely linked. In addition, we found that there is no one source that combines these two topics, and that by using historical and modern photographs we could produce a book that is both attractive and useful.

A Disclaimer

We must now state what this book is not. We are not trained historians and have not tried to write a definitive history book. Rather, this is a collection of anecdotes and facts that seem to us important. We have provided references to scholarly history sources, which we recommend to the reader. We make no apologies for the geology, however.

Abandoned combine west of Oxford, (October, 1978). Oxford Peak, underlain by Late Proterozoic quartzite of the Brigham Group, is in the background.

Organization

The book is organized into two primary parts. The first covers the geology and history of eastern Idaho from a topical and chronological point of view. The geology review should be especially useful for those wishing ready access to the Idaho geological literature. The second part contains regional snapshots of each part of eastern Idaho, complete with maps and references. Each of these snapshots is self-contained and covers trail routes, geology and interesting historical elements of eastern Idaho.

We spent a great deal of time and had some fun assembling and taking the pictures in this book. The captions, especially of the historical photos, are important and contain details not found in the text.

We wanted to publish the book through ISU in an attempt to keep the project in Pocatello. ISU Press published the first edition. We are delighted that the second edition is published by the Idaho Museum of Natural History.

Geography and Culture

The southeastern corner of Idaho, largely Mormon, has always had conflicting loyalties. After cruel political and religious persecution in the late 19th century, Idaho Mormons have good reason to feel estranged from the rest of their geographically awkward state. Their cultural and religious ties are with Utah to the south.

Pocatello

Pocatello has been the transition zone, the interface, between the "true" Idaho of the Snake River Plain, and the southeastern corner. Located at the mouth of Portneuf Narrows, the water level route to the Snake River Plain, Pocatello is the Gate City to the Pacific Northwest. It is a railroad town and a melting pot, a windy place where people came and went under the instructions of Oregon Short Line managers from Omaha. After years of economic stability, Pocatello in 1996 is one of the fastest growing cities in the Pacific Northwest.

Old Tom Mountain from Rock Creek in the Portneuf Range, looking southwest, (October, 1985). Marsh Valley in foreground. The stark mountains await the winter snows.

Nestled along the Portneuf River in what had been a sage-covered treeless valley, Pocatello has treated its natural environment cruelly. It grew with sprawling industrial sites and phosphate plants built where subject to reduced tax liabilities, but sited in the worst location for air pollution of the city downwind to the east.

Pocatello welcomed the U.S. Army Corps of Engineers who built in 1965 a concrete flood control channel which imprisons the Portneuf River. The channel is a manifestation of pragmatism that lacks environmental sensitivity.

But Pocatello is a city without an upper class. In a fundamentally blue-collar town with no landed aristocracy who stayed for generations, practicality repeatedly won out over aesthetics. So it goes.

Living in Southeastern Idaho

Although southeastern Idaho lacks craggy mountains, its ranges are wide and long, generally well-watered, and easily accessible by vehicle and by foot. These are gentle green mountains, home to deer, elk, and nowadays, cattle. They are places where solitude is the rule.

The weather in southeastern Idaho is gentle, but erratic. Multi-year long cycles of drought and wetness are normal and farming is always a chancy business. The climate is normally neither very cold in winter nor

Postcard view of a bull elk on the Pocatello West Bench, late 1930s. View looks east. Note the Portneuf River has been channelized with rip-rap, but the concrete channel has not been built. West Sublette is the east-west street east of the Portneuf River. The south end of Highland Boulevard is the street west of the River. The square white building is the present Pocatello Floor Covering store and showroom. The spire to the left of Red Hill is St. Joseph's Catholic Church. Abe Lillibridge collection, Idaho State University.

very hot in summer, and never uncomfortably humid. Many residents think the weather is close to ideal.

Many people from eastern Idaho think they live in one of the most beautiful places in the United States. One woman from Preston, returning home after years away, remarked that she was glad to see that it was still true that in Cache Valley the sky is bluer and the clouds are whiter than anywhere else she had been. It is to such people that we dedicate this book.

Acknowledgments

Production of this book was supported by the Ida Sarver Kackley and Lois Lynch Kackley Bear River Endowment to Idaho State University, presented by Evan, Ellis and Alvin Kackley—1974. Invaluable assistance in preparation of the photographs and graphics of the book was provided by Lisa Anderson, Dan Bruner, José Bunzow, Michelle Byrd, Susan Duncan, Caryn Elliott, Randy Gaines, Scott Gerwe, Glenn Harvey, Brian Hawk, Dee High and Dave Myers. We are grateful to Ron Hatzenbuehler, ISU History Department, and Dave Rodgers and Tom Ore, ISU Geology Department, for invaluable reviews. We thank the Bannock County Historical Museum, Idaho Museum of Natural History, Eli Oboler Library, Ketchum-Sun Valley Community Library and the Smithsonian Institution for use of photographs. Aerial photography would have been impossible without H. Thomas Ore, our pilot and friend. We are especially indebted to our friends and mentors Leigh Gittins and "Doc" Evan Kackley. Finally we thank each other, for patience and good humor, during the four year production of this book.

Recent References on Idaho History

Arrington, Leonard J., 1994, History of Idaho, 2 vols.: Moscow, Idaho, University of Idaho Press.

Idaho Humanities Council, 1994, Idaho and the American West, Boise, Idaho, 36 p.

Idaho State Historical Society, 1976, Idaho, An Illustrated History: Boise, Idaho State Historical Society , 250 p.

Peterson, F. Ross, 1976, Idaho: A Bicentennial History: New York, Norton, 292 p.

Schwantes, Carlos, 1991, In Mountain Shadows: A History of Idaho: Lincoln, Nebraska, University of Nebraska Press, 203 p.

Satellite image photograph of eastern Idaho. The view extends from near Mackay in the upper left, to north of Burley in the lower left, Malad Summit in the lower right, and Heise in the upper right. American Falls Reservoir is in the lower center, surrounded by irrigated farmland. The black splotches on the Snake River Plain are lava flows, with Craters of the Moon in the middle left, the Great Rift in the lower center, and Hell's Half Acre in the upper right center. U.S. Geological Survey photo.

Introduction to Geologic Diagrams

One of the premises of this book is that much of the geographic and economic history of southern Idaho is controlled by its geology. Thus a basic understanding of that geologic history is necessary to more fully appreciate the anthropocentric, indeed, Eurocentric, events of the last 150 years.

The discussion of the history of the earth requires reference to time periods of the past and their approximate ages. These terms, like "Proterozoic" and "Cretaceous," are not part of the vocabulary of normal Americans, and they can be intimidating. The time spans and hierarchy of these geologic periods are listed in the Geologic Event Table (pages 8 and 9), which will help those unfamiliar with the geologic time scale to decipher the following discussion.

Geologists work with geologic maps, which show, instead of the topography, the rock type and geologic structure. A geologic map shows the rock or sediment type that one would find at a certain place.

A second type of standard geologic diagram is the stratigraphic column, which shows the sedimentary rocks present in an area as if they were stacked on top of each other like a layer cake. Such stratigraphic columns are synthesized, in deformed country like Idaho, from exposures in different mountain ranges.

A third standard geologic diagram is a cross section, which views the earth as if it were cut open and seen from the side. Geologic cross sections are interpretative, since the relations can generally not be observed directly. Only in areas of deep canyons or high mountains can natural cross sections be observed. In most cases cross sections require inference about subsurface structure. Sometimes drill holes or geophysical exploration provide data from which cross sections can be constructed.

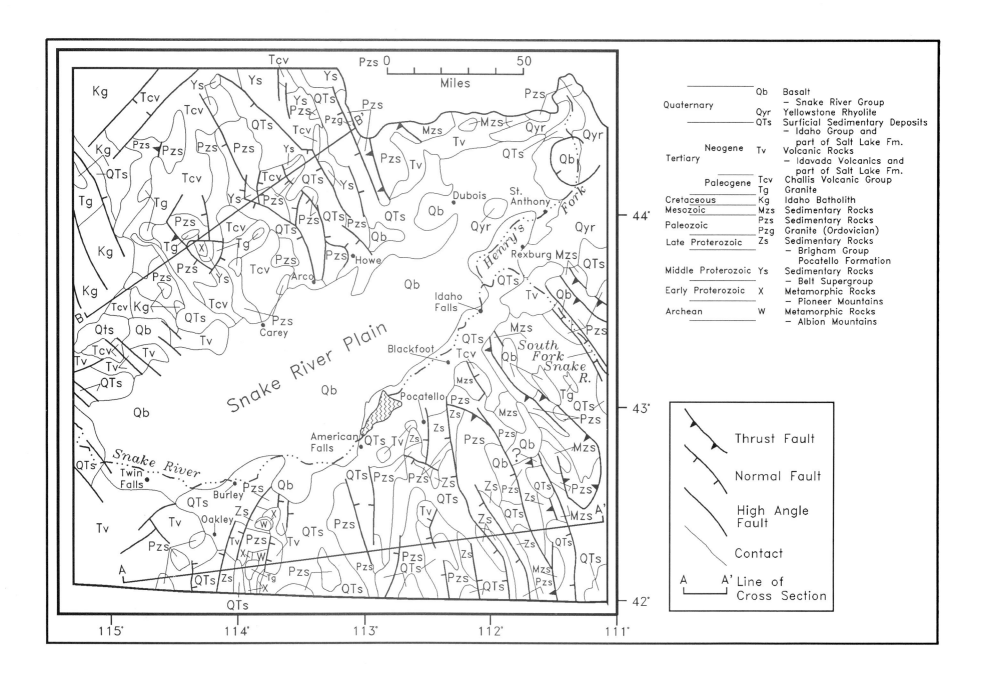

Geologic map of eastern Idaho (simplified and modified from the geologic map of Idaho, published by the Idaho Geological Survey).

4

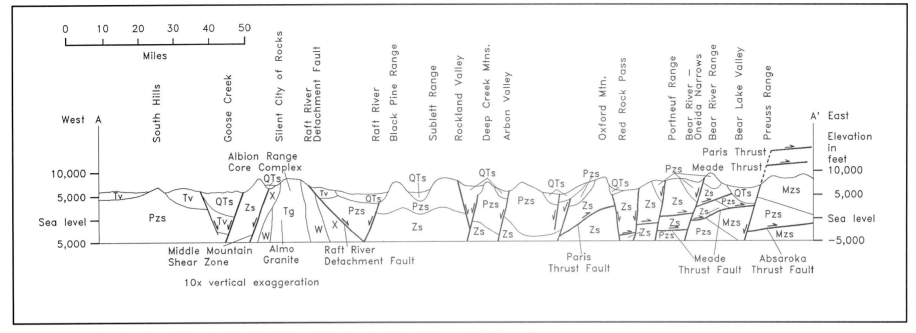

Geologic cross section along line A-A', south of the Snake River Plain, from the Twin Falls area to the Montpelier area.

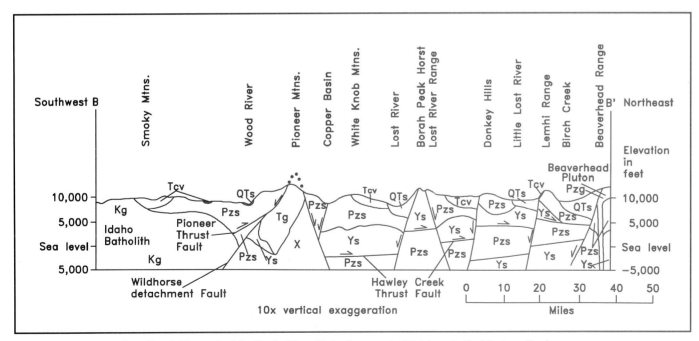

Geologic cross section along line B-B', north of the Snake River Plain, from west of Ketchum to the Montana Border.

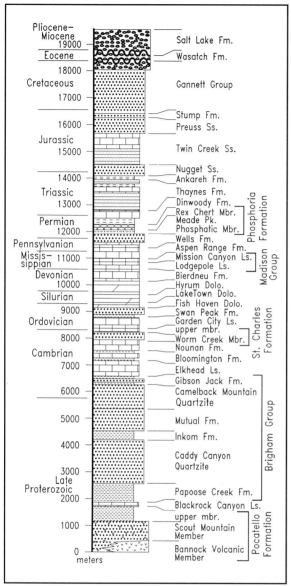

Composite stratigraphic column for the northern Portneuf and Bannock Ranges. Thicknesses from Trimble (1976), Link and LeFebre (1983), and Pogue (1984).

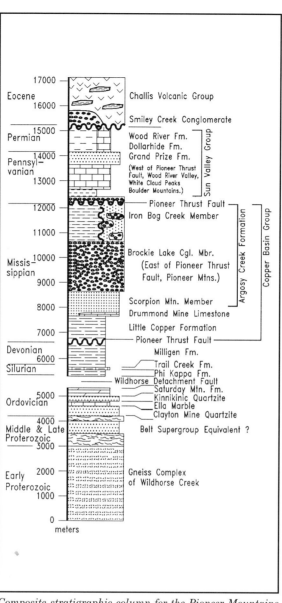

Composite stratigraphic column for the Pioneer Mountains west of Mackay (after Link and Hackett, 1988; Link and others, 1992; Link and others, 1996).

Relations between Geology, Topography and Drainage Systems in Idaho

Topography and geography are controlled by geologic structure and rock type. The great topographic diversity of southern Idaho reflects the several geologic provinces of the area. The southeastern part of the state contains relatively high and moist mountains and valleys of the Idaho-Wyoming thrust belt. Much of southern and east-central Idaho north of the Snake River Plain belongs to the arid Basin and Range Province. The economic heart of agricultural Idaho is the irrigated sagebrush desert of the Snake River Plain. North of the plain from Ketchum westward are the high and rugged mountains of central Idaho underlain by the intrusive rocks of the Idaho batholith. Here much of the land is wilderness and tourism has replaced mining as the primary source of income.

Idaho Drainage Systems and Diverse Geology

The topography of southern Idaho is varied and dramatic. The fundamental reasons for this diversity are geological: the recency of volcanism and uplift of ranges along normal faults. This rough topography reflects a complex geologic past.

Water flows downhill, forming river systems, which effectively cover the earth. These drainage patterns assume great importance to humans, but in eastern Idaho they are in some sense geologic accidents: the result of streams finding routes across areas of recent volcanic activity and uplifted mountain ranges. In geologically mature landscapes, streams tend to follow geologic structure, but in the geologically young landscapes of southern Idaho, stream courses are often either superposed (that is running across older geologic structures that were formerly buried), or disrupted (deranged) by lava flows which act as dams.

River systems carve drainage systems downward toward their ultimate base level. Rivers in southern Idaho over the last twenty million years have drained across active and changing geologic provinces, which have profoundly affected them. In most of southern Idaho water flows into the Snake River and ultimately the Pacific Ocean. However, the Lake Bonneville basin of western Utah, southern Idaho and eastern Nevada is an area of interior drainage. Its base level is the ever-changing level of the evaporating Great Salt Lake.

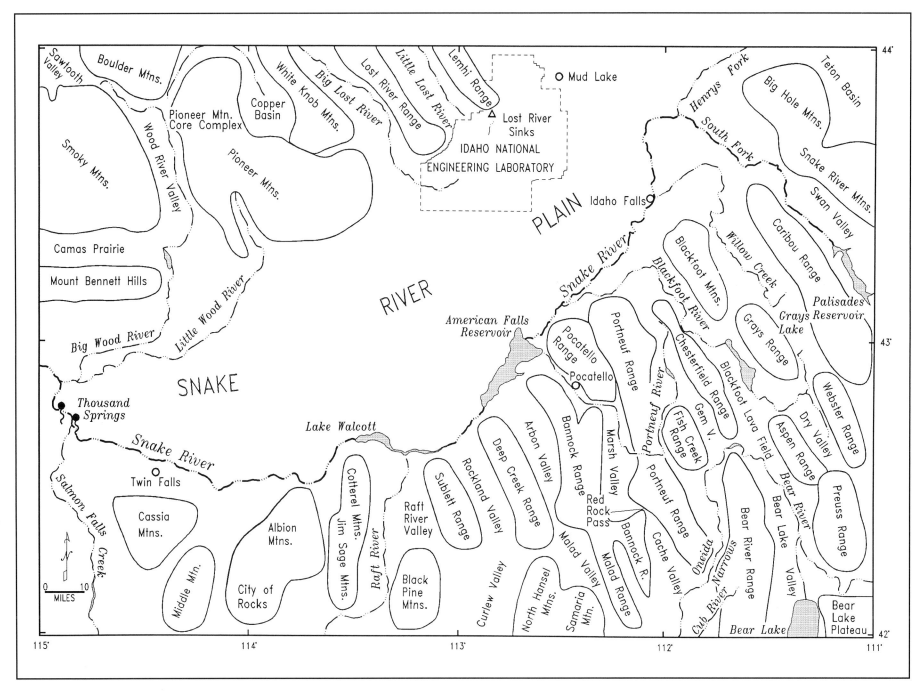

Drainage and mountain range map for eastern Idaho.

Era	Period	Epoch and Age in years	Events
Quaternary	Holocene (Recent)		Normal faults of the Intermountain Seismic Belt in the Basin and Range Province Deposition of blanket of loess on much of the area south and east of Pocatello Eruption of basalt lava flows at Craters of the Moon, the Great Rift, and Hell's Half Acre north of Blackfoot
		—12,000—	
	Pleistocene		Lake Bonneville Flood (14,500 years ago) with retreat to Provo Shoreline until 11,000 years Late Wisconsin glaciation and most recent rise of Lake Bonneville (30,000 to 12,000 years ago) Formation of the ancestral American Falls Lake, visited by giant land mammals (75,000 years ago) Eruption of tuff cones at Menan Buttes (about 70,000 years ago) Eruption of Basalt of Portneuf Valley (600,000 years) causes diversion of Bear River, formation of Lake Thatcher and cutting of Oneida Narrows Rhyolite domes formed at Big Southern Butte, East and Middle Buttes Eruption of Snake River Group of basalt lava on the Snake River Plain and in the Blackfoot Lava Field Catastrophic eruption of rhyolite ash flows of Yellowstone Volcanics (2 Ma, 1.2 Ma, and 600,000 years) Multiple glacial and interglacial intervals cause lakes to form in several lowlands in Idaho
		—2 Ma—	
Tertiary	Neogene	Pliocene	Formation of Lake Idaho on the western Snake River Plain. Primitive horses buried near Hagerman. Superposed streams cut Portneuf Narrows, Garden Creek Gap, Bear River Canyon at Lava Hot Springs Basin and Range faulting and Snake River Plain volcanism continues; Basaltic eruptions at Massacre Rocks.
		—5 Ma—	
		Miocene	Teton Mountains start to rise (5 to 10 m.y. ago) Volcanic ash of Salt Lake and Starlight Formations deposited in valleys south of the Snake River Plain Series of rhyolite caldera eruptions migrate northeastward along the Snake River Plain, from the Bruneau-Jarbidge center in SW Idaho, to the Twin Falls area (Idavada volcanics, to the Pocatello area (lava on Howard Mountain, to the Rexburg Caldera (Heise volcanic field, 6 Ma). About 17 m.y. ago Yellowstone-Snake River Plain Hot Spot originates in southeast Oregon Basin and Range faulting begins generally moving outward in time from central Nevada
		—24 Ma—	
	Paleogene	Oligocene	Generally Idaho is a topographic plateau; few Oligocene sedimentary rocks remain. Intrusion of Almo Pluton at what is now the Silent City of Rocks and final uplift of core complexes.
		—37 Ma—	
		Eocene	Eruption of Challis Volcanic Group Formation of gold-bearing mineral deposits of the Trans-Challis fault system Intrusion of granitic stocks in Sawtooth Range, Boulder Mountains, and elsewhere in central Idaho Metamorphism and intrusion in Pioneer Mountains and Albion Mountains core complexes Deposition of fluvial Wasatch Formation in SE Idaho and lacustrine Green River Formation in SW Wyoming
		—58 Ma—	
		Paleocene	Major uplift of Laramide basement blocks in northwest Wyoming (Wind River, Gros Ventre, Ancestral Teton Ranges), with continued thrusting in thrust belt Major extinction event, withdrawal in interior seaway and drop in worldwide sea level
		—66 Ma—	
Mesozoic	Cretaceous		Formation of rich silver-lead-zinc veins near Hailey and Bellevue Intrusion and mineralization of the Idaho batholith (mainly Late Cretaceous) Deposition of Gannett Group in foreland basin that passed eastward into a shallow sea Peak of thrust faulting and folding of the Idaho-Wyoming thrust belt Metamorphism in core complexes of Pioneer and Albion Mountains in hinterland of Sevier orogenic belt
		—144 Ma—	

Table of Geologic Events in Southern Idaho

Mesozoic	Jurassic		Subsidence in the foreland basin east of the Sevier orogenic belt; deposition of sandstones in E Idaho Formation of Sevier orogenic belt, with magmatic belt on the west and fold-thrust belt to the east
		— 208 Ma —	
	Triassic		Establishment of thick carbonate bank of the Thaynes Formation with shallow evaporite lagoon to the east Deposition of continental redbeds in thrust belt, last vestige of the Ancestral Rockies
		— 245 Ma —	
Paleozoic	Permian		Phosphate-rich Phosphoria Formation deposited in biologically productive shallow sea Sun Valley and Oquirrh basins continue; these are last major marine deposits as sea level falls in Triassic
		— 286 Ma —	
	Carboniferous	Pennsylvanian	Sun Valley and Oquirrh Groups deposited in basin inboard of mountainous areas to the south (Ancestral Rockies) and west (reactivated Antler or western oceanic highland)
		— 320 Ma —	
		Mississippian	Carbonate bank of the Madison Group covers much of Northern Rockies Deep water turbidites of Copper Basin Formation and McGowan Creek Formation deposited in basin east of the uplifted Antler orogenic belt
		— 360 Ma —	
	Devonian		End of passive western American continental margin. Formation of silver-lead-zinc in Milligen Formation.
		— 408 Ma —	
	Silurian		Formation of regional carbonate bank of Laketown Dolomite
		— 438 Ma —	
	Ordovician		Deposition of the Swan Peak and Kinnikinic Quartzites and Fish Haven Dolomite Intrusion of granitic plutons in the Beaverhead and Salmon River Mountains
		— 505 Ma —	
	Cambrian		Early complex life thrives in carbonate banks now seen in Cambrian limestones. Carbonate was formed during rapid crustal subsidence after separation of North America from Antarctica or Australia Major encroachment of the paleo-Pacific ocean over western U.S. (transgression of the shoreline)
		— 540 Ma —	
Pre-cambrian	Proterozoic	Late	First complex multicellular life evolves in latest Proterozoic time Deposition of Brigham Group of gravelly sandstones and siltstones in braided streams and shallow seas Glaciation, continental rifting and basaltic volcanism recorded in the Pocatello Formation
		— 1000 Ma —	
		Middle	Formation of huge, shallow-water intracratonic basin of the Belt Supergroup in western Montana and east-central Idaho (rocks are called Lemhi Group in Idaho) Formation of mineral deposits of the Cobalt and Blackbird areas
		— 1600 Ma —	
		Early	Deposition of the Elba Quartzite in the Albion Mountains and Wasatch Range Metamorphism of crust in Pioneer Mountains Intrusion of mafic dikes in the Teton Range about 1500 Ma
		— 2500 Ma —	
	Archean		Intrusion and high-grade metamorphism in core of Albion Mountains and Teton Range

Geologic Events in Southern Idaho. Columns read upward through time. Ma = million years (1,000,000 years).

The Snake River Plain-Yellowstone Hot Spot and its effect on drainage patterns

Over the last seventeen million years, a topographic uplift or plateau, like the Yellowstone National Park area today, has moved northeastward across Idaho (Malde, 1991; Pierce and Morgan, 1992). This northeastward migration is caused by the southwestward movement of the North American tectonic plate over a fixed hot spot, or area of production of molten rock or magma. The passage of the topographic uplift associated with the hotspot produced a northeast-progressing highland, from which streams drained to the north and south. Thus, the Continental Divide, at the headwaters of the Snake River, has migrated eastward across eastern Idaho. Streams which presently drain toward the Snake River Plain, from the north and south, formerly drained away from the volcanic plateau.

Subsidence of the plateau in the wake of passage of the Hot Spot allowed the Snake River to carve its west-flowing course along the southern margin of the lava field, and resulted in capture of streams which formerly drained south and east, away from the highland. Marsh Valley, among others, formerly drained southward toward the Lake Bonneville Basin, and has only drained northward through Portneuf Narrows since the Hot Spot passed to the northeast of Pocatello several million years ago. It is as if the west-flowing Snake River, over the last few million years, has eaten its way eastward, capturing the water of drainages to the north, east, and south, and, now, with the help of irrigation systems less than 100 years old, spreads that water on the fertile soil of the Land of Famous Potatoes.

Drainage Systems, Rails and Trails

The great river systems of the American west were the routes of Native American trails for hundreds of years before the advent of Europeans. They became railroad routes in the late 19th century.

The routing of the Oregon Trail along the Bear and Snake Rivers was primarily controlled by earlier Native American and trapper's routes, combined with the fact that wagons could not negotiate rough lava fields. The Hudspeth Cutoff, on the other hand, was a direct and geographically arbitrary route located with little prior planning. Between Soda Springs and the Raft River Valley, it cut across six mountain ranges, far from reliable stream systems, and is today not followed by any hard-surface roads.

Simplified geologic map of the central and southern Rocky Mountains. The Oregon Trail crossed the Continental Divide at the south end of the Wind River Mountains, and headed west across the Green River Basin to the Idaho-Wyoming Thrust belt (heavy lines) and the Snake River Plain.

1. trends of structures in Idaho-Wyoming Thrust belt.

2. Laramide basement uplifts containing Archean and Proterozoic igneous and metamorphic rock.

3. Late Cretaceous foreland basins.

4. Paleocene and Eocene basins.

5. Eocene lakes.

From King (1977). Used by permission of Princeton University Press.

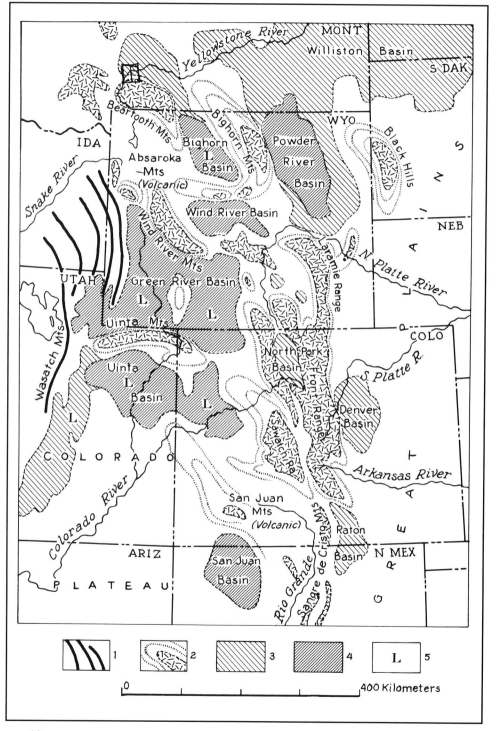

10

Later, when the Utah & Northern Railway was constructed, it followed the path of the Bear River north to Cache Valley, and then the Lake Bonneville Flood route north to Portneuf Narrows, the site of Pocatello Junction, and the Snake River Plain. From there the railroad followed the Snake River north to Eagle Rock (Idaho Falls), and then the basalt lava plain to Monida Pass and Montana.

The Oregon Short Line mainly followed the Oregon Trail from east to west across Idaho. Where the immigrants' wagons headed north at Soda Point to avoid the Gem Valley lava field, the rails headed directly across Gem Valley and down the lava-filled Portneuf River Canyon past Lava Hot Springs and Inkom to Portneuf Narrows. The railroad also cut directly west across the basalt lava plain from American Falls to Shoshone.

Geologic Provinces along the Oregon Trail

The route of the Oregon Trail was generally followed by the transcontinental Oregon Short Line railroad. This Overland Route traverses several geologic provinces from the Great Plains to the Pacific Ocean.

The Wyoming Rockies and Basins

The country of central Wyoming belongs to the stable North American craton, whose metamorphic and igneous rock foundations crystallized in Archean time more than 2500 million years ago. The topography of this area is controlled by mountain structures made in the Laramide orogeny, 70 to 50 million years ago. Generally, the Laramide orogeny consisted of large uplifts of Archean rocks of the Wyoming province, which punched upward through their thin Paleozoic and Mesozoic sedimentary cover. Examples include the Wind River Range, Owl Creek Mountains, Ancestral Teton Range and Gros Ventre Range. In between the Laramide uplifts, basins subsided, including the Green River and Wind River Basins, which now produce petroleum and natural gas.

Idaho-Wyoming Thrust Belt

Near Fort Bridger in southwestern Wyoming the Oregon Trail entered the Idaho-Wyoming thrust belt. Today the thrust belt contains vast, largely unpopulated, forested mountains. The area is underlain by a thick succession of sedimentary rocks that was deposited off the subsiding edge of North America in Proterozoic, Paleozoic, and Mesozoic time and then compressed, folded, and thrust as much as 100 miles

---

Strange Doings with Drainages in Southeastern Idaho

One of the fascinating elements of the geography of southeast Idaho is the contortions of its streams and drainage basins. In a few square miles of relatively flat valley bottom near Soda Springs are streams draining south into the Bear River, north to the Blackfoot River, and west to the Portneuf River. The Bear River flows south into Cache Valley and the Great Salt Lake; the Portneuf River drains south, then west and then north, cutting through the Portneuf and Bannock Ranges toward Pocatello and the Snake River; the Blackfoot River drains north from the Blackfoot Lava field and down a twisted, lava-filled canyon to empty into the Snake River near the site of the original Fort Hall.

Pioneer geologist F.V. Hayden (1883, p. 409) described the lava fields and recognized the odd drainage patterns:

> The region of the Blackfoot River ... is covered in all its lowest portions with flows of basalt which had their origin in craters that still show between the Blackfoot, Bear and Portneuf Rivers. The pouring out of basalt must have occurred extensively.

The courses of the Bear, Portneuf, and Blackfoot Rivers seem contorted, and they are. Within the last million years, eruption of basaltic lava from the Blackfoot-Gem Valley lava field dammed the former northerly course of Bear River through northern Gem Valley and down the canyon of the present Portneuf. The Bear was forced to turn south at Sheep Rock (Soda Point), to flow into southern Gem Valley and the Lake Bonneville basin of Cache Valley. The drainage divide between the Blackfoot and Bear Rivers north of Soda Springs is a marsh formed above a basalt lava flow. There is no topographic barrier, but water drains downhill both to the north and south. The two hydrologic systems are connected in the subsurface, as demonstrated by the effects on ground water levels in the Bear River system near Soda Springs produced by the filling of the Blackfoot Reservoir in the mid-twentieth century.

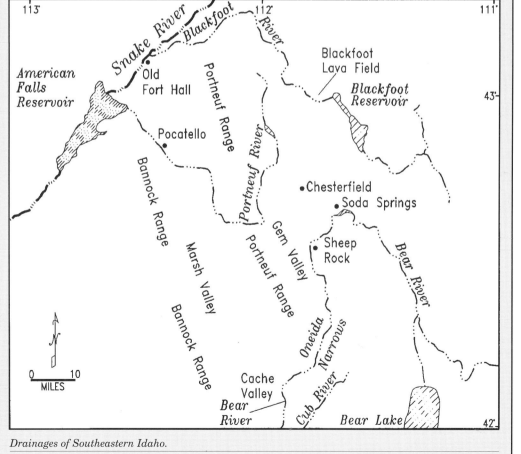

Drainages of Southeastern Idaho.

Folds in Jurassic rocks (mostly Twin Creek Formation) in the Crawford thrust sheet just west of Geneva, Idaho. Aerial view looks north, U.S. Highway 89 follows the transverse valley in middle distance, (August, 1984).

eastward toward the continent during the Sevier orogeny (about 130 to 55 million years ago in late Mesozoic and early Tertiary time). The Idaho-Wyoming thrust belt is just one segment of the Cordilleran thrust belt that contains folded and thrusted sedimentary rocks along the North American Cordillera from Alaska south to Mexico.

Basin and Range

At Bear Lake Valley the Oregon Trail entered the Basin and Range Province, an area affected during the last ten million years by extensional forces, creating uplifted ranges and downdropped valleys bounded by normal faults. The Basin and Range Province overlaps the Idaho-Wyoming thrust belt in the area from Montpelier to Pocatello. It extends northeast to Jackson Hole, west across southern Idaho to the Albion Range and north across the Snake River Plain to east-central Idaho east of Mackay.

North of the Snake River Plain in east-central Idaho is the northern part of the Basin and Range Province, with the huge Lost River, Lemhi, and Beaverhead Ranges separated by the sparsely settled and arid Lost River, Little Lost River-Pahsimeroi, and Birch Creek Valleys.

Gateway to the Snake River Plain

Along Interstate 15 and U.S. Highway 30, and the Union Pacific Railroad line, Portneuf Narrows serves today as the gateway from the Basin and Range to the Snake River Plain. Pocatello, at the mouth of Portneuf Narrows, is thus located at the junction between the Basin and Range, Thrust Belt, and Snake River Plain.

This change in geologic structure is a fundamental cause for the major topographic, climatic, and cultural change at Pocatello, from the agricultural valleys, flanked by tree-covered mountains, of southeastern Idaho, to the open, windswept, irrigated desert of the Snake River Plain.

Snake River Plain
Columbia Plateau Province

The Snake River Plain-Columbia Plateau Province is a vast, relatively flat, but dry and rough area of basalt and rhyolite lava erupted in the last 17 million years and today cut by deep canyons.

Formation of the Snake River Plain began with inception of volcanic activity of the Snake River Plain-Yellowstone Hot Spot in southwestern Idaho about 17 million years ago. The origin of this volcanic activity is not well understood, but is probably related to a plume of heat from the Earth's mantle (a "Hot Spot"), which melted the lower crust and produced the lava which now covers much of southern Idaho.

South-Central Idaho and
the Idaho Batholith Country

West of the Lost River Valley is the complex area of the Pioneer, Boulder, Smoky, and Salmon River Mountains. Much of this country has potential for mineral resources contained in Paleozoic black shales, and much of it is largely untrammeled wilderness. The Copper Basin and Wildhorse Creek areas on the east side of the Pioneer Mountains contain some of the most beautiful mountain country in Idaho. In the high Pioneers, east of Ketchum, Early Proterozoic metamorphic rock is exposed, in a "metamorphic core complex", which contains an uplifted part of the middle continental crust. West of the Big Wood River and north of the Salmon River, much of the country is underlain by granitic rocks of the Idaho batholith, which were intruded in Cretaceous time, and have since been uplifted by several miles. Eocene volcanic rocks of the Challis Volcanic Group cover much of the eastern and southern sides of the batholith.

Rocks of the Eastern Idaho Mountains

Late Proterozoic Sedimentary Rocks

The oldest rocks in the southeast Idaho thrust belt belong to the Pocatello Formation (750 to 700 million years old), which is exposed in the Bannock Range from the Pocatello area south through Oxford Mountain and almost to the Utah border. The Pocatello Formation contains two unique rock types, metamorphosed basaltic lava or greenstone, and dark-brown or gray rock known as diamictite, which contains clasts of older rocks, ranging from pebbles to boulders in size, floating in a matrix of sand and clay. Some of this diamictite was deposited as glacial-marine till.

The Brigham Group overlies the Pocatello Formation, and contains mainly sandstone or quartzite. The Brigham Group is exposed in much of the Portneuf, Bannock, and Bear River Ranges. The Wilbert Formation in the southern Beaverhead and Lemhi Ranges is correlative. The sediments which now make up the Brigham Group were deposited from about 700 to about 530 million years ago, during the time when complex life forms were developing. However, the sandstones of the Brigham Group were inhospitable places for latest Proterozoic and early Cambrian life to leave fossilized remains, and so the Brigham is largely devoid of fossils. The Brigham (named for Brigham City, which was named for, of course, Brigham Young) was deposited in shallow oceans and wide alluvial plains near the shorelines of those oceans.

Some of the micaceous quartzite or "Oakley stone" found on the flanks of the Albion Range south of Burley is probably correlative to parts of the Brigham Group. The distinctive bright green Elba Quartzite, now quarried at Park Valley, Utah, is older, of Middle Proterozoic age. It has been metamorphosed so that the chromium-rich clay minerals have recrystallized to green, shiny plates of mica.

Paleozoic Limestones and Sandstones

A thick sequence of carbonate rocks (limestone and dolomite), of early Paleozoic age (530 to 300 million years) lies above the Brigham Group and is present in most of the mountains of eastern Idaho. These rocks were deposited on broad carbonate platforms in warm seas off the western edge of the paleo-North American continent, settings not dissimilar to today's Bahama Banks or Great Barrier Reef. In many places the Paleozoic limestones contain invertebrate fossils, including trilobites, bryozoans, brachiopods, corals, and molluscs, which allow determination of their age and the precise conditions under which they were deposited.

Surface streams are rare in the limestone country. The limestone cliffs are highly porous and most of the water sinks into the subsurface. In places extensive cavern systems exist, as at Minnetonka Cave west of St. Charles. Large springs form where the subsurface

Diamictite, or pebbly mudstone, of the Scout Mountain Member of the Pocatello Formation north of Portneuf Narrows. Note quartzite boulder above head of hammer. These rocks were deposited by glacial marine ice sheets about 750 million years ago when North America was attached to Antarctica or Australia, and Idaho was apparently in a low latitude, (July, 1979).

Overturned syncline in Cambrian and Late Proterozoic Camelback Mountain Quartzite, Brigham Group, in Mill Creek, south of North Putnam Mountain, Fort Hall Indian Reservation, (September, 1986).

Fossil of intact head of colonial coral Favosites, Permian Snaky Canyon Formation, east side of Lost River Range, (July, 1990).

water (groundwater) intersects the land surface. Such springs supply important parts of the municipal water supplies of southeast Idaho. They are easily contaminated and their purity must be guarded carefully.

Thin units of fine-grained sandstones or quartzite are present within this stack of Paleozoic limestones in the Swan Peak Quartzite of Ordovician age and the Wells Formation of Pennsylvanian age. These sandstones represent times when wedges of quartz sand, eroded from distant mountain ranges, prograded over the carbonate platforms.

Also present in some limestone units are gray and black chert beds and nodules, which weather to distinctive pebbles of hard flint. This chert formed from dissolved skeletons of silica-secreting invertebrates, which also existed in the warm shallow seas.

Some of the limestone has been altered to the crystalline carbonate rock dolomite. In this process original fossils are generally destroyed and the result is a light or dark gray rock that preserves bedding structures but little of the fine detail found in limestone.

Southeast Idaho Phosphate Mining

Probably the most important geologic unit to the economic history of southeast Idaho is the Permian Phosphoria Formation. This black limestone, shale, and phosphate rock contains the most persistently profitable mineral resource in the Gem State: Phosphate. Though Idaho has earned more money over its history from silver mining, Phosphate has been the most important source of mineral wealth since World War II. The rock is mined in open pits at several locations north of Soda Springs, and at the now closed Gay Mine east of Fort Hall. The ore is processed at plants in Pocatello and Soda Springs into elemental phosphorus and super phosphate which is used for fertilizer. Early phosphate mines, now abandoned, are found near Paris, Montpelier, and Soda Springs.

In 1991 the J.R. Simplot Company completed a slurry pipeline to carry phosphate ore from its mine at Smoky Canyon in western Wyoming to its plant in Pocatello, thus freeing the company from the need to use the Union Pacific railroad to move the ore. Trains of ore cars are not about to disappear totally, however, as the new FMC mine in Dry Valley north of Soda Springs, will continue to use rail transport.

Origin of Phosphoria Formation

The Phosphoria Formation was deposited in an unusually productive shallow seaway, nourished by upwelling of nutrient-rich cold waters. The invertebrate organisms lived and died so rapidly that the phosphatic material in their soft tissues did not go back into solution in the ocean water, which is the normal case, but was buried and preserved in the smelly black mud. This mud, now hardened to phosphate rock, contains not only economically important deposits of phosphate, but other trace metals, including uranium, vanadium, and silver. Though phosphate slag was used for years as a paving material in southeastern Idaho, Environmental Protection Agency regulations in the 1980s stopped most of this practice because of possibly harmful radiation levels in the slag.

Mine Reclamation

The southeastern Idaho phosphate industry has responded to federal laws requiring mine reclamation with energy and enthusiasm. All open-pit mines must now be reclaimed; filled in with rock and soil not processed for phosphate, and revegetated with grasses and trees to make the area suitable for grazing and recreation. In 1994 the Monsanto Company won an award from the Forest Service for Best Mine Reclamation efforts in the U.S.

Aerial view of the Conda Mine, now abandoned, northeast of Soda Springs, (June, 1992).

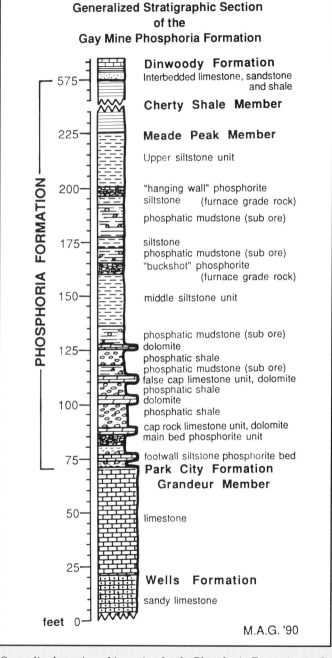

Generalized Stratigraphic Section of the Gay Mine Phosphoria Formation

PHOSPHORIA FORMATION

575 —

Dinwoody Formation
Interbedded limestone, sandstone and shale

Cherty Shale Member

225 —

Meade Peak Member

Upper siltstone unit

200 —
"hanging wall" phosphorite
siltstone   (furnace grade rock)
phosphatic mudstone (sub ore)

175 —
siltstone
phosphatic mudstone (sub ore)
"buckshot" phosphorite
              (furnace grade rock)

150 —
middle siltstone unit

125 —
phosphatic mudstone (sub ore)
dolomite
phosphatic shale
phosphatic mudstone (sub ore)
false cap limestone unit, dolomite
phosphatic shale
dolomite

100 —
phosphatic shale
cap rock limestone unit, dolomite
main bed phosphorite unit

75 —
footwall siltstone phosphorite bed
Park City Formation
Grandeur Member

50 —
limestone

25 —

Wells Formation
sandy limestone

feet 0 —

M.A.G. '90

Generalized stratigraphic section for the Phosphoria Formation in the Gay Mine area (from Link and others, 1990)

Mesozoic Continental Strata

Rocks of Mesozoic age in the southeast Idaho thrust belt include thick limestones of Triassic and Jurassic age and even thicker sandstones and shales of Cretaceous age. They were deposited before and during the thrust deformation, in basins which subsided because they were loaded down by the weight of advancing thrust sheets. These rocks are exposed on Highway 89 east of Montpelier, and on the Tincup highway east of Wayan, but the most spectacular place to see Mesozoic rocks is Raymond Canyon, Wyoming, just south and east of Geneva, Idaho.

Soft Cenozoic Rocks in the Valleys

The rocks that partially fill the valleys of southeast Idaho differ in fundamental ways from those that underlie the mountains. First, the valley fill is predominantly young, less than 10 million years old, and contains the imprint of volcanic activity associated with the Snake River Plain. There are large quantities of tuff, a distinctive white sedimentary rock made of collapsed shards of glass and derived from clouds of ash given off by volcanic eruptions on the Snake River Plain. Other parts of the valley fill are conglomerate, often with a red matrix. These coarse-grained rocks were carried by streams from adjacent mountains and deposited as the valleys were lowered along range-bounding faults. Lacustrine limestones also make up parts of the valley fill.

The Thrust Belt of Southeastern Idaho

The geological pioneers who surveyed southeast Idaho in the 1880s for the U.S. Geological Survey recognized that the structure of the folded strata here resembled better known thrust and fold belts like those in the Appalachians and the Alps. George R. Mansfield, who worked extensively in southeast Idaho in the early part of the 20th century, mapped these folds and a large thrust fault, the Bannock thrust, which he recognized in Montpelier and Georgetown Canyon, and west of Soda Springs on the east flank of the Bear River Range. Better understanding of how sedimentary formations deform when subjected to lateral compression, plus much data produced as the result of petroleum exploration, have refined our conception of the thrust faults of southeast Idaho.

In the southeast Idaho thrust belt we now recognize, from west to east, the Paris-Putnam, Meade, and Absaroka thrust faults, each of which forms the lower boundary for "thrust plates" or "sheets," which include the sedimentary rocks above the faults.

The sedimentary formations of the thrust belt were folded and broken much like a thin layer of wet cohesive snow ahead of a snow shovel. The results are geologic folds with amplitudes of 5,000 to 10,000 feet and thrust faults which move layers over one another with up to 50 miles of displacement. Thrust plates

Raymond Canyon, south of Geneva, Idaho. View looks east across Sublette Ridge. The rocks in the canyon dip steeply eastward and include the Pennsylvanian Wells Formation at the mouth of the Canyon to the Jurassic Twin Creek Formation where the steep topography ends. Small mines near the mouth of the canyon are in the Permian Phosphoria Formation, (September, 1984).

contain particular sets of sedimentary formations and economic mineral deposits, and are 10,000 to 20,000 feet thick. For example, all the phosphate mined in southeastern Idaho is from the Meade thrust plate, while the best prospects for oil production are in the Darby thrust plate, below the Absaroka thrust fault.

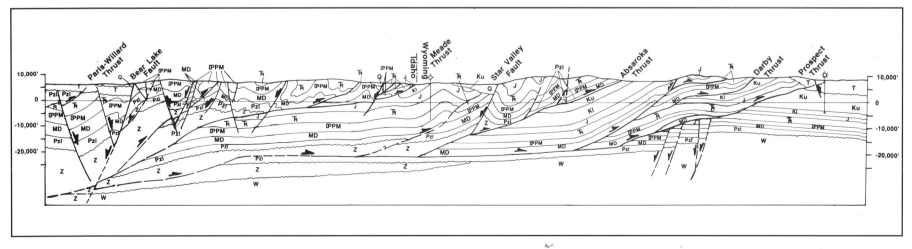

Cross section of the Idaho-Wyoming Thrust belt from near Montpelier to north of Evanston, Wyoming, approximately along the route of the Oregon Trail and the Union Pacific Railroad, after Dixon (1980). Symbols are as follows: W—Archean; Z—Late Proterozoic; Pzl—Lower Paleozoic rocks (Cambrian, Ordovician, Silurian); MD—Mississippian and Devonian rocks; lPPM—Permian, Pennsylvanian, and Mississippian rocks; Tr—Triassic rocks; J—Jurassic rocks; Kl—Lower Cretaceous rocks; Ku—Upper Cretaceous rocks; T—Tertiary rocks; Q—Quaternary unconsolidated deposits.

15

Views of Thrust Faults

Crawford thrust fault, looking northwest at Cokeville Butte, north of Smith's Fork of the Bear River, near Cokeville, Wyoming, just east of the Idaho border. The conical hill is held up by upper Paleozoic Phosphoria and Wells Formations, folded into an anticline, the west limb of which is most prominent. The southwest-dipping Crawford thrust fault is immediately right (east) of the hill, in the gully below the left end of the left snowfield. Below the Crawford thrust are Cretaceous rocks, (April, 1984).

Hogsback thrust fault, North LaBarge Creek, western Wyoming thrust belt. Thrust fault is at line of trees above the light cliffs. Light-colored Cretaceous rocks below the thrust form the front of the mountain. Cambrian Gros Ventre Formation (mainly shales) forms the slopes above the thrust at the top of the hill. Paleocene sandstones form the cliffs on top of the hill and provide a minimum age for movement on the thrust, (August, 1977).

Willard thrust fault on the west face of the Wasatch Range south of Brigham City, Utah. Thrust fault lies in the trees above the light cliff (Cambrian Tintic Quartzite). The Tintic lies nonconformably on Archean and Early Proterozoic Farmington Canyon Complex. Above the thrust fault is the Early Proterozoic Facer Creek Formation and the Late Proterozoic formation of Perry Canyon which contains evidence of Late Proterozoic glaciation, (July, 1982).

Large anticline (left) with small amplitude folds on right skyline, upper Paleozoic limestones, east side Lost River Range north of Borah Peak, view looks northwest, (July, 1990).

Keyser Creek anticline, above the Darby thrust, looking north in Little Grey's River, northwest Wyoming. Folded rocks are Jurassic Twin Creek Formation, (September, 1981).

Rocks of Central Idaho

Central Idaho Black-Shale Mineral Belt

In the mountains around Sun Valley the stratigraphic units are different, and generally darker-colored, than in southeast Idaho thrust belt or in the area from the Lost River to the east. Here, in the Pioneer, Boulder, and Smoky Mountains, are thick Lower Paleozoic black shales, such as the Devonian Milligen formation, which occupies much of the low country east and west of the Wood River Valley. The Milligen contains mineralized black shales, from which rich silver-lead-zinc veins were mined following an exploration boom in the 1880s. In the southern Pioneer Mountains are over 15,000 feet of Mississippian conglomerates and sandstones of the Copper Basin Formation, deposited in a deep-sea fan environment north and east of a highland that may have stood under the present Snake River Plain. Above the Milligen formation in the Wood River area are thick calcareous siltstones and sandstones of the Pennsylvanian and Permian Sun Valley Group (including the Wood River Formation), which were deposited in deep water west of a carbonate bank that existed in what is now the Lost River Range area.

Idaho Batholith

The Idaho batholith, generally of Late Cretaceous age (75-100 Ma) formed the roots of a continental volcanic arc, which is now eroded away. The magmatic activity was caused by the subduction of the Pacific Plate beneath North America during Cretaceous time. The batholith consists of two lobes, the southern Atlanta lobe and the northern Bitterroot lobe, separated by Proterozoic metamorphic rocks of the Salmon River arch.

Metamorphic Core Complexes

After intrusion of the Idaho batholith, there was a general relaxation of compression after Mesozoic crustal thickening. The general process of uplifting and thinning of overthickened crust results in the juxtaposition of ductilely deformed high-grade metamorphic lower crust against brittlely deformed low-grade metamorphic upper crust. This process has produced the metamorphic core complexes which are present along the length of the North American cordillera. In southern and central Idaho the Pioneer Mountains and the Albion-Raft River Mountains are metamorphic core complexes.

Bare hills west of the Wood River Valley, looking northwest from north of Bellevue, (December, 1987). Colorado Gulch is immediately south of the kinked ridge. The rich silver and lead strikes of the Wood River Valley in the 1880s were mainly in black shales in these hills.

Pioneer Mountains

At the same time as the Challis volcanic rocks were erupted, the Pioneer Mountains metamorphic core complex was rising. Low-angle extensional and strike-slip faults formed in the Boulder and Pioneer Mountains northeast of Ketchum. The general sequence of events was 1) Cretaceous intrusion ending by 70 million years ago; 2) formation of northwest-striking high angle faults as well as low-angle oblique-slip faults, ending about 45(?) million years ago; this faulting stripped sedimentary cover from the Pioneer Mountains; 3) volcanic activity of the Challis volcanic episode and faulting of the northeast-striking Trans-Challis fault system; intrusion of the Summit Creek stock in the core of the Pioneer Mountains at about 48 million years ago; 4) intrusion of late-stage granite plutons (Sawtooth, Boulder, Pioneer and Smoky Mountains) and related rhyolite volcanism about 44 million years ago, 5) final uplift and unroofing of Pioneer Mountains core complex (37 to 34 million years ago); the Summit Creek stock was beheaded by this faulting and its upper portion moved northwestward by as much as 23 km.

The view from Pioneer Cabin, above Sun Valley, of the cirques at the head of Hyndman Creek, Pioneer Mountains, (July, 1987). The rugged cirques are carved from Proterozoic and Paleozoic metamorphic rocks as well as Eocene granite. Pioneer Cabin was built as a ski base cabin in the 1930s during early development of the Sun Valley resort.

Folded sedimentary rocks in the high Boulder Mountains, north of Ketchum, looking south to the Pioneer Mountains. The peaks on the skyline, in the Pioneer metamorphic core, are made of metamorphic and igneous rock, some as old as 2300 million years, (July, 1987).

The Albion Range and The Silent City of Rocks

In the Albion Mountains, the oldest rocks are gneisses of the Archean Green Creek Complex. These are overlain by several Proterozoic and Paleozoic sedimentary formations which have been much folded and faulted. The domal shape of the core complex is evident in the form of Mount Harrison south of Albion, on which the Pomerelle ski area is built (Miller and others, 1983). The principle structural zone along which the core complex was uplifted south of Oakley is the Middle Mountain Shear zone, which occupies the valley of Birch Creek and much of Middle Mountain. This shear zone ceased moving about 35 million years ago.

The Silent City of Rocks, along the California Trail west of Almo, exposes the Almo Pluton, intruded about 32 million years ago, after uplift of the core complex had largely ceased (Bandy, 1992). There are probably other plutons under the northern Albion Range, but these have not been exposed by erosion.

The north face of the Devil's Bedstead, the most prominent peak of the northern Pioneer Mountains (11,865 feet high). The Bedstead can be seen from a large area to the east and north in the Lost River Valley. View looks south up the valley of Kane Creek from the Summit Creek road. The Bedstead is made of Eocene intrusive rock. The Wildhorse detachment fault, separating lower from upper plates of the Pioneer Mountains metamorphic core complex, is in the saddle immediately east (left) of the Bedstead. In the shadows in the foreground along Kane Creek are humpy mounds made of moraines formed by the Kane Creek glacier during the Potholes glaciation (about 20,000 years ago). These lie on flat river terraces formed during the earlier Copper Basin (Bull Lake) glaciation, (July, 1993).

View of the Silent City of Rocks, southern Albion Range, southwest of Almo, looking northeast from the summit of Bath Rock, (September, 1992). The Oligocene City of Rocks lobe of the Almo Pluton forms the exfoliating and jointed terrane in the foreground. The Archean Green Creek Complex underlies the darker colored ridges on the skyline.

The cumulative offset on these normal faults is much greater than the observed topographic relief because the upraised mountains are continually being eroded and the downdropped valleys filled with the debris carried down from the mountains. For example, just north of Downey, the floor of Marsh Valley is about 5,000 feet elevation and the summit of Oxford Peak to the south is just over 9,000 ft. But gravity studies demonstrate that beneath Downey are about 10,000 feet of valley fill, so that the "real" or structural floor of the valley is at 5,000 feet below sea level. The net displacement on the normal faults in southern Marsh Valley is thus at least 15,000 feet, not accounting for any erosion off the top of Oxford Mountain.

A normal fault which produces a major earthquake like that at Borah Peak with offset of 6 feet every 2,000 years (a net movement rate of 0.04 inches per year), will produce 15,000 feet of offset in 5 million years. Such rates appear reasonable based on geologic and paleoseismic data.

The total amount of lateral extension undergone by southeast Idaho over the last 16 million years is as much as 40 miles, at rates of 3.7 to 5.0 inches/year. Thus it is about 20 miles farther from Pocatello to Montpelier than it was 16 million years ago.

The west face of the Lost River Range, above the Big Lost River Valley. View looks northeast from the Burma Road, northwest of Mackay. The range is made up of folded Proterozoic and Paleozoic sedimentary rocks. The Lost River normal fault runs along the base of the mountains, and has been active over the last few million years. Huge alluvial fans radiate from the steep canyons and spread out over the valley. Borah Peak is the jagged high point on the north (left) end of the view. It is underlain by the Silurian Laketown Dolomite and Devonian Jefferson Formation. Leatherman Peak is on the extreme right, south of a normal fault that drops upper Paleozoic rocks down to the south, (July, 1993).

Basin and Range Faulting

The latest structure and modern topographic relief of the eastern Idaho mountains was produced by Basin and Range faulting, which began about 17 million years ago, long after thrusting and folding ceased. The map pattern of mountain ranges in the Great Basin of Idaho and Nevada has been likened by the pioneer geologist Major Clarence E. Dutton, who worked for the J.W. Powell Survey from 1875 to 1891, as "an army of caterpillars crawling northward out of Mexico." These sinuous mountain ranges are the product of

block faulting that resulted from the extension of the earth's crust. Steep faults, dipping more than 60°, form the boundaries of the ranges. The valleys between ranges are either "grabens" or blocks downdropped on two sides, or half-grabens, downdropped on only one side. In eastern Idaho, Bear Lake Valley and Cache Valley are grabens, while most of the rest of the Basin and Range valleys are half grabens, with normal faults only on their east sides.

The west face of the Boulder Mountains north of Ketchum, view to the northeast. A normal fault that runs through the low hills in the foreground has uplifted the mountains above the Wood River Valley. The white rocks in the cliffs at the base of the range are Eocene granite. The dark rocks on the summits are Devonian Milligen Formation and Pennsylvanian and Permian Wood River Formation, (October, 1991).

The Borah Peak Area and the October, 1983 Earthquake

Borah Peak fault scarp cutting irrigation ditch along Rock Creek, (November, 1983). Scarp is about 2 meters high. View looks south, Borah Peak in background.

View of Borah Peak and the October 1983 fault scarp looking east from U.S. Highway 93, during a cool and snowy year, (July, 1993). The cliffs in the center of the view are Devonian Jefferson Dolomite. The white rock at the summit is the Silurian Laketown Dolomite.

Intermountain Seismic Belt

Active faulting continues today along the eastern margin of the Basin and Range Province, along what is known as the Intermountain Seismic Belt. This belt extends from Salt Lake City along the Wasatch Range through Logan, Preston, to Soda Springs, and then north to Star Valley, Jackson Hole, and Yellowstone Park. Another branch of this belt extends generally northeastward through central Idaho from near Stanley and the Sawtooth Mountains through the Lost River, Lemhi and Beaverhead Ranges to Yellowstone Park.

Graben formed along the Borah Peak fault scarp, (October, 1983). Photo taken looking south. Graben was over 2 meters deep.

View of Borah Peak looking south from Willow Creek summit, (July, 1994). A syncline in Lower Paleozoic rocks forms the summit east ridge.

View looking northeastward up the East Fork of the Big Lost River, west of Copper Basin. The sagebrush-covered bedded rocks across the river are conglomerates deposited immediately before eruption of the Eocene Challis Volcanic Group. The jagged dark rock in the middle, Castle Rock, is composed of andesite lava. On the horizon is Porphyry Peak, one of the centers of Challis volcanism, (July, 1993).

Challis Volcanic Group & Intrusive Rocks

Throughout Central Idaho, a flare-up of intrusion, volcanic activity, extensional faulting along northeast-striking faults of the Trans-Challis fault system, and formation of major mineral deposits, occurred in Eocene time from about 52 to 44 Ma. The general pattern is of intermediate or mafic volcanic activity first, with the biggest concentration at about 48 Ma, followed by granitic intrusion and eruption of rhyolite lavas at around 44 Ma. Much of the country between Mackay, Ketchum and Challis is covered with these volcanic rocks. Shallow intrusive igneous bodies, or plutons, formed at the same time.

The Yellowstone-Snake River Plain Volcanic Province

Coincident with the wave of extensional faulting of the Basin and Range was volcanic activity in the Snake River Plain-Yellowstone Province. The Snake River Plain-Yellowstone volcanic center originated about 17 million years ago near the southwest corner of Idaho. As the North American Plate has moved southwestward, this volcanic center has migrated in a northeast direction across southern Idaho, at the speed of 4.5 mm per year (Rodgers and others, 1990; Pierce and Morgan,

1992). The most recent volcanic eruption was centered under Yellowstone Lake.

Bolide Hypothesis

The book "Roadside Geology of Idaho" (Alt and Hyndman, 1990) attributes the origin of the Snake River Plain-Yellowstone Hot Spot to the impact of huge meteorite or "bolide." There is no geologic evidence for this rather outrageous claim. The bolide hypothesis is based on circumstantial evidence and provocative inference; it is hypothesis, not scientific fact.

Model for Volcanism as the Hot Spot Passes

The general model for Snake River Plain-Yellowstone volcanism has been pieced together from the bits of exposed volcanic rocks in canyons and margins of the Snake River Plain. Readers should remember that though there is considerable evidence for much of this scheme, models of tectonic causes for the hotspot are hypotheses that must be tested further.

The "Hot Spot" or plume of heat generated in the earth's mantle, is thought to first melt the continental crust, producing explosive eruptions of light-colored lava or ash, with the composition of rhyolite. These eruptions coincide with collapse of calderas (topographic depressions formed after the rhyolitic volcanic eruptions) which form above what had been magma chambers. Deeper in the subsurface are slowly cooling batholiths of granite.

The volcanic activity has generally migrated eastward, so that the rhyolite present in the Snake River Canyon near Twin Falls is about 10 million years old, the rhyolite cliffs southwest of Pocatello are 8 million years old, and the cliffs along the Snake River at Heise and at the southern end of the Lemhi Range are 4 million years old.

After the rhyolite eruptions have ceased, dark lava known as basalt is erupted, and covers over the subsided rhyolite topography. The basalt lava which now covers the Snake River Plain, Gem Valley, and Blackfoot

View looking southwest along the axis of the Snake River Plain at East Butte, Middle Butte, and Big Southern Butte. The Pioneer Range is in the right background, (March, 1990).

Conglomerate interbedded with rhyolitic ash, Starlight Formation, The Cove, south of the Blackfoot River, Fort Hall Indian Reservation. This conglomerate was deposited in Neogene braided stream and alluvial fan systems that were periodically choked by great volumes of white ash produced by eruptions on the Snake River Plain, (October, 1987).

Lava fields is the product of this tail-end volcanic activity within the last 3 million years. Some of the basalt is erupted from fissures which extended northwest-southeast across the Snake River Plain. The Great Rift, from Craters of the Moon to the Crystal Ice caves near American Falls is one of these fissures.

The three Buttes which rise above the surface of the basalt northwest of Blackfoot are products of rhyolite volcanic activity long after passage of the Hot Spot. They are rhyolite domes, produced by the squeezing up of thick, viscous rhyolite. They have domed up the cover of basalt, like strong slow monsters rising from a frozen lake. Big Southern Butte is dated at about 300,000 years. East Butte is about 600,000 years old. Rhyolite of the core of Middle Butte did not poke through the basalt cap, and cannot be dated. The reason Middle Butte has such a different profile from the other two, is that it exposes only tilted basalt lava flows, rather than the more irregularly weathering rhyolite.

Small volcanic centers existed off of the main axis of the Snake River Plain. Three of these are the Massacre Rocks area southwest of American Falls (basalt only), the Hawkins Basin-Dairy Creek area in the Bannock Range north of Malad, and the Blackfoot Lava field north of Soda Springs. China Hat north of Soda Springs is a rhyolite dome in the Blackfoot Lava field.

In the evolution of the passing volcanic center and topographic plateau, it is thought that after rhyolite

Basaltic cinder cone south of Grace, formed within the last 100,000 years. Coarse, welded scoria is visible at lower left. This is overlain by channel-fill deposits of lapilli to fine ash, and then by laterally continuous planar beds of lapilli to fine ash. Colluvium and loess form the top of the exposure. Arrow points to 20 cm volcanic block in fine ash bed, (September, 1984).

eruptions cease, thermal doming of the land surface is reduced and the area subsides back to near its prior elevation. This is the basic reason why it is downhill from Yellowstone National Park to Boise. The Hot Spot now occupies the Continental Divide in Yellowstone and the country to the west has subsided in the wake of the mantle plume.

Snake River Plain, east of Shoshone, (July, 1991). View looks south at a basalt cinder cone built on a shield volcano, less than 1 million years old. A summer thunderstorm passes in the background.

Spheroidal weathering of the Cub River diabase sill along Cub River Canal, east of Preston. The Cub River diabase is of Miocene age and was intruded less than 10 million years ago. It intrudes conglomerate of the Mink Creek Member, Salt Lake Formation. Spheroidal weathering is typical of igneous rocks that have regularly spaced orthogonal (right-angle) joints, (September, 1984).

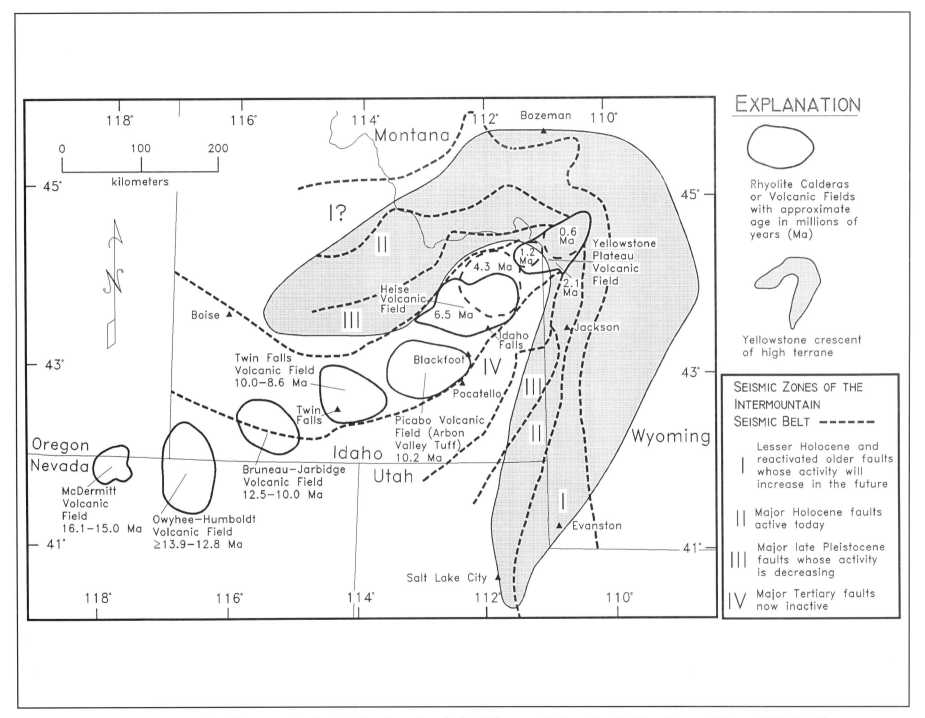

Major geologic features in the western United States associated with the late Cenozoic track of the Yellowstone Hot Spot. Simplified from Pierce and Morgan (1992, Fig. 23).

View of Hagerman Fossil Beds National Monument, which includes the light-colored cliffs on the west side of the Snake River near Hagerman. The sediments that bear hundreds of different species of fossils are about 3 to 4 million years old and belong to the Pliocene Glenns Ferry Formation, (May, 1995).

Lakes on the Snake River Plain

As the western Snake River Plain subsided in the wake of the passage of the Hot Spot, large fresh water lakes and river flood plains formed. These have been generally grouped under the rather fuzzy concept of "Lake Idaho." Fossils of now-extinct mammals, especially an early horse, are found at Hagerman Fossil Beds National Monument west of Hagerman. The light-colored sands and silts contain river channel deposits in which several complete skeletons of horses and other large animals have been found.

Glaciation in the Mountains of Idaho

The Pleistocene (the last 2 million years) has been a time of climatic conditions alternating between glacial and non-glacial, with a periodicity of about 100,000 years. There are also smaller cycles with periodicities of a few thousand years. In conjunction with a lowering of the earth's temperature by a few degrees, snowfields have built up, and reflectivity and cloudiness have increased.

During the cooler and wetter parts of the cycles, glaciers formed in the higher mountains of Idaho. The Yellowstone Plateau and Jackson Hole areas were extensively glaciated, as were the Sawtooths, Pioneers, the high Lost River, Lemhi, and Beaverhead Ranges to the east and the Albion Range south of the Snake River

Plain. In the Wyoming Rockies, the last two glacial advances are termed "Bull Lake" (maximum about 140,000 years ago) and "Pinedale" (maximum about 20,000 years ago). In the Copper Basin area these advances are termed "Copper Basin" and "Potholes," and in the Wood River Valley they are called "Prairie Creek" and "Boulder Creek" (Evenson and others, 1982; Evenson and others, 1988). An earlier, pre-Bull Lake advance is named the "Pioneer" glaciation.

During glacial advances, ice builds up and flows down valleys. At the terminus and sides of valley glaciers, poorly sorted sediment is deposited in moraines. In front of the glaciers, abundant meltwater flows downstream. This sediment-charged water deposited the high-level river terraces present today in the valleys of the Big Lost and Big Wood Rivers.

Big Lost River Floods

Recent work has determined that the Big Lost River flooded one or more times, carrying boulders from the Copper Basin area all the way to the Snake River Plain at Box Canyon south of Arco (Rathburn, 1993). The last of these floods occurred about 16,000 years ago, at the same time as the Lake Missoula floods in northern Idaho and over two thousand years before the Lake Bonneville Flood in southern Idaho (O'Connor, 1990, 1993). Such Pleistocene floods are part of the mythology of cultures from around the world.

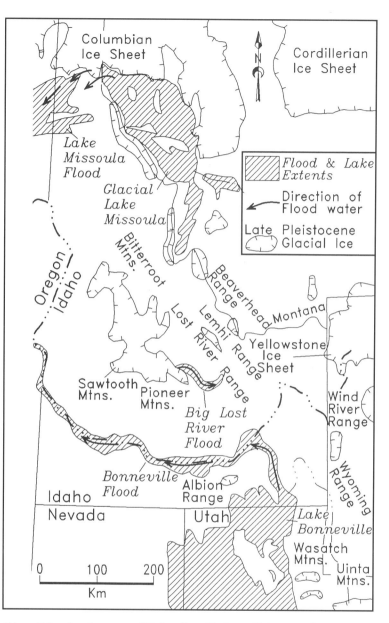

(Above) Map showing areas of Idaho affected by latest Pleistocene glaciation and the Bonneville, Missoula and Big Lost River Floods (slightly modified from Cerling and others, 1994). Glaciation was present both north of the Snake River Plain and in the Albion Range south of the Plain.

(Left) Boulder carried by an iceberg in the Big Lost River flood about 17,000 years ago. This picture was taken south of Arco, near the route of the Goodale Cutoff (March, 1995). The 2 foot diameter boulder was carried from the Copper Basin area in the Pioneer Mountains, a distance of almost 100 miles.

Glaciation in the Mountains of South-Central Idaho

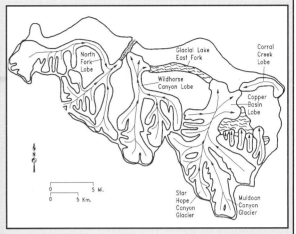

Reconstruction of ice margins, fluvial, and lacustrine systems at the maximum of Copper Basin glaciation, probably about 120,000 years ago (redrawn from Evenson and others, 1982).

Alturas Lake, with Perkins Lake in front of it, view looks west toward granitic rocks of the Sawtooth Mountains from over Stanley Basin. Both lakes are dammed by recessional moraines and bounded on the sides by lateral moraines. Moraines are probably about 20,000 years old, (July 1987).

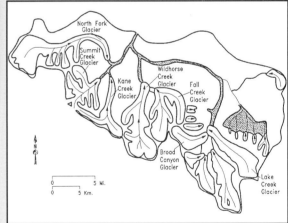

Reconstruction of ice margins and fluvial systems at the latest and smallest of the glacial advances of the Potholes glaciation, about 20,000 years ago (redrawn from Evenson and others, 1982).

View looking southeast into Copper Basin. The fluted ridges on the left and in the foreground are glacial moraines deposited during the Copper Basin and Potholes glaciations. The three large canyons in the background are from right to left (southwest to northeast) Star Hope, Muldoon, and Lake Creeks. Glacially carried boulders lie by the side of the road, (July, 1993).

Lake Bonneville and its Flood

Bonneville Basin

The Bonneville basin is a product of the Basin and Range faulting, which, starting about 17 million years ago, uplifted the Sierra Nevada Mountains on the west side of Nevada, the Wasatch Range in northeastern Utah, and the many ranges in between. Water that falls on these ranges does not reach the ocean, but flows to closed basins, of which the Bonneville basin is the easternmost.

The effect of climate change in the Lake Bonneville basin (the entire area that drains toward the modern Great Salt Lake, in western Utah, southernmost Idaho, and eastern Nevada) was to produce large lakes during the colder wetter glacial periods. During interglacial periods these lakes shrunk, and existed as saline water bodies like the present Great Salt Lake.

Calibration of Dating Methods

Geologists use several different methods to place ages on events related to Lake Bonneville and the Pleistocene in general. Radiocarbon years are based on the broadly applied method of dating organic material less than 30,000 years old with the naturally occurring isotope of carbon. Other methods of dating have been calibrated to tree rings and the growth rings of corals and are defined in "calibrated" years, which yield ages generally 10 to 20% older than radiocarbon years (Cerling and others, 1994). Radiocarbon years are used in this book.

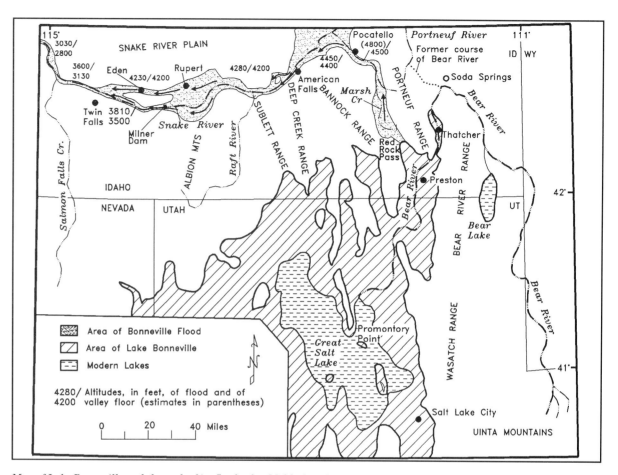

Map of Lake Bonneville and the path of its flood, after Malde (1968).

Field filled with basalt boulders dropped by the Lake Bonneville flood, south of Hagerman, (Oct. 1995). These are the "petrified watermelons."

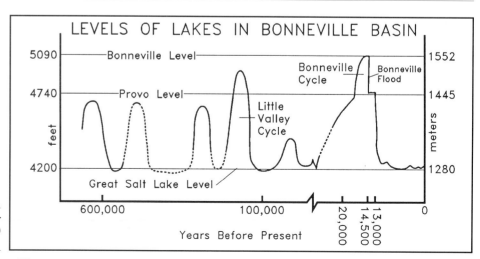

Quaternary lake levels in the Bonneville basin, after Currey and others (1984) and McCoy (1987).

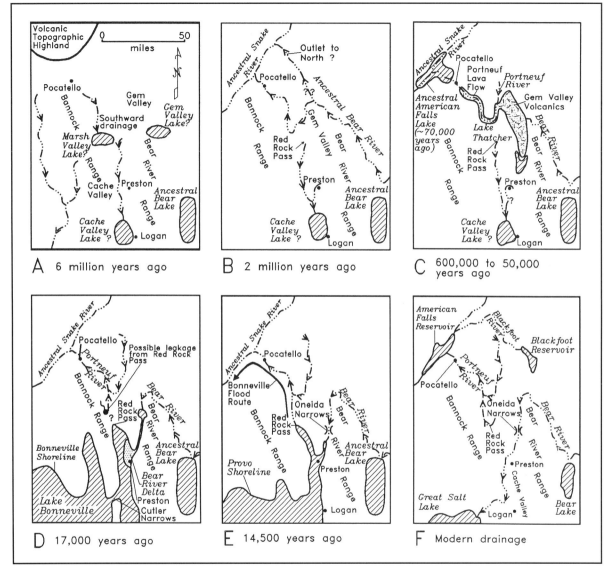

Steps in the Development of Drainage in Southeast Idaho,
expanded from Mahoney and others (1987).

A—Miocene (6 million years ago)
Topographic high of Yellowstone Hot Spot is present northeast of Pocatello. Valleys drain southward away from the volcanic plateau. The southeast Idaho mountains are largely buried in tuffaceous basin fill. Lake basins exist in southern Marsh Valley and southern Cache Valley.

B—Early Pleistocene (2 million years ago)
The Ancestral Bear River probably drained northward through Gem Valley and across the Portneuf Range through what is now the Portneuf River Canyon. Alternatively, it may have drained northward across the northern end of the Portneuf Range. Drainage in Marsh Valley has reversed from southward to northward; superposed river canyons have been cut in eroding valley fill.

C—Lake Thatcher and ancestral American Falls Lake, between 600,000 and about 50,000 radiocarbon years ago
Pleistocene basaltic volcanism in Gem Valley formed a lava field which blocked the northward surface drainage of Bear River. About 600,000 years ago two basalt flows moved 50 miles down the Portneuf River Canyon to the site of Pocatello (Scott and others, 1982). Lake Thatcher formed in southern Gem Valley as northward drainage was blocked. Bear River may have drained southward into Lake Thatcher or may have lost much of its water to subsurface flow through porous basalt flows. The ancestral American Falls Lake formed about 70,000 years ago, dammed up by the Cedar Butte Basalt Flow just northeast of Massacre Rocks.

D—Lake Bonneville (about 50,000 to 14,500 radiocarbon years ago)
The southward cutting of Oneida Narrows, by Bear River, about 50,000 years ago, plus the wetter climate of the Pinedale glaciation, were instrumental in causing the rise of Lake Bonneville. The maximum lake level at 5090 feet may have been controlled by subsurface leakage through limestones at Red Rock Pass (D.E. Fortsch, Idaho State University, oral communication, 1993). The diagram shows the maximum extent of the lake northward into Gem Valley and the extent of the Bear River Delta (stippled). Ancestral American Falls Lake no longer existed (Hearst, 1990).

E—Lake Bonneville Flood and Provo shoreline (14,500 radiocarbon years ago)
The Bonneville Flood emptied northward after failure of the alluvial dam at the Zenda Threshold, just north of Red Rock Pass. In the American Falls area, the floodwaters spread out. Some of them flushed down the modern Snake River channel, but some went north and west down Lake Channel, to return to the Snake River near what is now Massacre Rocks. A lake stood at the Provo shoreline (the bedrock lip at Red Rock Pass) for about a thousand years until it began to rapidly recede about 13,000 years ago.

F—Modern Drainage Patterns
The Bear River flows first north and then south into the Great Salt Lake. The Portneuf River flows first south and then north through Portneuf Narrows to the Snake River Plain. The headwaters of the Blackfoot, Portneuf, and tributaries to the Bear are all located in flat marshy ground underlain by young basalt lava north and west of Soda Springs.

Aerial view looking north at Red Rock Pass. The Butte in the center of the valley is underlain by Cambrian limestone. The headwaters of Marsh Creek drain directly south, toward the camera and then turn 180° and head north into the freshly excavated flood channel. The dam to Lake Bonneville consisted of coalesced alluvial fans which nearly covered Red Rock Butte. According to D.E. Fortsch, (ISU Geology Department), Lake Bonneville water may have leaked through underground (karst) caverns in the Butte and controlled the lakes highest level. A post-flood earthflow can be seen on the left of the photo, (April, 1992).

Lake Bonneville shorelines near Brigham City, Utah. The Bonneville level is the upper one, at about 5090 feet. The next prominent level is the Provo shoreline at about 4,740 feet, which the lake occupied for a few hundred years before retreating toward its present level, (July, 1982).

Shorelines and Canals

The Mormon Pioneers took full advantage of the ancient shorelines of Lake Bonneville and built their towns and irrigation canals along them. It was as if the area had already been leveled and surveyed!

The Rise of Lake Bonneville

Although lakes had existed in the Bonneville Basin periodically for 15 million years, the largest and deepest of these existed only 30,000 to 14,500 radiocarbon years ago, and it is this lake that we refer to as "Lake Bonneville."

The rise of Lake Bonneville was caused by both climatic change and the diversion of the drainage of the Bear River into the Bonneville Basin. The Bear, which comprises about a third of the fresh water input into the Great Salt Lake today, had formerly flowed into the Snake River, possibly through the present canyon of the Portneuf River at Pocatello. The Bear River was diverted south, into southern Gem Valley, by basaltic volcanic eruptions near Bancroft around 600,000 years ago. These eruptions also produced the Basalt of Portneuf Valley, which flowed down the Portneuf River canyon through Lava Hot Springs, Marsh Valley, Inkom, and

Pocatello. The diversion of the Bear through Oneida Narrows and into the Bonneville Basin and the cool climates of the most recent (Pinedale or Wisconsin) glacial period, caused the rise of Lake Bonneville. Lake Bonneville rose from near the modern level of Great Salt Lake today (4210 feet) at 30,000 years ago to the Bonneville Shoreline at 5090 feet about 17,000 years ago. At Red Rock Pass, the lowest point on the lake margin, alluvial fans from the adjacent Bannock and Portneuf Ranges had coalesced above bedrock of Cambrian limestone. As Lake Bonneville rose, leakage of water through the alluvial fan gravels plus though caverns in the limestone possibly controlled the level of its maximum shoreline at 5090 feet.

In southeastern Idaho, Lake Bonneville occupied the entire Cache Valley, the extreme southern end of Gem Valley, much of Malad Valley, and the area around Holbrook and Stone.

Bear River Narrows looking east from near Garland, Utah. The Lake Bonneville shoreline is the level of the top of the grain fields. Through this narrow canyon Lake Bonneville emptied into Cache Valley as its flood was pouring down through Red Rock Pass into Marsh Valley. Today the main north-south line of the Union Pacific Railroad winds through the narrow canyon at Cutler Dam, (May, 1983).

The Lake Bonneville Flood in the Pocatello Area

The flood removed the Basalt of Portneuf Valley from the Portneuf Narrows area, where the water was 300 feet deep and moving at 60 miles per hour. As the water slowed down in the Pocatello area it deposited boulders up to 12 feet in diameter in the downtown Pocatello area. A flat delta deposit known as the Michaud Gravel was laid down northwest of Pocatello, and is the present site of the city of Chubbuck and the Pocatello airport.

Basalt boulders up to 8 feet in diameter on North Main Street, downtown Pocatello, (April, 1990).

View of Portneuf River Valley and Pocatello, Idaho, looking northwest from Portneuf Hill, south of Portneuf Narrows, (March, 1982). The Portneuf River meanders in a valley widened by the Lake Bonneville Flood about 14,500 years ago. Some of the river's meandering has been curtailed by construction of the Union Pacific Railroad. In the upper left, just west of the railroad tracks, the Portneuf enters a flood control channel built by the U.S. Army Corps of Engineers after much of downtown Pocatello was flooded in February, 1962 and 1963.

The Basalt of Portneuf Valley forms the dark escarpment northeast of the railroad. At least two lava flows can be seen. About 600,000 years ago, these flowed down the canyon of the Portneuf River from a source area near Bancroft in Gem Valley. Interstate 15 makes sweeping curves that parallel the edge of the lava flows. The dry Highway Pond can be seen in the middle distance.

Lake Bonneville Flood

The catastrophic Lake Bonneville Flood occurred about 14,500 (radiocarbon) years ago. The Lake Bonneville Flood was about 3,000 years after the Big Lost River floods and the Lake Missoula floods (Rathburn, 1993, O'Connor and Baker, 1992). The point of outflow was at Zenda, a few miles north of Red Rock Pass, between Swan Lake and Downey, at the north end of Cache Valley. The flood carried the upper 350 feet of water in Lake Bonneville northward through Marsh Valley to Pocatello and the Snake River, and lowered the lake to the Provo shoreline level (4,740 feet), the level of bedrock at Red Rock Pass (Malde, 1968). The total volume of the Lake Bonneville Flood is estimated to have been 4,750 cubic km (or 1,150 cubic miles) of water, with a peak discharge lasting about 8 weeks (Jarrett and Malde, 1987; O'Connor, 1990, 1993). The peak flow was about one million cubic meters per second at Red Rock Pass. This flow is around 500 times the maximum discharge of the Snake River ever recorded at Idaho Falls. For comparison, the average discharge of the Amazon River is 170,000 cubic meters per second. The topography left behind by the flood is called scabland topography and is manifested in dry waterfalls, alcoves, scoured bedrock surfaces and Boulder bar accumulations along the flood path.

The cause of the flood is not known. One possibility is that an earthquake of the Intermountain Seismic Belt weakened part of the alluvial fan material that was serving as the dam to the lake. Another possibility is that the leaking water simply eroded its own piping system which undermined the overlying gravel.

After the flood, the lake stood at the Provo shoreline (4,740 feet) until about 13,000 years ago. It filled the lower portions of Cache and Malad Valleys and had an outlet, north into Marsh Creek. When the climate began to rapidly become drier, the lake began to recede, and the Great Salt Lake, at most 40 feet deep, is the modern remnant. The present lake level was reached by about 11,500 years ago.

The rise and fall of the lake caused changes in streams that entered it. When the lake stood at the Bonneville level, it reached as far north as Grace, in Gem Valley. At the Provo level the shoreline was farther south, near Preston. The gradient and speed of water flow in Bear River was drastically changed by these levels. The wide Bear River canyon at Preston has been eroded since the retreat below the Provo level, only 13,000 years ago.

After passing north from Red Rock Pass to Marsh Valley, Portneuf Narrows and Pocatello, the flood emptied into a flat area along the Snake River which had been occupied, about 70,000 years ago, by the ancestral American Falls Lake. Water ponded here and then flooded down into the Snake River Canyon near Massacre Rocks. This flood scouring produced the abandoned "Lake Channel," north of Massacre Rocks.

View looking south from Howe Point at the south end of the Lemhi Range to the Sinks of the Big Lost River and the Big Southern Butte in the background (June, 1996). This was a wet spring and there is a great deal of water both flowing in the rivers and standing in ponds in the sinks area. Although it is not obvious, the entire flat area between the cows and the dark escarpment, is covered with standing water.

Big Lost River Rest Area, U.S. Highway 26, (July, 1993).

Disposal of Wastes at the Idaho National Engineering Laboratory

At the INEL, the water table is 200 to 1000 feet below the ground surface, though its elevation is observed to change from wet to dry years by at least 80 feet. The groundwater flows at a rate of 5 to 20 feet per day through layers of basalt lava and rubble zones between the flows. The aquifer has a distinct top (above which the rock is not saturated, and bottom (below which the permeability is apparently too low to allow water to flow).

Disposal of radioactive wastes at the INEL has not harmed the water quality in a major way. Traces of radionuclides have been detected in the aquifer south of the INEL, having migrated up to 7.5 miles in 20 years. Injection wells which discharged waste water used for cooling nuclear reactors were operated from 1953 to the mid 1980s. A plume of tritium, or heavy hydrogen, had migrated past the edge of the INEL by 1985, but has begun to shrink since the injection wells were closed down. Only natural background levels of radiation are detectable at the Thousand Springs area west of Twin Falls.

All this is not to say that nuclear waste disposal at the Idaho National Engineering Laboratory must not be closely monitored. Indeed, Idaho politicians should consider the effects of federally funded nuclear waste disposal on tourism and quality of life in southern Idaho. We probably would not gain from a change in the state motto to "Idaho—Famous Waste Dumps."

As of October 1991 a Department of Energy report revealed that the following nuclear waste inventory existed for the entire INEL:

Spent Fuel	700 metric tons
High-level nuclear waste	423,000 cubic feet
Low-level nuclear waste	5,088,891 cubic feet
Stored transuranic waste	1,323,323 cubic feet
Buried transuranic waste	2,016,486 cubic feet
Contaminated soil	1,977,640—5,509,140 cubic feet

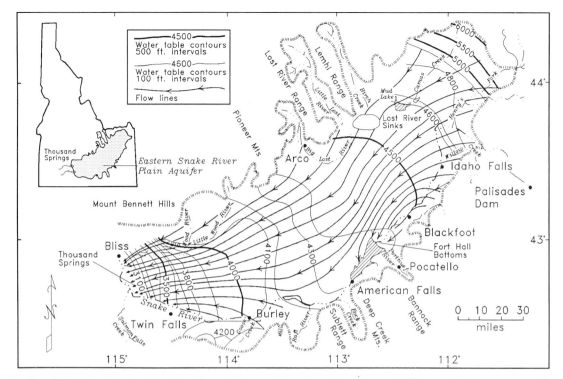

Snake River Plain Aquifer, showing directions of flow and locations of outlets at the Thousand Springs area northwest of Twin Falls.

this from wells and the rest from canals. This extensive irrigation system is the primary reason that Idaho has the highest per capita water consumption in the U.S.

The Snake River aquifer is a complex system, with multiple layers of high permeability. It discharges 8 million acre feet of water per year in the famous Thousand Springs area on the north wall of the Snake River canyon from Twin Falls to Hagerman. Most of the commercially produced trout in the United States are grown there.

The Snake River Plain is underlain by fractured and rubbly basalt lava flows, which form a highly permeable aquifer. Interbeds between the basalt layers are mainly sand, silt and clay, with smaller amounts of volcanic ash. Within basalts, permeable zones are mainly the tops and bottoms of lava flows, with columnar jointing in between providing slower vertical transmission of water. Rhyolite that underlies the basalt does not have high permeability, as many of the pore spaces are filled with chemical precipitates.

Water which falls mainly as snow in the mountains north and east of the eastern Snake River Plain is absorbed into the basalt in many places along the northern margin of the plain. The most obvious is the Sinks of the Big Lost River east of Howe, where waters of the Big and Little Lost Rivers, and Birch Creek sink into the lava plateau.

Geologic Setting of Water and Idaho

Ground Water

In the desert country of eastern Idaho, people have generally placed a value on irrigation water close to the level of motherhood, apple pie, and Family Home Evening. Although most irrigation water today is provided from surface sources and wells, many an early homestead was located next to a spring.

Ground water issues forth in springs where the water table intersects the land surface. In most cases these springs contain water that has fallen upslope, been absorbed into the ground, and spent a few weeks to thousands of years travelling to the point of issue.

Hot springs

Hot springs are present across southern Idaho in diverse geologic settings on both sides of the Snake River Plain. Generally, these springs are produced by the very slow circulation of meteoric (rain) water to

depths of 8,000 to 10,000 feet where it is heated to near 80°C (Ralston and others, 1980; 1983). These waters then recirculate to the surface as hot springs. Studies from oil wells drilled in the 1970s reveal that the geothermal gradient in southeast Idaho is generally high, ranging from 19 to 61°C per kilometer depth, with an average near 40°C/km. The average geothermal gradient for the global continental crust is 26°C/km.

The residence times of waters in these systems (the time between the water falling as rain and it emerging from a hot spring) is surprisingly long: in most places in southeast Idaho it is over 25,000 years for hot springs over 25°C.

Snake River Plain Aquifer

The most famous aquifer in Idaho is that of the Snake River Plain, which controls the economy of much of southern Idaho north and west of Pocatello (Stearns and others, 1938). Three million acres of farmland on the Snake River Plain are irrigated, with about 1/3 of

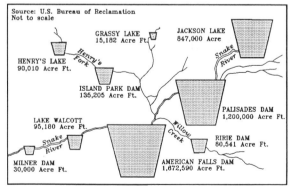

Dams and their storage on the Snake River system. Source: U.S. Bureau of Reclamation.

Irrigation and its Effect on the Snake River Plain Aquifer

Dams were put on the Snake River at Milner, Minidoka, and American Falls in the early 1900s. The extensive irrigation essentially recycles the Snake River water, drawing it out of the river, and returning it to the river or the aquifer downstream. When the amount of irrigation on the Snake River Plain is reduced, output from the springs goes down also. The level of the aquifer rose dramatically after initiation of irrigation, but the level stabilized after a new equilibrium was reached. In the last 25 years, the level has begun to fall slowly.

Fundamentally, the Snake River Plain Aquifer is so large, with so much water running through it, and with residence times on the order of 100s of years, that it will be hard for man's efforts to change it much. Point sources of pollution certainly exist, but the dilution factor prevents them from becoming regional problems.

Water quality of the Snake River Plain aquifer is adversely affected by several human activities, most importantly agriculture. Runoff from fertilizer, feedlots, and potato processing plants has produced local acute pollution of the aquifer.

Another potential source of pollution is the Idaho National Engineering Laboratory. Voluminous and expensive monitoring programs are being conducted to determine the extent of INEL-caused pollution. The bottom line appears to be that the dry climate on the Snake River Plain combined with the huge volume of water in the Snake River Plain aquifer act to limit the amount of radionuclides that have reached the aquifer and then to dilute them below detection limits.

References cited in this chapter

Armstrong, F.C., and Oriel, S.S., 1965, Tectonic development of Idaho-Wyoming thrust belt: American Association of Petroleum Geologists Bulletin, v. 49, p. 1847-1866.

Bandy, P.J., 1992, Structural and kinematic analysis of the City of Rocks lobe of the Almo Pluton, Cassia Co. Idaho: An application of granite tectonics: M.S. Thesis, Idaho State University and Boise State University, Pocatello and Boise, Idaho, 105 p.

Cerling, T.E., Poreda, R.J., and Rathburn, S.L., 1994, Cosmogenic ^{3}He and ^{21}Ne age of the Big Lost River flood, Snake River Plain, Idaho: Geology, v. 22, p. 227-230

Currey, D.R., Atwood, Genevieve, and Mabey, D.R., 1984, Major Levels of Great Salt Lake and Lake Bonneville: Utah Geological and Mineral Survey Map 73, scale 1;750,000.

Dixon, J.S., 1982, Regional structural synthesis, Wyoming salient of Western Overthrust Belt, American Asso-

ciation of Petroleum Geologists Bulletin, v. 66, no. 10, p. 1560-1580.

Evenson, E.B., Cotter, J.F.P., and Clinch, J.M., 1982, Glaciation of the Pioneer Mountains: A proposed model for Idaho: *in* Bonnichsen, Bill, and Breckenridge, R.M., editors, Cenozoic Geology of Idaho, Idaho Bureau of Mines and Geology Bulletin 26, p. 653-665.

Evenson, E.B., Breckenridge, R.M., and Stephens, G.C., 1988, Field Guides to the Quaternary Geology of Central Idaho: *in* Link, P.K., and Hackett, W.R., editors, Guidebook to the Geology of Central and Southern Idaho: Idaho Geological Survey Bulletin 27, p. 201-244.

Hayden, F.V., 1883, Twelfth Annual Report of the U.S. Geological and Geographical Survey of the Territories--Wyoming & Idaho, for the year 1878: Washington, Government Printing Office.

Hearst, Jonena, M., 1990, Paleontology and depositional setting of the Duck Point local fauna (Late Pleistocene, Rancholabrean) Power County, Southeastern Idaho: M.S. Thesis, Pocatello, Idaho, Idaho State University, 275 p.

Huerta, Audrey D., 1992, Lake Creek Fault: Evidence of Pre-Challis shear within south-central Idaho: M.S. Thesis, Pocatello, Idaho, Idaho State University, 57 p.

Jarrett, R. D., and Malde, H. E., 1987, Paleodischarge of the late Pleistocene Bonneville Flood, Snake River Idaho, computed from new evidence: Geological Society of America Bulletin v. 99, p. 127-134.

King, P.B., 1977, The Evolution of North America, revised edition, Princeton, New Jersey, Princeton University Press, 197 p.

Link, P.K., Nielson, J.W., McDonald, C., and Smith, J.L., 1990, History and geology of the J.R. Simplot Company Gay Mine, Bingham County, Idaho: *in* Robinson, Lee, editor, 1990 Symposium on Engineering Geology and Geotechnical Engineering: Pocatello, Idaho, Idaho State University, College of Engineering, p. 24-1 to 24-12.

Mahoney, J.B., Link, P.K., Henkelman, J.J., McCalpin, J., and Smith, B.L., 1987, The Bear River Landslide Complex, Preston, Idaho: Geologic considerations and historical perspectives: *in* McCalpin, J., editor, Proceedings of the 23rd Symposium on engineering geology and soils engineering: Boise, Idaho, Idaho Department of Transportation, p. 306-353.

Mahoney, J.B., Link, P.K., Burton, B.R., Geslin, J.K., and O'Brien,J.P., 1991, Pennsylvanian and Permian Sun Valley Group, Wood River Basin, South-Central Idaho: *in* Cooper, J.D., and Stevens, C.H., eds., Paleozoic Paleogeography of the Western United States—II: Pacific Section, Society of Economic Paleontologists and Mineralogists Publication 67, p. 551-579.

Malde, H.E., 1968, The catastrophic late Pleistocene Bonneville Flood in the Snake River Plain, Idaho: U.S. Geological Survey Professional Paper 596, 52 p.

Malde, H.,E., 1991, Quaternary geology and structural history of the Snake River Plain, Idaho and Oregon: *in* Morrison, R.B., editor, Quaternary Nonglacial Geology: Con-

terminous U.S., Boulder, Colorado, Geological Society of America, The Geology of North America, volume K-2, p. 251-281.

McCoy, W.D., 1987, Quaternary aminostratigraphy of the Bonneville Basin, western United States: Geological Society of America Bulletin, v. 98, p. 99-112.

Miller, D.M., Armstrong, R.L., Compton, R.R., and Todd, V.R., 1983, Geology of the Albion-Raft River-Grouse Creek Mountains area, northwestern Utah and southern Idaho: *in* Gurgel, K.D., editor, Geologic excursions in the Overthrust Belt and Metamorphic core complexes of the Intermountain Region: Utah Geological and Mineral Survey, Special Studies 59, p. 1-62.

O'Connor, J.E., 1993, Hydrology, hydraulics, and geomorphology of the Bonneville flood: Geological Society of America Special Paper 274, 83p.

O'Connor, J.E. and Baker, V.R., 1992, Magnitudes and implications of peak discharges from Glacial Lake Missoula: Geological Society of America Bulletin, v. 104, p. 267-279.

Oriel, S.S., and Armstrong, F.C., 1986, Tectonic development of Idaho-Wyoming thrust belt: Authors' commentary, *in* Peterson, J.A., editor, Paleotectonics and sedimentation: American Association of Petroleum Geologists Memoir 41, p. 267-279.

Pierce, K.L., and Morgan, L.A., 1992, The track of the Yellowstone Hot Spot: Volcanism, faulting, and uplift: *in* Link, P.K., Kuntz, M.A., and Platt, L.B., editors, Regional Geology of Eastern Idaho and Western Wyoming: Geological Society of America Memoir 179, p. 1-53.

Ralston, D.R., and six others, 1980, Interactions of mining and water resource systems in the southeastern Idaho Phosphate Field: Idaho Water Resources Research Institute Research Technical Completion Report, Project C-7651, Moscow, Idaho, University of Idaho, 214 p.

Ralston, D.R., and six others, 1983, Thermal Ground water Flow Systems in the Thrust Zone in southeastern Idaho: Idaho Water and Energy Resources Research Institute, Research Technical Completion Report, Moscow, Idaho, University of Idaho, 336 p.

Rathbrun, Sara L., 1993, Pleistocene cataclysmic flooding along the Big Lost River, east central Idaho: Geomorphology, v. 8, p. 305-319.

Rodgers, D.W., Hackett, W.R., and Ore, H.T., 1990, Extension of the Yellowstone Plateau, eastern Snake River Plain, and Owyhee Plateau: Geology, v. 18, p. 1138-1141.

Scott, W.E., Pierce, K.L., Bradbury, J.P., and Forester, R.M., 1982, Revised Quaternary stratigraphy and chronology in the American Falls area, southeastern Idaho, *in* Bonnichsen, Bill, and Breckenridge, R.M., editors, Cenozoic Geology of Idaho, Idaho Bureau of Mines and Geology Bulletin 26, p. 581-595.

Stearns, H.T., Crandall, L., and Steward, W.G., 1938, Geology and groundwater resources of the Snake River Plain in southeastern Idaho: U.S. Geological Survey Water Supply Paper 774, 268 p.

References on Idaho Geology

The geological literature on Idaho is extensive. A few key book references are listed below. Individual papers are cited or listed in appropriate places throughout the book. All of these sources can be found in the University Libraries in Pocatello and Boise. U.S. Geological Survey publications may be obtained from Publication Sales Offices in Spokane and Salt Lake City. Idaho Geological Survey publications may be obtained from the main office in Moscow.

In general, a geological dictionary (for example, *Dictionary of Geological Terms,* edited by R.L. Bates and Julia A. Jackson, (3rd edition, 1984, Doubleday Anchor Press) will be useful for those of the general public who are adventuresome enough to track down and try to understand this scientific literature.

The best general book on Idaho geology is by Terry Maley, *Exploring Idaho Geology* (1987, Mineral Land Publications, P.O. Box 1186, Boise, Idaho, 83701, 232 p.). An early geological summary of Idaho is by Edward F. Rodenbaugh (*Sketches of Idaho Geology* 1953, Caldwell, Idaho, Caxton Printers, Ltd. 267 p.). Ralph W. Maughan, Northside farmer from Rupert, has written an entertaining and wise commentary on *Anatomy of the Snake River Plain: An Amateur's View* (1992, Pocatello, Idaho, The Idaho State University Press, 69 p.).

Recent Books on the Geology of Southern and Eastern Idaho

Alt, D.D., and Hyndman, D.W., 1989, Roadside Geology of Idaho: Missoula, Montana, Mountain Press Publishing Company, 393 p.

Alt, D.D. and Hyndman, D.W., 1995, Northwest Exposures— A geologic story of the Northwest: Missoula, Montana, Mountain Press Publishing Co., 443 p.

Beus, S.S., editor, 1987, Rocky Mountain Section of the Geological Society of America: Centennial Field Guide, Volume 2, Boulder Colorado, Geological Society of America, 475 p.

Bonnichsen, Bill, and Breckenridge, R.M., editors, 1982, Cenozoic Geology of Idaho: Idaho Geological Survey Bulletin 26, 725 p.

Burnett, Betty, 1985, Goodale's Cutoff: Overland Journal, Winter 1985, p. 30-34.

Chamberlain, V.E., Breckenridge, R.M., and Bonnichsen, Bill, editors, 1989, Guidebook to the Geology of Northern and Western Idaho and Surrounding Area: Idaho Geological Survey Bulletin 28, 156 p.

Chapin, C.E., and Zidek, J., editors, 1989, Field excursions to volcanic terranes in the western United States, Volume II: Cascades and Intermountain West: New Mexico Bureau of Mines and Mineral Resources Memoir 47, 285 p.

Fisher, F.S., and Johnson, K.M., editors, 1995 Geology and Mineral Resource Assessment of the Challis 1° x 2° Quadrangle, Idaho: U.S. Geological Survey Professional Paper 1525, 204 p.

Kerns, G.L., and Kerns, R.L., editors, 1985, Orogenic patterns and stratigraphy of north-central Utah and southeastern Idaho: Utah Geological Association Publication 14, 328 p.

Link, P.K., editor, 1994, Hydrogeology, Waste Disposal, Science and Politics: Proceedings of the 30th Symposium on Engineering Geology and Geotechnical Engineering: Pocatello, Idaho, College of Engineering, Idaho State University, 652 p.

Link, P.K. and Hackett, W.R., editors, 1988, Guidebook to the geology of central and southern Idaho: Idaho Geological Survey Bulletin 27, 319 p.

Link, P.K., Kuntz, M., and Platt, L.B., editors, 1992, Regional geology of eastern Idaho and western Wyoming: Geological Society of America Memoir 179, 312 p.

McIntyre, D.H., editor, 1985, Symposium on the geology and mineral deposits of the Challis 1° x 2° Quadrangle, Idaho: U.S. Geological Survey Bulletin 1658, 227 p.

Miller, W. Roger, editor, 1987, The thrust belt revisited: Wyoming Geological Association 38th Field Conference Guidebook, Jackson Hole, Wyoming, September 8-11, 1987, 404 p.

Northwest Geology, 1982, volume 11, Tobacco Root Geological Society, 1981 Field Conference, September 8-13, 1981, Pocatello, Idaho, 76 p.

Northwest Geology, 1996, Geology of the Crook in the Snake River Plain, Twin Falls and vicinity, Idaho: Northwest Geology, v. 25, 123 p.

Roberts, Sheila, editor, 1990, Geologic field tours of western Wyoming and parts of adjacent Idaho, Montana, and Utah: Wyoming Geological Survey Public Information Circular no. 29, Laramie, Wyoming, 191 p.

Ruebelmann, Kerry L., editor, 1989, Snake River Plain-Yellowstone Volcanic Province, Jackson, Wyoming to Boise, Idaho, July 21-29, 1989, Field Trip Guidebook T305: Washington D.C., American Geophysical Union, 103 p.

Schmidt, C.J., and Perry, W.J., Jr., 1988, editors, Interaction of the Rocky Mountain Foreland and the Cordilleran thrust belt: Geological Society of America Memoir 171, 582 p.

Snoke, A.W., Steidtmann, J.R., and Roberts, S.M., editors, 1993, Geology of Wyoming: Geological Survey of Wyoming Memoir No. 5, 2 vols. plus map packet.

Wilson, James R., 1992, Field Guide to geologic excursions in Utah and adjacent areas of Nevada, Idaho, and Wyoming: Utah Geological Survey Miscellaneous Publication 92-3, 482 p.

Worl, R.G., Link, P.K., Winkler, G.R., and Johnson, K.M., editors, 1995, Geology and Mineral Resources of the Hailey 1° x 2° Quadrangle and the Western part of the Idaho Falls 1° x 2° Quadrangle, Idaho: U.S. Geological Survey Bulletin 2064, Chapters A-R.

Recent U.S. Geological Survey Maps of large areas of Eastern Idaho and Vicinity

Fisher, F.S., McIntyre, D.H., and Johnson, K.M., 1993, Geologic map of the Challis 1° x 2° quadrangle, Idaho: U.S. Geological Survey Miscellaneous Investigations Series Map I-1819, scale 1:250,000.

Hladky, F.R., Kellogg, K.S., Oriel, S.S., Link, P.K., Nielson, J.W., and Amerman, R.E., 1991, Geologic map of the eastern part of the Fort Hall Indian Reservation, Bannock, Bingham and Caribou Counties, Idaho: U.S. Geological Survey Miscellaneous Investigations Series Map I-2006, scale 1:50,000.

Hobbs, S.W., Hays, W.H., and McIntyre, D.H., 1991, Geologic map of the Bayhorse area, central Custer County, Idaho: U.S. Geological Survey Miscellaneous Investigations Series Map I-1882, scale 1:62,500.

Kuntz, M.A., and twelve others, 1992, Geologic map of the Idaho National Engineering Laboratory and adjoining areas, eastern Idaho: U.S. Geological Survey Miscellaneous Investigations Series Map I-2330, scale 1:100,000.

Love, J.D., Reed, J.C., Jr., and Christiansen, A.C., 1992, Geologic Map of Grand Teton National Park, Teton County, Wyoming: U.S. Geological Survey Miscellaneous Investigations Series Map I-2031, scale 1:62,500.

McIntyre, D.H., and Hobbs, S.W., 1987, Geologic map of the Challis Quadrangle, Custer and Lemhi Counties, Idaho: U.S. Geological Survey Geologic Quadrangle Map GQ-1599, scale 1:62,500.

Oriel, S.S., and Platt, L.B., 1980, Geologic map of the Preston 1° x 2° quadrangle, Idaho and Wyoming: U.S. Geological Survey Miscellaneous Investigations Series Map I-1127, scale 1:250,000.

Scott, W.E., 1982, Surficial geologic map of the eastern Snake River Plain and adjacent areas, 111° to 115° W, Idaho and Wyoming: U.S. Geological Survey Miscellaneous Investigations Map I-1372, scale 1:250,000.

U.S. Geological Survey, 1975, Geologic Map of Yellowstone National Park, U.S. Geological Survey Miscellaneous Geologic Investigations Series Map I-711, scale 1:125,000

Whitehead, R.L., 1986, Geohydrologic Framework of the Snake River Plain, Idaho and Eastern Oregon, U.S. Geological Survey Hydrologic Investigations Map HA-681, scale 1:1,000,000

Whitehead, R.L., 1992, Geohydrologic Framework of the Snake River Plain Regional Aquifer System, Idaho and Eastern Oregon, U.S. Geological Survey Professional Paper 1408-B, 32 p.

Worl, R.G., Kiilsgaard, T.H., Bennett, E.H., Link, P.K., Lewis, R.S., Mitchell, V.E., Johnson, K.M., and Snyder, L.D., 1991, Geologic Map of the Hailey 1° x 2° quadrangle, Idaho: U.S. Geological Survey Open-File Report 91-340, scale 1:250,000.

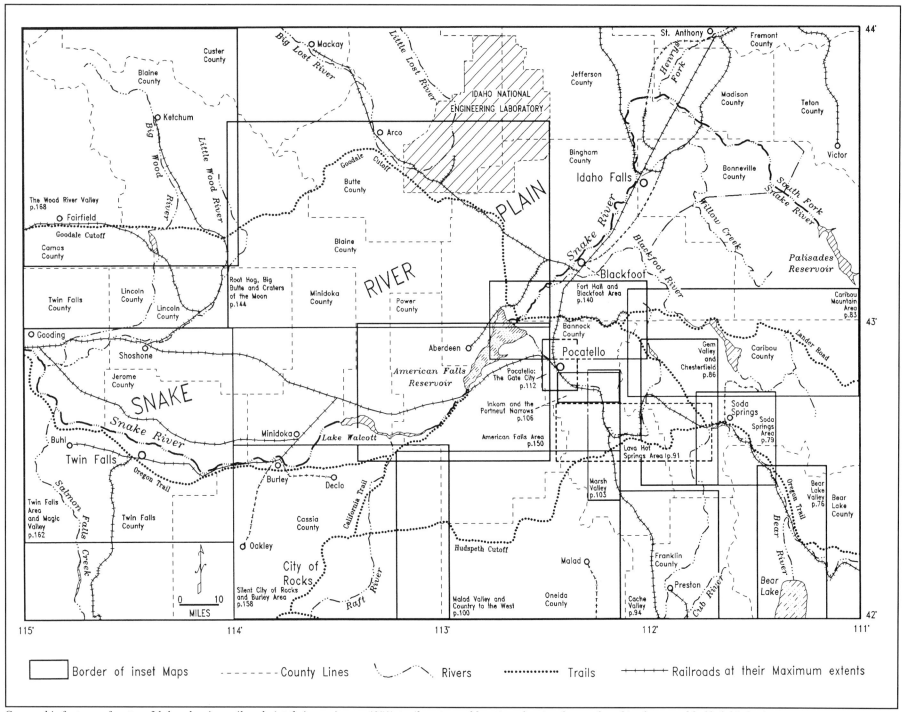

Custer
County

Blaine
County

Mackay

Big Lost River

Little Lost River

IDAHO NATIONAL
ENGINEERING LABORATORY

Jefferson
County

St. Anthony

Fremont
County

Henry's Fork

Madison
County

Teton
County

Victor

Ketchum

The Wood River Valley
p.168

Fairfield

Goodale Cutoff

Camas
County

Arco

Goodale Cutoff

Butte
County

Blaine
County

Bingham
County

Idaho Falls

Bonneville
County

Snake River

South Fork Snake River

Willow Creek

Palisades
Reservoir

PLAIN

RIVER

Blackfoot River

Caribou
Mountain
Area
p.83

Twin Falls
County

Lincoln
County

Lincoln
County

Minidoka
County

Power
County

Root Hog, Big
Butte and Craters
of the Moon
p.144

Blackfoot

Fort Hall and
Blackfoot Area
p.140

Bannock
County

Gem Valley
and
Chesterfield
p.86

Caribou
County

Lander Road

Gooding

Shoshone

Jerome
County

SNAKE

Snake River

Aberdeen

American Falls
Reservoir

Pocatello

Pocatello:
The Gate City
p.112

Inkom and the
Portneuf Narrows
p.106

Soda
Springs

Soda
Springs
Area
p.79

Buhl

Twin Falls

Oregon Trail

Minidoka

Lake Walcott

Lava Hot
Springs Area p.91

American Falls Area
p.150

Twin Falls
Area
and Magic
Valley
p.162

Salmon Falls Creek

Twin Falls
County

Burley

Declo

California Trail

Marsh
Valley
p.103

Bear
Lake
Valley
p.76

Bear
Lake
County

Oregon Trail

Oakley

Cassia
County

Silent City of Rocks
and Burley Area
p.158

City of
Rocks

Raft River

Hudspeth Cutoff

Malad

Franklin
County

Preston

Bear River

Cub River

Bear
Lake

0   10
MILES

Malad Valley and
Country to the West
p.100

Oneida
County

Cache
Valley
p.94

Border of inset Maps   County Lines   Rivers   Trails   Railroads at their Maximum extents

Geographic features of eastern Idaho, showing railroads (at their maximum, 1950), trail routes and location of regional maps found in the second half of this book.

34

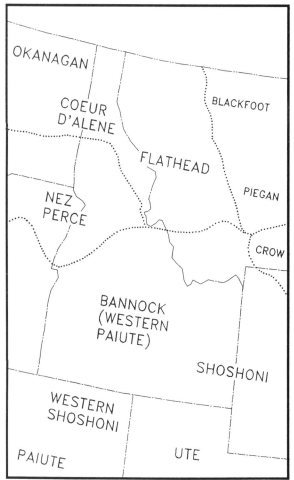

Map showing general areas inhabited by Native American tribes in Idaho, early 1800s. Modified from Beck and Haase (1989, map 8).

Native Americans and the Fur Trappers

The Pacific Northwest was populated by several native tribes and all early European visitors had contact with one or more of them. These relationships ranged from friendly visits to violent encounters. Overall, at the outset, relationships were cordial and often mutually advantageous. As time went on and the threat of loss of food sources and free movement increased, tensions developed to the detriment of the native population. The superior technology of the Europeans, their unity and cohesive purposes, plus the overwhelming influence of military power, forced native populations into increasingly unfavorable circumstances and resulted ultimately in their total subjection.

Native Populations

Native populations were widespread, although seldom in large social groups. To the white men, the Native Americans had apparent homogeneity, but cultural and language variations were extensive. The popula-

Petroglyphs on basalt boulder south of Ross Park in Pocatello. The dark surface of basalt was particularly easy to carve and is one of the main places where Native American rock art is found. The petroglyphs are less than 10,000 years old, (October, 1992).

tions have been classified by five distinct language groups: north of the Salmon River were the Kutenai (Flathead), the Coeur d'Alene and the Nez Perce; south of the Salmon were the Shoshoni (or Shoshone) and the Northern Paiute (now known as Bannock). Most of these identifying names are French words.

The two southern groups differ from the three northern groups both in language and in culture. Today, almost all of the Shoshone and Bannocks live on the Fort Hall Indian Reservation. The Shoshone form the great majority. A few tribal members live on the Duck Valley Reservation in southwestern Idaho.

Antiquity of Native Americans in Idaho

Archeology keeps pushing back in time estimates of how long native populations have lived in the Snake River Plain area. Excavations of inhabited sites now indicate there have been humans in southern Idaho for at least 11,000 years. Whether these residents were the ancestors of the current tribes is a subject of debate (Swanson, 1972; Lohse and Holmer, 1990). Certainly, peoples existed in the wetter, more habitable areas of the Pacific coast for a longer period. Over time, settlement spread into arid desert lands as far south as the Mexican border and into the deserts of southern Idaho and northern Utah.

Prior to the introduction of the horse, the Indians of Idaho apparently lacked permanent band organization, formal chieftainship and tribal political unification; rather they existed in groups of family-clusters. By the mid-eighteenth century, however, contacts with European culture and the acquisition of horses brought about a transformation in the native way of life. Political organization developed, new sources of food became available, and increased mobility permitted wide-ranging contacts with other native populations. Apparently, yearly festivals took place, attended by tribes from eastern Oregon and Washington, along with the northern and southern Idaho tribes mentioned above and tribes from Utah.

The Bannock and the Shoshoni

Very early in this development, members of the Northern Paiute (Bannock) population from Oregon who adopted the horse culture began to associate with the mounted Shoshoni bands, joining them in hunting expeditions. They intermarried and ultimately became bilingual and culturally and politically integrated. Sven Liljeblad (1959) noted that nowhere was there a Bannock society separated culturally and politically from the Shoshoni society. Thus he considered this to be not the combination of two differing cultures, but of two different languages into a new culture. The Paiute speakers who melded into the Shoshoni horse groups called themselves "pannakwaty," meaning, presumably, "being on the west side" (of the water, or river). Early white men writing of this used various terms such as "Pannacks" or "Bonacks" and ultimately the term came to be "Bannock."

The range of the Shoshoni-Paiute tribes was in southern Idaho and northern Utah. Identification of various groups was often related to their foods, such as

Portrait of Pat Tahee (Tyhee), early 1900s. Mary Garvey photograph, Wrensted collection, Idaho Museum of Natural History.

Portrait of two Native American Women, Old Wazipe (left) and "Old Mari: ci"; photo taken between 1895-1912, probably before 1900. Benedicte Wrensted Photograph, Idaho Museum of Natural History.

"Sheepeaters," "Salmon eaters" and "Buffalo eaters." The names changed often and had little significance to the tribes themselves. Such terms did not denote culturally distinct, politically independent tribes and are interchangeable, depending on circumstances.

The two languages (Shoshone and Paiute) still exist on the Fort Hall Reservation, although very few can now speak Paiute. The culture and skills which sustained the native tribes of southern Idaho have nearly disappeared; most of the cultural attributes now propounded have been relearned in recent times, through efforts to reestablish old values.

> **As Dr. Sven Liljeblad stated in 1959:**
> "Whether the Indians will survive as a separate people or be entirely absorbed by the white man's society is a question the future must solve."

References on Idaho Native Americans

Boag, P.G., 1993, "The Indians of this Place are Snakes in the Grass" The Overlander Perspective on Native Americans in Southern Idaho, 1836-1860: Idaho Yesterdays, v.37, no.3, p.16-26.

Liljeblad, Sven, 1959, Indian People of Idaho, in S. Beal and M. Wells, eds., History of Idaho: Pocatello, Lewis Historical Publishing, p. 29-59.

Liljeblad, Sven, 1960, The Indians of Idaho: Idaho Yesterdays, v. 4, no. 3, p. 22-28.

Lohse, E.S., and Holmer, R.N., editors, 1990, Fort Hall and the Shoshone-Bannock: Pocatello, Idaho, The Idaho State University Press, 59 p.

Madsen, B.D., 1980, The Northern Shoshoni: Caldwell, Idaho, The Caxton Printers, Ltd., 259 p.

Madsen, B.D., 1986, Chief Pocatello: The "White Plume": Salt Lake City, University of Utah Press, 142 p.

Madsen, B.D., 1958, The Bannock of Idaho: Caldwell, Idaho, The Caxton Printers Ltd., 382 p.

Merkley, Anne, 1994, Cultural Contrast and Material Change: The Wrensted-Garvey photographs of Northern Shoshone and Bannock Indians: M.A. Thesis, Department of Anthropology, Idaho State University, 296 p.

Swanson, Earl, 1957, "Since time immemorial . . . " The Problem of Shoshone Chronology: Idaho Yesterdays, v. 1, no. 4, p. 21-26.

Swanson, Earl H., 1972, Birch Creek: Human Ecology in the Cool Desert of the Northern Rocky Mountains, 9000 B.C.-A.D. 1850: Pocatello, Idaho, The Idaho State University Press.

Indians at the Fort Hall Drug Store, about 1895. The numbers are as follows. 1. Tom Edmo; 2. Chas. Deepwater; 3. Percy Edmo; 4. Canaker (Canker) Johnson; 5. Johnnie Gibson; 6. Geo. Edmo, 7. Chief Arimo; the white man is Cye Napper, druggist. Abe Lillibridge collection, Eli Oboler Library, Idaho State University.

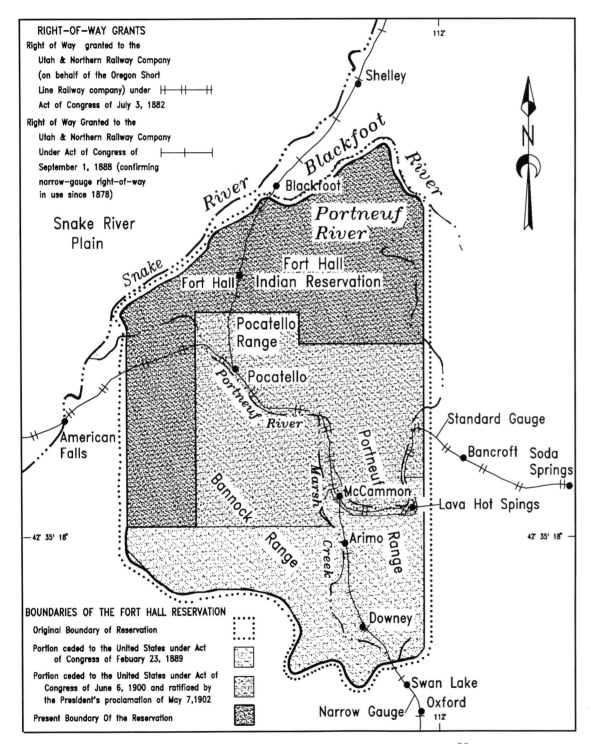

Snake River
Plain

112°

N

Shelley

Blackfoot River

Snake River

Blackfoot

Portneuf
River

Fort Hall
Indian Reservation

Fort Hall

Pocatello
Range

Portneuf River

Pocatello

American
Falls

Standard Gauge

Bancroft   Soda
Springs

— 42° 35' 18"

Marsh Creek

Bannock
Range

Portneuf Range

McCammon

Lava Hot Spings

42° 35' 18" —

Arimo

Downey

Swan Lake
Oxford

Narrow Gauge   112°

Teepees camped in the Pocatello Valley, 1895. View looks north to the west side of the valley near Grant Street at the Riverside Golf Course. Photo used courtesy of the Idaho Museum of Natural History and the Smithsonian Institution.

Painting in the Union Pacific Depot in Pocatello, painted by Bethel M. Farley in 1943, (picture taken in April, 1996). The view looks south toward Kinport Peak and the Bannock Range in 1878, with the narrow gauge railroad train headed north to Eagle Rock, Monida Pass, and the Montana mines. Chief Pocatello and his band survey the scene on the left, with Mink Creek and Scout Mountain behind them in the distance. The narrow gauge depot was probably a boxcar located, as shown, near the intersection of Jefferson Ave. and Alameda Road. The view is fictionalized as there was never a depot of this size.

The reduction in size of the Fort Hall Indian Reservation and early rail routes, 1868-1902. The Bannock and Shoshone were relocated to the Fort Hall Indian Reservation beginning in 1869. The original reservation was larger than modern day Bannock County and extended south to Red Rock Pass and east nearly to Bancroft. The growth of American civilization, especially the building of the railroads, caused two reductions of the reservation, in 1889 and 1902. Redrawn from Union Pacific Railroad map.

The Northwest Frontier 1800-1840

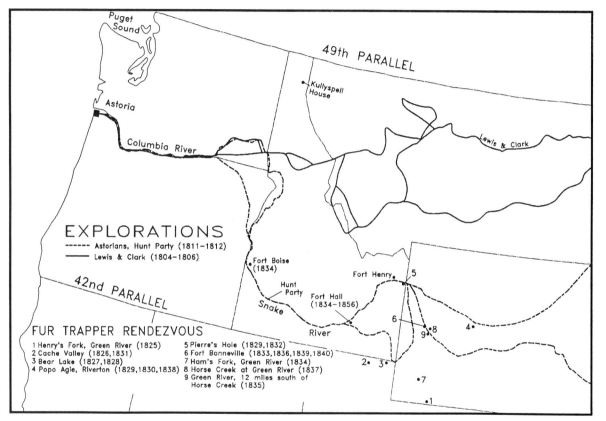

EXPLORATIONS

----- Astorians, Hunt Party (1811-1812)
——— Lewis & Clark (1804-1806)

FUR TRAPPER RENDEZVOUS

1 Henry's Fork, Green River (1825)
2 Cache Valley (1826,1831)
3 Bear Lake (1827,1828)
4 Popo Agie, Riverton (1829,1830,1838)
5 Pierre's Hole (1829,1932)
6 Fort Bonneville (1833,1836,1839,1840)
7 Ham's Fork, Green River (1834)
8 Horse Creek at Green River (1837)
9 Green River, 12 miles south of Horse Creek (1835)

Routes of Lewis and Clark and Hunt Party explorations plus locations of Mountain Men Rendezvous, early 19th century, after Lavender (1965) and Beck and Haase (1989, maps 25 and 26).

Dividing Territory Between Nations

As the 19th Century opened, the far northwest corner of the North American continent was almost unknown but was about to become an object of interest and conflicting claims. Little was known about the geography and resources of the area. The newly formed United States was occupied fully with the development of its east coast and with a growing interest in the Mississippi Valley. Most Americans found the Pacific Northwest just too far away. Explorers had sailed along the Pacific Coast, and by 1792, the mouth of the Columbia River had been discovered by the American captain Robert Gray. He was followed a month later by the British sea captain, George Vancouver, who gave his name to an island and to cities in Washington and British Columbia. Vancouver named Mt. Hood for his first mate and Mt. Rainier for the 1st Lord of the British Admiralty. In 1793, Canadian Alexander Mackenzie crossed the continent to reach the Pacific Ocean. Because of voyages by Spanish explorers, Spain made vague claims to the Pacific Northwest. Russians in Alaska were looking south.

Some American politicians and entrepreneurs advocated expanding trade between the new nation and the Orient through exchanging furs, obtained from native tribes on the Pacific Coast, for spices, silk and other exotic products. In 1800, incoming President Thomas Jefferson was among the visionaries who foresaw uses for the probable resources of the Northwest. While serving as United States Ambassador to France, he had learned of the possible fur trade in the western lands and he believed the United States would expand to the west.

The Louisiana Purchase

After a long period of secret treaties between Spain and France over the area vaguely referred to as "Louisiana," Spain returned control of the area to France by the secret treaty of San Ildefonso on October 1, 1800, although possession was not transferred until late 1802. Shortly thereafter, Napoleon Bonaparte, who needed money to finance his English wars, offered to sell the area to the United States. Napoleon feared that conflict with Great Britain would result in the loss of "Louisiana" without benefit to France. President Jefferson promptly accepted the offer, and in 1803, the Louisiana Purchase was made.

The boundaries of the area involved in the Louisiana Purchase were uncertain. It took a number of agreements over a period of years to establish the limits. Roughly, the Purchase involved the area drained by the Missouri and Mississippi Rivers, with the eastern boundary being the Mississippi River and the western boundary being the Continental Divide, excluding Texas. While none of the area of the Pacific Northwest was included, the Louisiana Purchase encouraged interest in and ultimately movement into the Northwest by both the United States and Great Britain.

The location of the boundary between the United States and Canada remained uncertain for many years. East of the Continental Divide, an international boundary at the 49th Parallel was settled in 1818 by the Treaty of Ghent, ending the War of 1812. The status of the Northwest area, west of the Divide, remained in dispute. The Treaty established the area as far north as Russia, at 54° 40' (the present southern boundary of Alaska at Juneau), as neutral ground, open to the citizens of both countries for a period of 10 years, at which time the matter of its ownership was to be taken up again. Russia's interest in the Northwest area was abandoned by 1812 when it devoted its efforts on the Pacific Coast to building posts in California in the vicinity of San Francisco.

Spain's interest in the area north of the 42nd Parallel was eliminated by the Adams-Onis Treaty of 1819 settling claims of the United States to Florida and areas in western North America. This was the origin of the arbitrary southern boundary of what was to become Idaho territory.

Commercial exploitation of the Northwest had not waited for the politicians to decide whose country owned what. Under the excuse of discovering what manner of territory the United States had acquired from France, Jefferson sent an expedition, under the joint command of Meriwether Lewis and William Clark, to the western border of the Louisiana Purchase. Secret orders were for the party to continue on to the Pacific Ocean.

Lewis and Clark

In 1804 the Lewis and Clark expedition set out, reaching the Pacific at the mouth of the Columbia River in late 1805. The report of this party together with the information from Alexander Mackenzie following his 1793 journey excited fur trapping interests in both countries and soon the area swarmed with trappers. This opened a 30 year period of competition and conflict. The disputes were finally settled in 1846 when the northern border between the United States and Canada was established by extending the line along the 49th Parallel to Puget Sound.

Aerial view looking southeast across the Snake River and the Fort Hall Bottoms, above the site of Old Fort Hall. Spring Creek meanders across the farmland in the upper part of the photo, (May, 1989).

The North West Company

Trappers ranged over the broad area of the Northwest beginning in 1807 with a party from the British commercial North West Company under the leadership of David Thompson. In 1808 Thompson established a trading post in what was to become northern Idaho, where the Clark Fork River enters Lake Pend Oreille, and named it Kullyspell House. American trappers of Manuel Lisa's Missouri Fur Company, meanwhile, were working the upper Missouri River area. A small party under Andrew Henry, escaping from the fierce Blackfeet Indians in the Three Forks area (now south-ern Montana), moved over the mountains into today's Idaho and, in the fall of 1809 built a wintering post on the Henry's Fork of the Snake River near present day St. Anthony, known ever since as Fort Henry.

The Astorians

The entrepreneur and aggressive American fur merchant John Jacob Astor, in 1811, sent two expeditions to establish a permanent post in the Northwest. One party moved by sea in the good ship Tonquin, to the mouth of the Columbia River and built Fort Astoria. The second expedition was an overland party, under the direction of Wilson Price Hunt, that traveled through southern Idaho, reaching Astoria in 1812. The Hunt Party was the first American group to explore the Snake River.

Astor's venture failed when British interests acquired Fort Astoria under the threat of capture by naval units during the War of 1812. Thereafter, most of the fur trapping and trading west of the Rocky Mountains was handled by British interests, first by the North West Company; and after the 1821 merger with Hudson's Bay Company, by that company until the 1850s.

Overtrapping to make a Barren Zone

The trappers of both countries ranged throughout the Northwest. Concern over intrusions by American trappers prompted Hudson's Bay Company to depart from its usual emphasis on conservation and to embark on a plan to establish a barren zone along the Snake River in eastern Idaho by trapping out all fur bearing animals. The policy was pursued vigorously in the 1820s by British explorer-trapper Peter Skene Ogden. It largely succeeded in reducing the supply of available pelts until well into the 1830s.

American fur interests involved mainly independent trappers who operated mostly in the Rocky Mountains east of the Snake River although some adventurous trappers occasionally moved into the areas of British dominance. There were also a few American companies that employed their own trappers in the Missouri River watershed east of the Continental Divide. These diverse and hardy mountain men covered the huge territory of the northwest, incidentally exploring streams, mountain passes, animal routes and other features, so that by the time fur trapping diminished in the late 1830s, the nature of the terrain was well known.

Trading Posts: Fort Hall

Settlers were beginning to move into and through the Snake River area in the 1840s and 1850s, but settlement was almost nonexistent in what was to become Idaho. By the time the northern boundary of the United States had been established in 1846, the only places of permanent residence in the entire vast area east of the Cascades were Fort Hall and Fort Boise in the valley of the Snake River. Fort Hall, near the intersection of the Blackfoot River and the Snake, was established in 1834 by Nathaniel J. Wyeth, an American businessman who built the post in order to dispose of trading goods for which he had no use. Fort Boise, near the intersection of the Boise River and the Snake in western Idaho, was built in 1834 by Hudson's Bay representatives to neutralize Fort Hall's influence. Hudson's Bay Company ultimately acquired and operated both posts until the 1850s when the Company withdrew entirely from the United States. American fur trappers held annual Rendezvous at various spots in the Rocky Mountain area. Two rendezvous (1829 and 1832) were held in Idaho, both in Pierre's Hole (Teton Valley).

When the fur trade industry deteriorated in the 1840s Idaho had become less desirable as a source of furs, mainly due to overtrapping. Idaho, lacking good farmland or discovered mineral wealth, was totally undesirable as a place of settlement to the pioneers moving west around this time. However, there were areas eagerly sought after by settlers and miners in Oregon and California to the west. The final expansion of the United States westward across the entire continent was about to begin.

References

Beck, W.A. and Haase, Y.D., 1989, Historical Atlas of the American West: Norman, Oklahoma, University of Oklahoma Press, 78 maps.

Lavender, David S., 1965, The Great West: New York, N.Y., American Heritage Publishing Co.

Lohse, E.S. and Holmer, R.N., editors, 1990 (2nd printing 1992), Fort Hall and the Shoshone-Bannock: Pocatello, Idaho, The Idaho State University Press, 60 p.

Site of Fort Hall on the south bank of the Snake River. The fort was established by Nathaniel J. Wyeth in 1834. The walls of the Fort are visible, though indistinct, in the ground halfway between the wide turn-around at the end of the road and the trees at the edge of the river. To the right (northeast) of the Fort the straight track of the trail to the Fort crosses the rough ground and slough, heading southwest. Most sources claim that this was the main Oregon Trail, but we believe that in later years the main Trail did not pass the Fort, see text, (May, 1989).

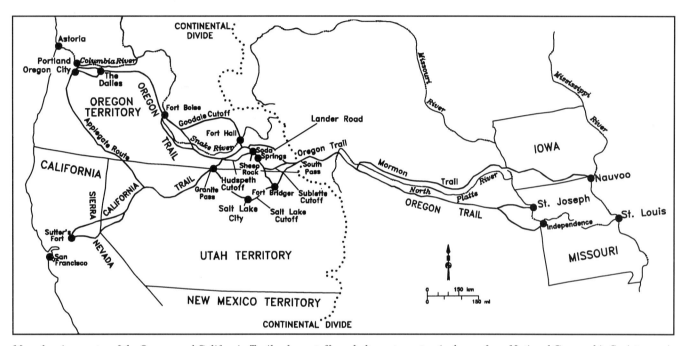

Map showing routes of the Oregon and California Trails plus cutoffs and alternate routes, (redrawn from National Geographic Society map).

Replica of Oregon Trail wagon, east of Declo, Idaho, (July 1993). Wagon was part of the sesquicentennial (150th anniversary) Oregon Trail wagon train.

Birth of the Trails

For various reasons, in the 1830s and 1840s, interest began to grow throughout the settled parts of the United States in the area west of the Mississippi River. Here was land for the taking, places where people could get a new start in life. There were newspaper articles praising the little-known areas. Returning missionaries told of the wonders of the distant lands. A few people started out and the trickle of settlers grew.

Mountain men knew the way. There were animal trails to follow, streams and rivers to furnish water and enough feed for animals. The pioneering spirit of the country was aroused.

This was not an organized migration. The government did not establish programs to encourage travel to the West. No roads were built, no preparations for a mass movement of settlers were undertaken. The whole idea just grew. Small groups of people would decide to go west. Parties would gather at jumping off places where they joined others who were ready to go and a wagon train would be organized.

For the first few years, before guidebooks became available, it was necessary for a wagon train to hire a leader, usually a retired fur trapper, who knew the country and could help the inexperienced travelers find their way. Some of the pioneers were experienced in handling large numbers of animals and did not find the prospect of a 4 or 5 month trip into a wilderness to be daunting. Many, however, were from cities in the east or mid-west and had no concept of what they were getting into. It took a lot of courage, and not everyone had it. Many turned back.

Life was less complicated then. The American diet was limited and the usual foods could be carried easily. Barrels of flour or corn meal, in which eggs were stored for safe carrying, sides of salt pork and bags of beans made up the usual fare. Travelers expected to supplement these staples on the trail with vegetables, fish and game. Clothing was rough and simple.

The large Conestoga wagons, used in an earlier time when east coast settlers were moving into the Mississippi area, were unsuited for this movement. They were too bulky and heavy. Instead, the pioneers used smaller, slab-sided wagons which could be floated across streams. These were pulled either by horses or oxen. Families took everything they owned and brought all of their animals. The draft animals would be used in farming when the trip was over.

Oregon Trail ruts southeast of Chesterfield, (October, 1986).

The Oregon-California Trail

The Oregon-California Trail was around 2,200 miles long. Beginning around 1840, it departed from points along the Missouri River, such as Independence and St. Joseph, Missouri, and Omaha, Nebraska. In the early years, before the trail was improved and bridges were built, the trip took 4 to 6 months, depending on the weather, difficulties along the way, the experience of the travelers or their guide and so forth. In later years, the trip took somewhat less time.

Departure dates depended mainly on the weather. Teams could not travel until grasses began growing for feed. The ground had to be dry enough so the loaded wagons would not sink into mud. But the trip had to begin as early as possible so that the Sierra Nevada, the Blue Mountains and the Cascades could be crossed before winter snows caught the travelers. Departure was usually between mid-May and early June, depending on whether the spring was dry or wet.

The limitations imposed by the finite pulling power of draft animals tended to cause the Trails to follow water routes where possible. The relatively easy grade and open nature of the country at South Pass, Wyoming, the principal pioneer crossing of the Continental Divide, simplified the passage between the watersheds of the Atlantic and the Pacific.

In open areas, wagons could fan out over a broad area to avoid traveling in the dust of those in front, but in hilly areas this was not possible. Until brakes were put on wagons in the 1850s, steep descents were a problem. Sometimes ropes were used to lower each wagon or wheels would be chained so the wagon could slide down the grade. Runaway wagons were one of the many hazards of the trip, with damage to the loads and injury to passengers and draft animals.

Until 1847, the travelers were mainly settlers headed for Oregon. The Mormon emigration, led by Brigham Young to the promised Zion in Utah, started that year. The California Trail was lightly traveled until after the discovery of gold in 1848. Starting in 1849, travel greatly increased, most of it headed for the gold fields. One author estimates that between 1840 and 1860, the principal years of the trails, 300,000 people made the trip west, with approximately 47,000 Mormon Pioneers going to Utah, approximately 53,000 farmers ending up in Oregon and around 200,000 gold seekers traveling to California.

The Oregon-California Trails were not the only routes taken by pioneers. More persons traveled to California by other routes, overland along the Santa Fe Trail through the southwest deserts, by roads through central America and by ship to Panama or around Cape Horn.

Trail Routes

After the Oregon Trail negotiated South Pass, a variety of routes and cutoffs was utilized. Some pioneers followed the main, or original Oregon Trail across the Green River to Fort Bridger, near Evanston, Wyoming, then down the Bear River past Soda Springs, Idaho. Others took the Sublette Cutoff, a shorter but drier route reaching the Bear River in the vicinity of Cokeville, Wyoming. A few miles west of Soda Springs, at Sheep Rock (also called Soda Point), the Oregon and original California Trails headed northwest across

Following the Goodale Cutoff north toward the Big Butte. Photo taken south of Root Hog, (June, 1990).

Robust growth of sage and rabbitbrush along the Oregon Trail near Milner Dam, east of Twin Falls, (October, 1992).

Gem Valley. The trails crossed the headwaters of the Portneuf River north of what was to become Chesterfield, rounded the north side of North Putnam Mountain, and dropped down past Big Springs to the Snake River bottoms and the area of Hudson's Bay Company trading post of Fort Hall.

Hudspeth Cutoff

Beginning in 1849, most of the California-bound pioneers utilized Hudspeth's Cutoff, which departed from the main Oregon-California Trail by heading straight west at Sheep Rock. Hudspeth's Cutoff wound through mountainous country north and west of present-day Malad City before rejoining the California Trail on the west side of the Raft River Valley on Cassia Creek near the present day town of Malta. Hudspeth and his fellow guide Myers felt their route would save over one hundred miles. In fact, the route eliminated only around 25 miles and there was no saving of time. On top of that, the much more difficult Hudspeth route had less water and feed and was harder on animals and equipment. Nevertheless, thousands of Americans yet to come, true to their national temperament, would take the cutoffs, believing that by going west rather than northwest they would be able to get ahead of others and reach California first.

Lander Trail

Of the various routes of the trails, only one was deliberately laid out and constructed--the Lander Trail (or, to use its official, government-issue name: "The Fort Kearney, South Pass and Honey Lake Wagon Road"). With the growing population on the Pacific Coast in the

Writing by pioneers at Register Rock along the Oregon Trail in the Silent City of Rocks, (September, 1987).

1850s, there was need for an adequate military road to permit the movement of troops for protection of these areas. Sectionalism in Congress prior to the Civil War prevented agreement on a route for a railroad. As the next best thing, the U.S. Congress authorized construction of an adequate wagon road. Ultimately, the only part of the road to be constructed was from a point several miles east of South Pass to a junction with the Oregon Trail a few miles east of Fort Hall, running generally north of the Oregon-California Trails. The road opened in 1858, but while it had better water and feed than the main trail, it came too late to attract much travel and was not heavily used. The area traversed by the route north and east of Soda Springs remains today wild and beautiful country.

Salt Lake Cutoff

As the Latter-Day Saint towns in the Salt Lake Valley grew in the 1850s, increasing numbers of wagons followed the Mormon Trail west from Fort Bridger to the Salt Lake Valley and rejoined the California Trail southwest of the Silent City of Rocks. After that point was reached, all travelers to California used a single route, crossing Granite Pass in southern Idaho to reach the Humboldt River in northern Nevada. They then followed it to the Sierra Nevada. Most Oregon-bound pioneers took the main road past Fort Hall.

Fort Hall and West

Hudson's Bay supplies were expensive and many travelers could not afford them. Fort Hall was abandoned in 1856, without appreciable effect on the trail. Even when it was open, there was little reason for most pioneers to stop at the Fort. Staying on the southeast side of Spring Creek avoided a difficult stream crossing, so it seems logical that the main trail bypassed Fort Hall. Accounts are not very clear, but the ruts which are at the Fort do not seem to reflect travel by over 50,000 pioneers and their wagons.

South of Fort Hall the Trail headed southwest along Spring Creek to a crossing of the Portneuf River. The most-used trail followed the south side of the Snake River to the often difficult and dangerous Three Island Ford near present day Glenns Ferry, crossing to the north side and on to the Boise River Valley. An alternate route, which was drier and longer, stayed on the south side of the Snake to the mouth of the Boise River. Here the north-side travelers recrossed the Snake and a single route headed northwesterly through Oregon to The Dalles, where travelers could go down the Columbia by boat to the terminus of the Oregon Trail at Oregon City on the Willamette River south of Portland, or could use the Barlow Trail around Mt. Hood and on to the terminus.

Goodale Cutoff

There were several branches and cutoffs in Idaho. In the vicinity of Fort Hall, a somewhat difficult route headed north across the Snake River Plain and along the south side of the mountains of central Idaho to a junction with the main trail near present day Mountain Home. This was the Goodale or Jeffrey's Cutoff, which was opened as an emigrant route by John T. Jeffrey in 1852 or 1854. Timothy Goodale led a wagon train consisting of 1,095 people over the route in late summer, 1862. These emigrants and most who subsequently traveled the cut off, were miners and their families seeking gold in central or western Idaho.

Northside Route

Although most travelers crossed to the north side of the Snake River at Three Island Ford, it has been suggested by some that there was a trail along the north side of the Snake River all the way from Fort Hall. A total absence of surface water on the north side of the Snake River plus the lack of access for animals over the lava cliffs to the Snake River below would seem to preclude much use of a northside route.

Applegate Route

Some Oregon-bound travelers after 1846 followed the California Trail to western Nevada and then up into Oregon and the upper reaches of the Willamette River, along what was known as the Applegate Route. This longer, drier and much more dangerous route was not heavily used.

End of the Trail

The stream of families moving west by wagon continued at a reduced rate into the 20th Century. One could not, after all, easily ship one's total belongings and farm animals by train. It is said that use of the Oregon Trail came to an end not because of the railroads, but because of the automobile.

Wagon Ruts

There are many areas in southern Idaho where wagon ruts of the various routes can be seen. A few traces of the trails are clearly visible, but in most areas, farming activities or roads or civilization have obliterated the ruts. Very often the route of the trail can still be discerned, even in areas where the actual ruts are not visible, by a more luxuriant growth of grasses or

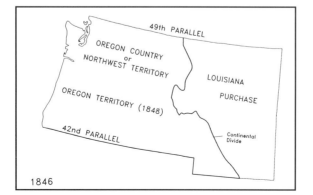

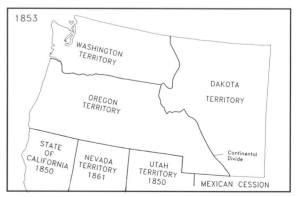

Territorial divisions before and after the Mexican War (1848), after Beck and Haase (1989, Map 41).

Aerial view of the Twin Sisters, at the south edge of the Silent City of Rocks. The Sisters were landmarks on the California Trail, which can be seen crossing through the gap in the rocks at the base of the photograph. The trail can be clearly seen to the right of the gap. The left Twin Sister is composed of Archean granitic gneiss that crystallized about 2.6 billion years ago. The right Twin Sister is made of Oligocene granite of the Almo Pluton that cooled about 30 million years ago, (September, 1988).

sagebrush where the droppings of millions of animals fertilized the soil. Often the wagon route can be more easily observed from the air than on the ground.

Marking the locations of the trails and the various cutoffs is a difficult and frustrating activity. Markers are commonly defaced and trail segments are destroyed each year by new construction and farming activities. Efforts to mark the trail are uneven and depend on the enthusiasm of local residents. Sometimes, overzealous residents have marked a trail's location incorrectly (see photo to right). Some trail-marking projects are becoming more effective, especially those of the Oregon-California Trails Association (OCTA) and its various state subsidiaries. The best single reference for locating the trail in Idaho is "The Oregon Trail Revisited" by Gregory M. Franzwa. The many diaries and journals of travelers which exist in various museums provide fascinating reading. Several books and pamphlets have been published about aspects of the trails and the western migration. A few references are listed at the end of this section.

References

Beck, W.A., and Haase, Y.D., 1989, Historical atlas of the American West: Norman, Oklahoma, University of Oklahoma Press, 78 maps.

Burnett, Betty, 1985, Goodale's Cutoff: Overland Journal, Winter 1985 issue, p. 30-34.

Carney, Ellen, 1992, The Oregon Trail: Ruts, Rogues and Reminiscences: Wayan, Idaho, Traildust Publishing Co., 332 p.

Etulain, R.W., and Marley, Bert W. editors, 1974, The Idaho Heritage: A collection of Historical Essays: Pocatello, Idaho, The Idaho State University Press, 230 p.

Franzwa, G.M., 1982, Maps of the Oregon Trail: Gerald, Mo, The Patrice Press, 292 p.

Franzwa, G.M., 1980, The Oregon Trail Revisited: Gerald Mo., The Patrice Press, 436 p.

Gibbons, B., 1986, The Itch to Move West: Life and Death on the Oregon Trail: National Geographic, v. 170, no. 2, p. 147-177.

Haines, Aubrey, 1973, Historic Sites along the Oregon Trail: Denver Service Center, National Park Service.

Harstad, Peter J., 1968, The Lander Trail, Idaho Yesterdays: v. 12, no. 3, p. 14-28.

Hill, W.E., 1987, The Oregon Trail: Yesterday and Today: Caldwell, Idaho, The Caxton Printers, Ltd., 179 p.

Lavender, David S., 1963, Westward Vision: The Story of the Oregon Trail: New York, McGraw Hill Book Co.,

Merrill, I.R., 1990 Tim Goodale and his cutoff: A major trail segment during and after the fourth emigration wave: Overland Journal, v.8 no.3, p. 9-16.

Paden, Irene D., 1943, The Wake of the Prairie Schooner: New York, The Macmillian Co.

U.S. Department of the Interior, Bureau of Land Management and Idaho State Historical Society, 1993, Emigrant Trails of Southern Idaho: U.S. Department of the Interior, Bureau of Land Management, Idaho State Office, 3380 Americana Terrace, Boise, Idaho 83706, 233 p.

U.S. Department of the Interior, Bureau of Land Management, Guide to the Lander Cutoff, Oregon Trail (Map): Bureau of Land Management, Wyoming State Office.

Unruh, J.D., Jr., 1982 (reprint), The Plains Across: Chicago, Illinois, University of Illinois Press, 364p.

Incorrect Historical Marker, corner of Carter St. and S. 5th Ave., Idaho State University Campus, Pocatello. The monument was corrected in 1993. The Oregon Trail did not cross the Portneuf River in the Pocatello area.

6

Mormon Settlement of Southeastern Idaho

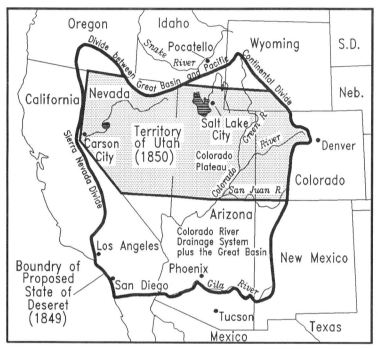

Map showing the borders of the State of Deseret as proposed by the Mormon leaders of Utah in 1849, (after Morgan, 1987).

run by the Mormon Church was offensive to many Americans.

California was admitted as a state in 1850. In 1851 the Territory (rather than the State) of Utah, which consisted of most of the central and eastern parts of Deseret, was established by Congress. Brigham Young became territorial governor. The choice of the name Utah, commemorating an Indian tribe the Mormons disparaged, was symbolic of the defeat of the Mormons' goals.

The State of Deseret lived on past its official death in 1851 in the Mormon way of life and the Mormon aspiration for home rule. Deseret lingered until the 1880s as a ghost state, with an active legislature (generally the same one that governed the Territory of Utah) that convened directly after the Utah legislature had adjourned. The "Deseret News" is the most visible remnant of the name which meant "honey bee" and was the symbol of the organized, patriarchal, communal system established by the Mormon apostles and pioneers. In many ways the validity of the concept of Deseret is demonstrated in the economic success of Utah and the worldwide expansion of the Mormon religion in the last 100 years.

Brigham Young and the State of Deseret

The Mormon Pioneers, led by Brigham Young to Utah in 1847, were Millennialists who believed the world would soon end. They saw themselves as estabishing the new Zion, where they would live in prosperity and autonomy during the prophesied destruction of the rest of godless humanity. The Lord had revealed to them via prophet Joseph Smith that they were God's Chosen People and that the national government was corrupt. From 1847 to 1894 there was recurring political conflict over the issue of whether the Saints were in control of their chosen land of Zion or whether their State of Deseret (or Utah) was subject to external governance from Washington D.C.

The Provisional State of Deseret was organized by the Mormon Church in 1849. It covered most of the Great Basin and Colorado River drainage basin. It extended on the east to the Continental Divide, and on the west to the Sierra Nevada and to what is now Los Angeles and San Diego. It demonstrated the grand scale with which the Mormon leaders thought and the unrestrained ambition with which they planned for the future.

The Mormons hoped that two states, Deseret and California, would be admitted to the union following the 1848 Treaty of Guadalupe Hidalgo. In this treaty, ending the Mexican War, Mexico ceded what is now New Mexico, Arizona, Nevada, California and Utah to the United States. The State of Deseret was proposed to Congress first in 1849, and three times further in the next 30 years, but the concept of a state organized and

The early Mormon leaders were articulate and inspiring writers.

"We have no business but to build up the kingdom of God, and preserve it and ourselves in it. Whether it is ploughing, sowing, harvesting, building, going into the canyon, or whatever it is we do, it is all within the pale of the kingdom of God, to forward his cause on the earth, to redeem and build up his Zion, and prepare ourselves." Brigham Young, December 27, 1857, quoted in Swetnam (1991, p. 7):

"The race is not always to the swift nor the battle to the strong, but to him that endures faithful to the end." Joseph F. Smith, September 30, 1877, paraphrasing Ecclesiastes, quoted in Swetnam, (1991, p. 57):

The "Utah War" and Johnston's Army

Driven by faith and well-supplied with the arrogance of God's Chosen People, Brigham Young and the twelve Mormon Apostles chose not to believe that the nationally mandated territory of Utah would stand. During the 1850s, the refusal by the Mormon leaders to accept the sovereignty of the United States government was seen by many national politicians as a manifestation of disloyalty to the U.S. similar to that being spawned in the secessionist movement of the South.

In 1857-58, a Federal army, led by Colonel A.S. Johnston, and commissioned by President Buchanan, was sent to Utah to establish control over the Mormons. Such an occupation, though certainly politically motivated, was not totally unprovoked. The early Mormons were zealous and proud of it; laws of the United States were sometimes held in disrespect; violent crimes against Gentiles (non-Mormons) were not uncommon. Perhaps the worst offense was the Mountain Meadows Massacre of 1857 in which a party of Gentile pioneers was decimated by Mormons in southern Utah.

The outcome of the occupation by Johnston's army was death of any reality of the lingering Mormon State of Deseret. Many of the far-flung Mormon settlements, from San Bernardino to Malad City, were abandoned in 1857, as the Saints retreated back to Utah. Salt Lake City was evacuated for a time and Brigham Young threatened to burn it to the ground rather than see it occupied by a "foreign army." In the end, the U.S. government peaceably imposed Governor Alfred Cumming on Utah.

Mormon Settlement of Idaho

There were six stages of Mormon settlement of present-day Idaho. In 1855, a preliminary settlement was attempted at Limhi (Lemhi) between present-day Leadore and Salmon. Fort Limhi was abandoned in 1858, because of Indian hostilities and as part of the retrenchment of Mormon expansion due to Johnston's army. A rush of migrants to Cache Valley occurred in 1860, after the occupation of Salt Lake City by Johnston's army. Franklin was founded in that year. In 1863, migration recurred, this time from Cache Valley to Bear Lake Valley, led by Mormon apostle Charles C. Rich. Within two years 16 separate communities had been founded. The fourth settlement group began in 1873 in what is now Cassia County and resulted in the founding of Elba, Almo, Albion and Oakley. In 1879, large groups moved from Cache Valley

into the Upper Snake River Valley. Eleven different communities were settled, including Rexburg, Menan, Salem, and Teton. Finally in the 1940s, and 1950s, farmers (Mormon and otherwise) migrated to the north side of the Snake River following the opening of reclamation projects in the Rupert and Emmett areas.

The Southern Boundary of Idaho

The northern boundary of Utah Territory was set at the 42nd Parallel, which had been the northern edge of Mexico at the time Spain gave up any claims north of this line in the Adams-Onis Treaty of 1819. The precise location on the ground of this boundary was a contentious issue, as most of the Mormon settlers in southeastern Idaho either believed they were, or wished they were, living in Utah (or Deseret), which was defined to included the drainage basin of the Bear River.

Oscar Sonnenkalb, a German surveyor, who lived in Oxford and Pocatello from 1881 to 1928 and describes life in early Idaho in an elegant little book edited by P.T. Harstad, quotes (1972, p. 2) a letter dated August 15, 1868 from LaFayette Cartee, Surveyor General of Idaho, who

> "urged the running of the boundary between the Idaho territory, Utah, and Nevada, at an early day . . . In the southern part of this country, particularly along the Bear River valley, is an extent of fertile country, and it is estimated that over 3,000 persons are settled here who refuse to pay taxes to this (Idaho) Territory, but pay both taxes and tithes to Utah . . . The consequence is, this country is, to all intents and purposes, disorganized."

A Government Survey in the early 1870s precisely located the 42nd Parallel and confirmed placement of the Idaho-Utah border. The U.S. Geological Survey places the date of the survey at 1871 (van Zandt, 1966). Sonnenkalb (Harstad, 1972) cites the date as 1872. Though no part of Utah had officially been north of the 42nd Parallel, a Mormon historian, quoted by Sonnenkalb, wrote that with the completion of the boundary survey,

> "that part of Utah north of the 42nd Parallel, became a part of Idaho, and the name of Oneida County was given to it."

Several times after 1872 the Mormon communities of the Bear River area attempted and failed to become annexed to Utah.

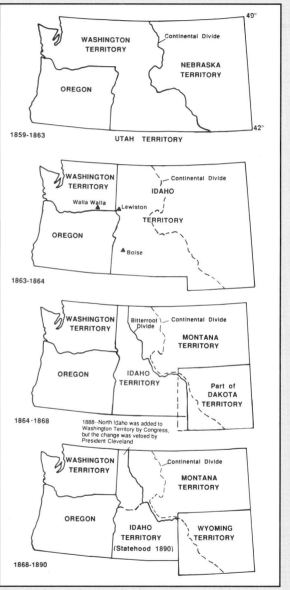

Historical map of various borders of the state of Idaho. After Wells (1966). Ironically the arbitrary southern border was never changed.

The master plans of the Mormon settlers were elegant and noble. Brigham Young sent these instructions to the new Idaho communities

"You are commencing anew, the soil, the air, the water are all pure and healthy. Do not suffer them to become polluted . . . Strive to preserve the elements from becoming contaminated . . . Keep your valleys pure, keep your towns pure, keep your hearts pure, and labor as hard as you can without injuring yourselves . . . Build cities, adorn your habitats, make gardens, orchards, and vineyards, and render the earth so pleasant that when you look upon your labours you may do so with pleasure, and that angels may delight to come and visit your beautiful locations . . . Your work is to beautify the face of the earth, until it shall become like the Garden of Eden." (Quoted in Arrington, 1979, p. 46).

The Effects of the Civil War in Eastern Idaho

Many Mormons viewed the outbreak of the Civil War in 1861 as the confirmation of Joseph Smith's prophecy that the national government was going to fall. The Mormon reluctance to support the Union was met during the war by U.S. Army opposition to Mormon expansion. The California Volunteers, led by Colonel Patrick E. Connor, were sent to Utah to keep watch on the Mormons when regular armed troops went east to serve in the Civil War. Connor hated Indians and to get even for Indian raids on white farmers and for raids on Oregon Trail emigrants, especially at Massacre Rocks along the Snake in the fall of 1862, his army massacred a large band of Shoshoni at Battle Creek north of Preston in January, 1863. This attack was partly designed to open up settlement of the area to non-Mormons (including the Morrisites, who were Mormon apostates), although it had the effect of allowing the Mormon population room to expand also.

The attitude of hostility toward Native Americans was not shared by Brigham Young and the Mormon settlers at least during initial settlement. Brigham noted that it was "manifestly more economical, and less expensive to feed and clothe (the Indians), than to fight them". He urged his followers to treat them with Christian values and respect:

"be just and quiet, firm and patient and benevolent, generous and watchful in all your intercourse with them; learn their language so that you can explain matters to them and pay them the full and just reward for their labor, and treat them in all respects as you would like to be treated" (Madsen, 1980, p. 30).

Polygamy and anti-Mormon laws

In Idaho the polygamy issue was to prove disastrous to Mormon goals for self-determination. Although fewer than 15% of Mormons were polygamists, many Church leaders were. This became a vehicle for religious persecution that resulted in the anti-Mormon political movement. From 1872 to 1892, this movement was dominant in Idaho politics. It molded the construction of the state.

In the 1870s and 1880s, Idaho Mormons voted Democratic as a bloc, as dictated by Church leaders. Due to Mormon block voting, the Democrats won the 1882 Idaho election despite a national Republican landslide. At a time so soon after the Civil War, when being Democratic came near to being equated with treason, this was fuel for anti-Mormon activism by Idaho Republicans. Furthermore, the polygamy issue became an emotional rallying point for individualistic Idahoans.

Edmonds-Tucker Act and Idaho Test Oath

In 1882, the U.S. Congress passed the Edmonds-Tucker Act, designed to eliminate polygamy. The Idaho Democratic party effectively betrayed its Mormon members soon after the 1882 election, by supporting anti-Mormon legislation in Idaho territory. The Idaho Test Oath, passed by the Idaho territorial legislature in 1884, disenfranchised anyone who "engaged in or belonged to an organization that advocated" bigamy or polygamy. The oath was designed to prevent Mormons from voting, holding political office, or sitting on juries. It succeeded. Prosecution of polygamist patriarchs led by U.S. Marshall Fred T. Dubois followed, and Mormon self-government became a dying dream.

"The effects of this unjust treatment of the Mormon population were, of course, very disastrous and disturbing ones. It poisoned all society relations between Mormons and Gentiles and led to many persecutions and unfriendly and hateful acts. Exaggerations in describing the supposed unhappy family relations of the Mormons were spread by their political enemies, and many settlers who had started a home and had successfully cultivated their lands left their farms in the fear of prosecutions and moved to new and remote valleys in the mountains to avoid spying in their family affairs."
(Oscar Sonnenkalb, *in* Harstad (editor, 1972, p. 17)).

"The Co-op" in Franklin, Idaho. Cooperative stores were part of the Mormon governance pattern. The building was built in the 1860s. Photo taken May, 1992.

The political cruelty of the anti-Mormon Idaho politicians of the 1880s fell on the broad shoulders of patriarchs who were accustomed to persecution and to fighting it with organization, community and faith. It was a classic harsh battle of late 19th century Victorian America. The end result of these political actions was to make the Mormons more self-sufficient and harden their opposition to the rest of the state of Idaho.

Idaho politicians have remained stubborn and cantankerous. Some aspects of Idaho politics have been as cruel in the 20th century as they were in the 19th.

State Boundaries

Just as North Idaho tried for 20 years to join with Washington, with which its economic system was more consistent, only to fail when the act of Congress establishing an expanded Territory of Washington was vetoed by President Cleveland in 1888, the Mormons of the Bear River area repeatedly tried and failed to be rejoined with their brethren in Utah.

Longtime Idaho historian Merle Wells (1978, p. 133) wrote

"The national election of 1888 (in which Republican Harrison defeated Democrat Cleveland) culminated a series of accidents responsible for Idaho admission with its ill-advised territorial boundary configuration."

The borders of Idaho territory had been fixed in 1868. The southern border was established at the 42nd Parallel, the northern boundary of Utah Territory. The western boundary was established in the Idaho Territorial Act of 1863. The eastern boundary was fixed by the establishment of Montana Territory in 1864, and when Wyoming Territory was established in 1868 the existing shape of Idaho was set. These geographically awkward territorial borders were adopted as the state borders in 1890. Idaho thus contains parts of three disparate economic and geographic regions: the southeast which is oriented toward Salt Lake City, the north, oriented toward Spokane, and the west-central part, or the "True Idaho," oriented toward Boise.

In 1889, Idaho's electorate ratified a constitution containing anti-Mormon provisions. Most Mormons did not vote in that election. Idaho was admitted as a Republican, anti-Mormon state in 1890.

Renunciation of Polygamy

Although Brigham Young died in 1877, the practice of polygamy, which became a major obstacle to economic and political success of the Mormons, was not renounced until Sept. 24, 1890, when new Mormon President Wilford Woodruff "was favored with a new plural marriage revelation." He denied that the Church had sanctioned polygamy during his presidency. His manifesto agreed to submit to the laws of Congress:

> "I now publicly declare that my advice to the Latter-Day Saints is to refrain from contracting marriages forbidden by the laws of the land" (Wells, 1978, p. 163).

Over a million dollars of Church property, which had been confiscated under the Edmonds-Tucker Act was returned on Feb. 10, 1894. Utah was admitted to the Union in 1896.

ZCMI Warehouse, in Pocatello, 1920s. Bannock County Historical Museum Collection.

Stone house, east of West Side Highway, Clifton, Idaho. House was probably built in the 1870s. The tree in the left background is a western larch (tamarack), common in forests of northern Idaho and Montana, but almost impossible to cultivate in the alkaline soils of southeast Idaho, (May, 1991).

The Cities of Zion

Chesterfield and nearly 500 other Mormon settlements from Mexico to Canada were planned as parts of a utopian vision presented by Joseph Smith and set down on paper as the plat of the city of Zion in 1833. The vision was of order, in a rigorous grid of streets aligned to the points of the compass. People would live in sturdy houses built of brick or stone, all set back from the tree-lined streets so as to make room for fruitful gardens and orchards.

For the people of Chesterfield, like so many other Mormon settlers throughout the American West, the old Christian metaphor of building Zion—the city of God on earth—became the reality of their daily lives.

Mormons in Idaho Politics

In the 1890s, Mormons began to join both political parties, although the Republican party only unwillingly. By February 1892, Idaho Republicans, led by William E. Borah, stated that they had ceased to suspect the Saints' intentions and welcomed the Mormons into the party. The Idaho Test Oath was repealed in 1895. It was not until 1982 that voters amended the Idaho constitution to remove the language barring Mormons from voting.

Throughout the 20th century Idaho, Mormons have tended to favor the Republican Party and most state legislators from southeast Idaho have been Republicans. Ironically, in the 1980s and 90s, several Mormon Democrats (John Evans, Richard Stallings, Larry Echohawk) have achieved state or national office, though southeast Idaho Republicans seldom have been influential outside their local constituencies, being overshadowed in state politics by Republicans from the Boise area.

References

Arrington, L.J., 1979, The Mormon Settlement of Cassia County, Idaho 1873-1921: Idaho Yesterdays, v. 23, no. 2, p. 36-46.

Bitton, Dennis, 1979, Peopling the upper Snake: The Second Wave of Mormon Settlement in Idaho: Idaho Yesterdays, v. 23, no. 2, p. 47-52.

Coates, L.G., Boag., P.G., Hatzenbuehler, R.L., and Swanson, M.R., 1994, The Mormon Settlement of Southeastern Idaho, 1845-1900: Journal of Mormon History, Fall 1994, v. 20, p. 46-62.

Harstad, P.T., editor, 1972, Reminiscences of Oscar Sonnenkalb, Idaho Surveyor and Pioneer: Pocatello, Idaho, The Idaho State University Press, 66 p.

Morgan, D.L., 1987, The State of Deseret: Logan, Utah, Utah State University Press, 201p.

Simmonds, A.J., 1980, Southeast Idaho as a Pioneer Mormon Safety Valve: Idaho Yesterdays, v. 23, no. 4, p. 20-30.

Simmonds, A.J., 1988, Idaho's Last Colony: Northern Cache Valley under the Test Oath, 1972-1896: Idaho Yesterdays, v. 32, no. 2, p. 2-14.

Swetnam, Susan Hendricks, 1991, Lives of the Saints in Southeast Idaho: Moscow, Idaho, The University of Idaho Press, 188 p.

Wells, M.W., 1966, Walla Walla's Vision of a Greater Washington: Idaho Yesterdays, v. 10, no. 3, p. 20-31.

Wells, M.W., 1978, Anti-Mormonism in Idaho, 1872-92: Provo, Utah, Brigham Young University Press, 197 p.

van Zandt, F.K., 1966, Boundaries of the United States and the several states: U.S. Geological Survey Bulletin 1212, 291 p.

Latter-Day Saint Temple along the Snake River in Idaho Falls, dedicated Sunday, September 23, 1945, (July 1992).

7

The Gold Road and Coming of the Railroads

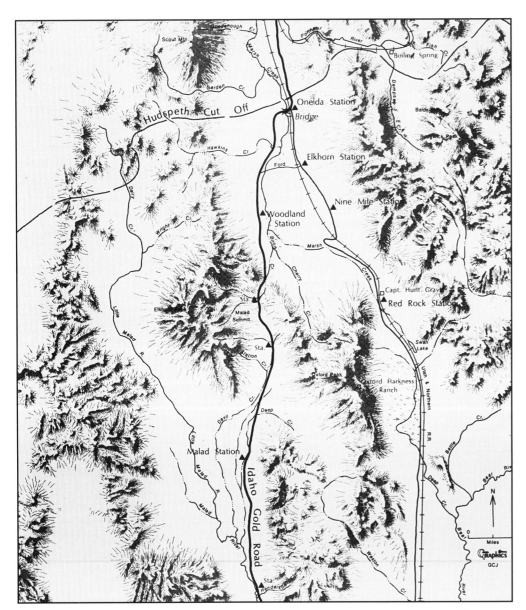

South half of the Idaho Gold Road from Malad Valley north to Oneida station (Arimo). Map shows many features of Malad and Marsh Valley in the period 1865-1885. From Gittins (1976). Used by permission.

The Idaho Gold Road

Before railroads were built there were stage lines and freight wagons. As trade increased between the Mormon settlements in Utah and the mines in Montana to the north, Ben Holladay, opened in 1864, a stagecoach service along the "Idaho Gold Road" from Corinne, Utah (on the transcontinental railroad) to Virginia City, Montana, via Eagle Rock. South of the Snake River two stage routes existed, the Bannock Road, which went northwest from Malad into Hawkins Basin and Arbon Valley, and the Portneuf Road followed by Holladay's stages, which went north, following present-day Interstate 15. The success of these stage lines plus the decision by the Mormon Church to build rails northward from Salt Lake City to Montana opened Idaho to the railroad era of the turn of the century.

Eagle Rock

In the early 1860s the Snake River was a major barrier on the trip north to the gold fields of Montana. In May, 1863, a ferry was constructed near the ford used by Indians to cross the Snake about nine miles upstream from what was then Eagle Rock. Matthew Taylor built the first bridge across the Snake River at Eagle Rock, using poles from Beaver Canyon, 80 miles to the north. The abutments were set in place on a frozen river in January, 1865. The bridge opened in May and stood a block south of present day Broadway Street bridge in Idaho Falls. The bridge was flooded and gave way in June, 1867. The bridge was rebuilt and lasted until 1889 when it was declared a public highway and replaced by an iron bridge. The name of Eagle Rock was changed to Idaho Falls in a referendum in January 1890.

Port Neuf Toll Bridge

In 1864 William Murphy built a cabin and a toll bridge on the Portneuf River in Marsh Valley (at present-day McCammon, then called Port Neuf), mainly to service the stage business of Ben Holladay and the growing freight wagon business. In 1865, Murphy's wife

Catherine became the first Anglo-American woman to live in Marsh Valley. Murphy acquired the Port Neuf toll road in 1866. He was a passionate and hot headed Irishman who died from the bullet of an Oneida County Sheriff during an argument outside a bar in Malad City in April, 1870.

After Murphy's death, Henry O. Harkness, a Civil War veteran who had been employed by Murphy to operate the toll store and gate in Beaver Canyon, south of Monida Pass, was requested by widow Catherine Murphy to take over operation of the stage line. A year later, in August, 1871 Henry Harkness and Catherine Murphy were married. In the next 40 years he built a farming and ranching empire, a power generation facility, a flour mill, and a hotel to serve the new railroad.

Stage Robbery

On July 13, 1856, over $60,000 in gold dust was stolen and three men were killed in a robbery of the Ben Holladay Overland Stage southeast of Inkom. The robbery probably took place north of Lower Rock Creek, near where Green Canyon joins the Portneuf River. The robbers were never caught, but Robbers Roost Canyon is named for them. The filings for possession of land for stations along the Holladay stage line had been filed on, only a few weeks before, in late June.

Replica of Union Pacific engine 119, one of the first engines on the transcontinental railroad, at Promontory Point National Historic Site, Utah (1978).

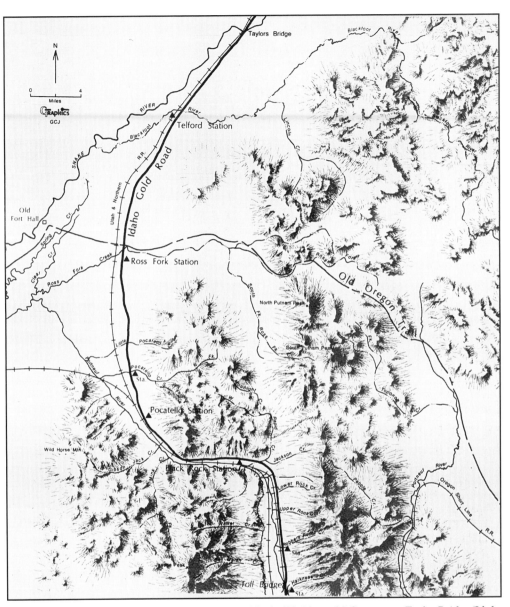

North half of the Idaho Gold Road map from the Port Neuf toll bridge at McCammon to Taylor Bridge (Idaho Falls) From Gittins (1976), used by permission.

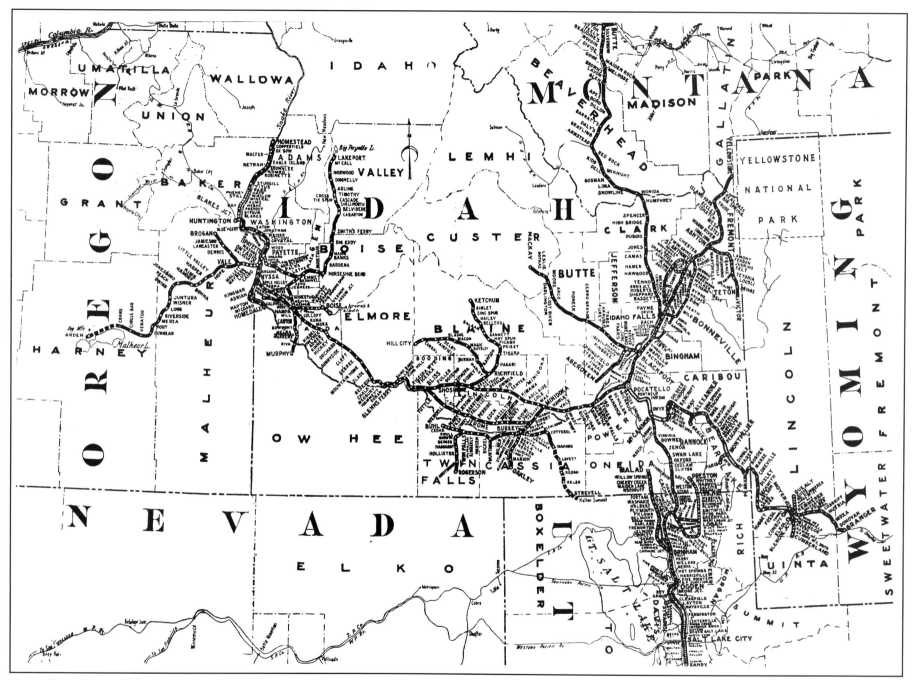

Map of Idaho Division, Union Pacific System at its maximum extent 1924 (from railroad timetable). Strevell branch was never built.

The Coming of the Railroads

By the middle of the 19th Century, the immense value of railroads to the American economy had become apparent. They were the only reliable means of transportation; they could operate in all kinds of weather and their ability to haul heavy loads permitted unparalleled growth of industry and the economy.

The need for rail transportation in the newly settled western areas was manifest, but until secession, neither Northern nor Southern politicians could agree to any route which did not originate in their territory. Almost at once after secession and the departure of Southern politicians, Congress adopted the Pacific Railroad Act of 1862 which provided for a transcontinental line linking the east with California roughly along the 43rd Parallel (that is through the newly created Idaho Territory).

Actual construction of the transcontinental rail line had to wait until financing became available after the Civil War. The first rails of Union Pacific Railway Company were not laid until 1865. After that, construction moved ahead with great speed. The Union Pacific Railway was building westward from Omaha, Nebraska, and the Central Pacific Railway was building eastward from Sacramento, California. Neither railroad passed through Idaho. The junction took place on May 10, 1869, at Promontory Point, in Utah just west of Brigham City at the north end of the Great Salt Lake. This was the cause for celebrations throughout the United States. For the first time, the east and west coasts were linked by a rapid, dependable form of transportation which permitted unlimited growth.

Residents of the new Territory of Idaho, established just 6 years earlier, were confident that after the junction of the transcontinental railroads, it would be only a short time until Idaho would be connected to the transcontinental line. They were shocked when Union Pacific management announced the company was financially incapable of building a line into Idaho. The area did not have enough commerce to justify the large expenses of construction.

Line of trees growing on roadbed of planned Utah-Northern Railroad at Johnson Reservoir north of Preston. The route was rejected after the reorganization of the Utah & Northern Railway in favor of a route across the Bear River and up Battle Creek, (May, 1992).

Across the sagebrush desert of the Snake River Plain west of American Falls, there were no towns. The sidings were named by the railroad planners. E.P. Vining, former general freight agent of the Union Pacific system, described how the names (Wapi, Minidoka, Kimama, Owinza, Ticeska, etc.) were derived.

> "It seemed evident to us both (Vining and Chief Engineer Blickensderfer), however, that if the names (of the stations) were Indian very few would know, or care, which particular Indian dialects they were selected from. We therefore turned to the Dakota (otherwise known as the Sioux) dialect, for the following reasons:
> First: it is one of the most euphonious of all the original American languages.
> Second: It had quite a large number of books printed in it, from which our selection could be made, and
> Third: The region inhabited by that tribe was the nearest to Idaho of any district of which the former considerations were true." (Idaho Yesterdays, 1959, v. 3, no. 3, p. 32.)

The Utah & Northern Railroad Company

Union Pacific also refused to construct a connection between Ogden and the Territory of Utah capital in Salt Lake City, just 32 miles away.

> Brigham Young, President of the Mormon Church and governor of the Territory, is alleged to have said something along the lines of:
> "The damned cusses! You'd think after all we did to help in the construction of the transcontinental railroad, they'd show us a little consideration."

In order to connect Ogden and Salt Lake City, to bring rail service to other areas of the Mormon Empire, and especially to connect Utah with the new mines in Montana Territory, the Mormon Church established several rail companies to construct and operate a rail network. The broad gauge Utah-Central connected Ogden with Salt Lake City.

To reach the Montana mines, a narrow gauge road called the Utah-Northern Railroad Company was established in 1871. From Ogden the road was planned to extend through Brigham City and Logan to the Bear River, then up the Bear to Soda Springs where church leaders owned property, and then through the mountains to the Snake River and on to Montana. While the area to be traversed was known to be rugged, it avoided the Fort Hall Indian Reservation. The proposed route was chosen over a water level route along Marsh Valley to the Snake River Plain, that had been recommended by surveyors.

The Utah-Northern Railroad was incorporated on August 21, 1871, and construction began at once. The road did not hire a railroad construction company to do the work but relied on the usual Mormon Church method of constructing public improvements: volunteer labor, utilizing their own equipment, would do the necessary construction in a cooperative, communal manner. Progress was painfully slow. By May 2, 1874, the line extended only 74 miles to Franklin, Idaho Territory, just across the Utah-Idaho border. Construction halted at this point. Lack of constant, remunerative sources of income, a grasshopper infestation in the neighboring farm lands and the economic Panic of

Similar view to previous photo at Johnson Reservoir, but taken in October, 1992, when the reservoir was empty.

Former grade of the Utah & Northern Railway in Marsh Creek south of Inkom. The narrow-gauge rails ran parallel with Marsh Creek road, between the road and the creek, on the right hand (west) side of the view. The railroad grade can also be seen in the center of the Marsh Creek Valley heading to the upper right. Dry waterfalls or alcoves can be seen on the Basalt of Portneuf Valley above the right of way. Here the Lake Bonneville Flood filled the valley and poured over into Marsh Creek. Interstate 15 is on the left. Meandering Marsh Creek was prone to flooding, which caused the railroad right of way to be relocated in 1882 with building of the Oregon Short Line along the east side of the valley, along the Portneuf River, (July, 1990).

the types of passenger cars on them and their routing. Union Pacific ran a complicated network of passenger trains on its Overland Route, and in its heyday the system worked with efficiency and style. We show Union Pacific timetables of several vintages in this book, because they were such elegant forms of written communication.

The Utah & Northern Railway and the Fort Hall Indian Reservation

The Fort Hall Indian Reservation had been created by presidential proclamation as a result of the Fort Bridger Treaty of 1868. The Treaty required that any roads constructed through the Reservation must be approved by a majority vote of the adult males of the Tribes involved, after payment to the Indians of just compensation.

In 1878, the rejuvenated narrow-gauge railroad, now named the Utah & Northern Railway Company, solved this problem by ignoring it, and began building north. Its route left the Bear River terminal north of Preston, crossed the River, and went up Battle Creek itself to a station about one mile east of Oxford, Idaho, then to Red Rock Pass and down Marsh Creek to the Inkom area, crossing the Portneuf River at Blackrock on a bridge that is still used. After passing through the Portneuf Gap, the tracks skirted the southwest side of the basalt lava flow of Portneuf Valley, and ran across what was to become the campus of Idaho State University to Pocatello Creek, and then north to the Ross Fork Agency and the Blackfoot River, the northern boundary of the Reservation. The trespass and failure to comply with the Treaty created tension between the parties and although the Bureau of Indian Affairs demanded compliance by the Railway Company, nothing was done about it. At one time in 1878, word came from the Ross Fork Agency (Fort Hall) that the Indians would accept 500 head of good cattle for letting the rails cross the Reservation but no official response was made to this offer and little was heard about it again.

The official position of the Railway Company's management was that the Congressional authorization for the road to build to Montana was granted after the Reservation was established, yet no mention of the Reservation appeared in the act of Congress; therefore, by implied revocation, Congress had relieved the Company of any obligation under the Treaty. There is no indication in the records that the Company seriously believed in this totally specious argument, but it made no attempt to patch things up with the Indians

1873 combined to dry up funds for construction. The line was gradually extended to the north, through what is now Preston and to the south side of the Bear River near Battle Creek, before full receivership took place; but construction by the Mormon Church essentially ended.

The narrow gauge road was purchased by interests associated with Union Pacific at a receiver's sale in 1878 and construction began again. Although the roadbed had been constructed for 14 miles north of Preston to Riverdale, the route up Bear River via Oneida Narrows was abandoned as being impractical. The grade was too steep and the mountainous terrain was too cold and would be difficult to operate in winter. Instead, the route suggested earlier by surveyors through Red Rock Pass north of the Bear River crossing and down Marsh Creek to the Snake River Plain

and then north to Montana was adopted. It would be cheaper to build, having no grades of consequence, except where the road came up Battle Creek out of the Bear River valley north of Preston, and would permit faster service. The water level route had one king-sized flaw: it ran directly through the Indian Reservation from Red Rock Pass to the Blackfoot River, a distance of 75 miles.

Railroad Timetables

The railroad timetable was, in its way, an art form, as well as a succinct way to communicate important information to those who operated and rode the trains. The timetable contained absolutely correct and legible maps, distances, elevations, and geographic information. It also contained the specifications of the trains,

Utah & Northern Railway narrow-gauge engine crossing the Snake River at Eagle Rock (Idaho Falls), about 1885. Photo is taken looking northeast from the west side of the river. In the background are the roundhouse which blew over in a windstorm in June 1886, and the shops that were moved to Pocatello in 1886-87. The bridge in the background is the original bridge at Eagle Rock built by Matthew Taylor. It was one block south of the present location of the Broadway St. bridge. In 1911 a retaining wall was built in the area of the two bridges when the Idaho Falls power plant was constructed downstream. Until that time there were really no falls in Idaho Falls. Abe Lillibridge collection, Idaho State University.

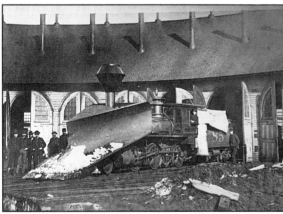

Utah & Northern Railway narrow-gauge roundhouse at Eagle Rock, about 1885. The roundhouse blew down in a windstorm in 1886. The large snow plow appears to engulf the tiny narrow-gauge engine. Clifford Peake collection, Bannock County Historical Society.

UNION PACIFIC RAILWAY.

IDAHO DIVISION.

SOUTHERN DISTRICT, UTAH AND NORTHERN RAILWAY.

OGDEN TO EAGLE ROCK.

TIME SCHEDULE NO. 2.

To take Effect Sunday, July 1st, 1883, at 12:05 A. M

For the Government and Information of Employes only.   The Company reserves the right to vary therefrom at pleasure.

ALL TRAINS WILL RUN DAILY.

BOUND NORTH						STATIONS.	Distance from Ogden	BOUND SOUTH					
SECOND CLASS No. 7 U & N Freight	SECOND CLASS No. 11 O S L Freight	FIRST CLASS No. 1 O S L Express	SECOND CLASS No. 9 U & N Freight	SECOND CLASS No. 5 O S L Freight	FIRST CLASS No. 3 U & N Express			FIRST CLASS No. 4 U & N Express	SECOND CLASS No. 6 U & N Freight	SECOND CLASS No. 10 O S L Express	FIRST CLASS No. 2 O S L Freight	SECOND CLASS No 12 O S L Freight	SECOND CLASS No 8 U & N Freight
	Dep 7.40 P.M	Dep 6.10A.M	Dep 10.30A.M			Ogden	204.8	Arr 4.30P.M	Arr 1.55 P.M	Arr 2.40 A.M			
	8.35	7.05	11.05		9.0	Hot Springs	195.8	3.55	1.00	1.45			
	8.45	7.17	11.12		10.4	Woodland	194.4	3.48	12.50	1.35			
	9.05	7.35	11.25		14.0	Willard	190.8	3.35	12.30 P.M	1.15			
	9.45	11.15 Dep	11.50 A.M		21.0	Brigham	183.8	3.10	11.25 A.M	12.35A.M			
	10.40	9.20	12.30 P.M		30.5	Honeyville	174.3	2.30	10.30	11.40P.M			
	11.10 P.M	9.50	12.50		35.5	Dewey	169.3	2.10	9.50	11.10			
	12.00 Night	10.40	1.17		41.5	Collinston	163.3	1.50	9.15	10.35			
	12.30 A.M	11.10	1.35		45.5	Cachill	159.3	1.35	8.50	10.10			
	1.00	11.40A.M	1.55		51.0	Mendon	153.8	1.00	8.00	9.20			
	Arr 1.00 Dep	Arr 12.25 P.M Dep 1.30 P.M	Arr 2.15 Dep 2.20		58.0	Logan	146.8	Dep 12.55 P.M Arr	Dep 7.30	8.50			
	2.57	1.57	2.50		62.7	Hyde Park	142.1	12.00 Noon	6.00	7.30			
	3.15	2.15	2.58		65.4	Smithfield	139.4	11.51 A.M	5.45	7.15			
	3.50	2.50	3.19		71.2	Richmond	133.6	11.32	5.10	6.40			
	4.30	Arr 3.30 Dep 3.40	3.40		78.0	Franklin	126.8	11.10	4.30	6.00			
	5.10	4.20	4.05		86.0	Freedom	119.8	10.47	3.45	5.20			
	Arr 5.40 A.M	Arr 4.50 P.M	Arr 4.20 P.M		90.0	Battle Creek	114.8	Dep 10.30A.M	Dep 3.15 A M	4.50 P.M			
	Dep 5.55 A M	Dep 5.10 P.M	Dep 4.30 P.M		90.0	Battle Creek	114.8	Arr 10.20A.M	Arr 2.20 A.M	3.30 P.M			
	6.25	5.40	4.45		93.7	Morrell	111.1	10.05	1.50	3.00			
	7.10	6.25	5.14		100.8	Oxford	104.0	9.37	1.00	2.10			
	7.30	6.50	5.27		104.3	Swan Lake	100.5	9.24	12.35 A.M	1.45			
	8.15	7.35	5.55		110.8	Calvin	94.0	8.55	11.50 P.M	1.00			
	Arr 8.45 Dep	7.55	6.05		114.0	Downey	90.8	8.45	11.30	12.40 P.M			
	9.30	8.40	6.32		121.0	Toombs	83.8	8.19	10.42	11.53 A.M			
	Arr 9.50A.M	Arr 9.00 P.M	Arr 6.45 P.M		124.5	Arimo	80.3	Dep 8.05 A.M	Dep 10.20 P.M	11.30A.M			
Dep 2.55 A.M	Dep 7.27 P.M	Dep 10.30 A M	Dep 9.30 A M	Dep 7.05 P.M		McCammon	78.3	Dep 7.45 A.M	Dep 9.40 P.M	Dep 10.30 A M	Arr 7.25 A.M	Arr 4.50 P.M	
3.22	7.10	11.10	10.20	7.20		Onyx	68.3	7.30	9.10	10.10	7.12	4.22	
3.52	7.54	11.45 A.M	10.55	7.38		Inkom	62.3	7.12	8.35	9.35	6.57	3.50	
4.15	8.05	12.17 P.M	11.27 P.M	7.55		Portneuf	56.5	6.55	7.45	9.03	6.45	3.28	
Arr 5.00 A.M	Arr 8.25 P.M	12.40 A M				Pocatello	50.1	6.25 A.M	8.45 P.M	Dep 6.25A.M	Dep 2.45 P.M		
	Dep 2.50 P M	Dep 1.45 A.M	Dep 9.20 P.M		166.3	Ross Fork	38.5	Dep 5.30 A.M	Dep 5.10 P.M	6.35 A.M			
	4.00	2.55	9.58		178.9	Blackfoot	25.9	4.52	4.00	5.25			
	5.10	Arr 4.07 Dep 4.17	10.33		191.1	Basalt	13.7	4.17	2.50	Dep 4.57 Arr 4.17			
	Arr 6.30 P M	Arr 5.40A.M	Arr 11.15P.M		204.8	Eagle Rock		Dep 3.35 A.M	Dep 1.30 P.M	2.45 A.M			
	Dep 2.35 P M	Dep 2.55 A.M	Dep 7.15A.M		348.0	Dillon		Dep 7.45 P.M	Dep 7.10 P.M	9.20 A.M			
	Arr 10.40 P M	Arr 10.35 A.M	Arr 11.25 A.M		416.8	Butte		Dep 3.30 P.M	Dep 11.25 A.M	Dep 1.20 A.M			
		Arr 12.40 P.M			442.9	Deer Lodge		Dep 2.15 P.M					

F. S. RAWLINS,
Train Dispatcher,
EAGLE ROCK.

W. P. P. ST. CLAIR,
Superintendent,
EAGLE ROCK.

W. B. DODDRIDGE,
Gen'l Supt,
OGDEN.

THOS. L. KIMBALL,
Ass't Gen'l Manager,
OMAHA.

S. H. H. CLARK,
Gen'l Manager,
OMAHA.

SPECIAL RULE NO 1.—Study rules well and know that you understand them. IMPORTANT CHANGES HAVE BEEN MADE
SPECIAL RULE NO 2.—FULL-FACED FIGURES indicate MEETING and PASSING POINTS.
SPECIAL RULE NO. 3.—U & N. Trains on this schedule will take their date at OGDEN and EAGLE ROCK.
SPECIAL RULE NO. 4.—Conductors and engineers when MEETING or PASSING trains must STOP and ascertain the numbers or names of such trains met or passed.
SPECIAL RULE NO. 5.—All trains and light engines passing able tracks at night where work or other trains are stationed, and no night operator, will notify such trains by leaving message with watchman what they are and time they passed.
SPECIAL RULE NO. 6.—Trains will not exceed schedule time except by special orders.
SPECIAL RULE NO. 7.—Trains will come to a full STOP before reaching U. C. crossing at Ogden.

SPECIAL RULE NO. 8.—Passenger trains must positively reduce speed over all switches to Ten (10) Miles an hour, and Freight Trains to Six (6) Miles an hour.
SPECIAL RULE NO. 9.—South Bound Trains will look out carefully for Helping Engines returning from MORRELL to BATTLE CREEK ahead of them.
SPECIAL RULE NO. 10.—Engines running without trains, or backing up pulling trains, will carry one Red Light at night, on rear of tank.
SPECIAL RULE NO. 11.—Engines helping trains carrying signals will duplicate the signals while helping the train. Conductors must notify Engineers of helping engines on their trains of any orders they may have.
*Trains do not stop except on SIGNAL.
NOTE.—Passengers may be carried upon trains five (5) and six (6) between Ogden and Oxford without permits.

JOINT TRACK.—All trains on joint track take their date at McCammon and Pocatello. Junction switches at McCammon and Pocatello will be set for standard gauge. All trains will register at McCammon.
Pocatello. Oregon Short Line Dispatcher will give all orders concerning the movement of trains between McCammon and Pocatello.

Union Pacific Railway, Idaho Division Timetable, Ogden to Eagle Rock, July 1, 1883; from Beal (1957), used by permission of Idaho State Historical Society.

UNION PACIFIC RAILWAY.
IDAHO DIVISION.
NORTHERN DISTRICT, UTAH AND NORTHERN RAILWAY.
EAGLE ROCK TO BUTTE.

TIME SCHEDULE NO. 2.
THIRD EDITION.
To take Effect Sunday, September 30, 1883, at 12:05 A. M

For the Government and Information of Employes only.   The Company reserves the right to vary therefrom at pleasure.

ALL TRAINS WILL RUN DAILY.

BOUND NORTH.   ## BOUND SOUTH.

Second Class. No. 11 Mixed.	Second Class. No. 9 Freight.	Second Class. No. 5 Freight.	First Class. No. 3 Express.	First Class. No. 1 Express.	Distance from Eagle Rock	STATIONS.	Distance from Garrison	First Class. No. 2 Express	First Class. No. 4 Express.	Second Class. No. 6 Freight.	Second Class. No. 10 Freight.	Second Class. No. 12 Mixed.
	Dep. 7.40P.M	Dep. 6.10A.M	Dep. 10.30A.M			Ogden	454.3	Arr. 4.30 P.M	1.55P.M	Arr. 2.40 A.M		
	Dep. .2.30A.M	Dep. 1.30P.M	Dep. 2.35P.M			Logan	396.3	Dep. 12.35P.M	Dep. 7.20A.M	Dep. 8.40P.M		
	Dep. 9.05P.M	Dep. 10.20A.M	Dep. 11.30P.M			**Eagle Rock**	249.5	Arr. 3.20 A.M	Arr. 12.00noon	Arr. 12.45A.M		
	10.00	11.10A.M	11.55P.M		8.5	Payne	241.0	2.55	11.10A.M	Dep 11.33P.M		
10.55A.M	12.00 Noon	12.20A.M			17.1	Market Lake	232.4	2.30	10.20	10.55		
12.05A.M	1.05P.M	12.52			27.6	Hawgood	221.9	1.58	9.15	9.55		
Arr. 1.13 Dep. 1.33	2.10	1.25			38.4	Camas	211.1	1.25	8.10	8.50		
3.00	3.20	2.00			50.1	Dry Creek	199.4	12.50	7.00	7.40		
4.00	4.20	2.30			58.9	High Bridge	190.6	12.23	6.05	6.45		
4.25	4.45	2.42			62.1	China Point	187.4	12.12A.M	5.45	6.25		
Arr. 5.00 Dep. 6.00	Arr. 6.15 Dep. 6.15	3.00			67.4	Beaver Canon	182.1	11.55P.M	5.15	Dep 5.33 Arr 5.33		
6.50	7.05	3.30			72.9	Pleasant Valley	176.6	11.30	4.35	4.55		
7.35	7.50	3.50			79.4	Monida	170.1	11.10	Dep 3.40 Arr 3.40	4.15		
8.30	8.45	4.17			88.2	Williams	161.3	10.42	2.45	3.20		
Arr. 9.15A.M	Arr. 9.30P.M	Arr. 4.40A.M			95.2	Spring Hill	154.3	Dep. 10.20P.M	1.55A.M	2.30P.M		
Dep. 9.35A.M	Dep. 10.10P.M	Dep. 4.50A.M			95.2	Spring Hill	154.3	Arr. 10.10 P.M	Arr. 12.15A.M	2.10P.M		
10.30	11.10P.M	5.22			105.7	Dell	148.8	9.38	11.10P.M	1.07P.M		
11.50A.M	12.20A.M	6.00			118.0	Red Rock	131.5	9.00	9.55	11.50A.M		
12.40P.M	1.10	6.27			126.7	Grayling	122.8	8.35	9.03	11.00		
1.30	2.00	6.55			135.4	Barratt's	114.1	8.08	Dep 7.58 Arr 7.58	10.10		
Arr. 2.30 Dep. 2.55	Arr. 2.45 Dep. 2.45	7.15			143.2	Dillon	106.3	7.45	Dep 7.10 Arr 7.45	Dep 6.50 Arr 7.31		
4.05	4.15	7.55			155.2	Apex	94.3	7.10	5.30	7.31		
4.45	4.55	8.15			161.7	Glen	87.8	6.45	4.45	7.00		
Arr. 5.55 Dep. 6.25	Arr. 6.00 Dep. 6.00	8.45			174.0	Melrose	75.5	Dep 5.53 Arr 5.53	3.35	Dep 6.00 Arr 5.30		
7.25	7.20	9.45			183.8	Lavell	65.7	5.15	2.35	4.30		
8.45	8.40	10.25			195.9	Feely	53.6	4.35	1.25	3.20		
9.15	9.10	10.40			199.9	Buxton	49.6	4.17	12.50	2.45		
Dep. 11.40P.M	9.45	10.33	Dep. 4.00P.M		205.0	Silver Bow	44.5	Arr 10.55A.M	Dep 3.30 Arr 11.33	12.30 P.M	Arr. 1.00P.M	
Arr. 12.25A.M	10.40P.M	10.30A.M	Arr. 11.25A.M	Arr. 4.25P.M	212.0	Butte	51.5	Dep 10.30P.M	Dep. 3.30P.M	11.25A.M	Dep. 1.20A.M	Dep .12.20P.M

DEER LODGE BRANCH.

BOUND NORTH.   ### BOUND SOUTH.

Second Class. No. 15 Mixed.	First Class No. 13 Express.	Distance from Eagle Rock	STATIONS.	Distance from Garrison	First Class No. 14 Express	Second Class. No. 16 Mixed.
Dep. 1.10P.M	Dep. 11.05A.M	205.0	Silver Bow	44.5	Arr 3.50P.M	Arr 11.30P.M
2.15	11.40A.M	216.3	Stuart	33.2	3.15	10.25
2.55	12.02P.M	223.6	Warm Springs	25.9	2.55	9.45
3.30	12.18	229.6	Race Track	19.9	2.38	9.10
Arr. 4.15 Dep. 4.50	12.40	238.1	Deer Lodge	11.4	2.15	Dep 8.25 Arr 7.24
5.25	12.57	243.8	Mullen	5.7	1.58	6.50
6.00P.M	1.15P.M	249.5	Garrison		Dep 1.40 P.M	6.15 P.M

F. S. RAWLINS, Train Dispatcher, Eagle Rock.   W. P. S. St. CLAIR, Superintendent, Eagle Rock.   W. B. DODDRIDGE, Gen'l Superintendent, Ogden.   THOS. L. KIMBALL, Ass't Gen'l Manager, Omaha.   S. H. H. CLARK, Gen'l Manager, Omaha.

SPECIAL RULE NO. 1.—Study rules well and know that you understand them. Important changes have been made.
SPECIAL RULE NO. 2.—FULL-FACED FIGURES indicate MEETING and PASSING POINTS.
SPECIAL RULE NO. 3.—Train 3 will wait at Silver Bow until Train 2 arrives.
SPECIAL RULE NO. 4.—Conductors and Engineers when MEETING or PASSING trains must STOP and ascertain the numbers or names of such trains they met or passed.
SPECIAL RULE NO. 5.—All trains and light engines passing side tracks at night where work or other trains are stationed, and on signal, will notify such trains by leaving message with watchman, what they are and time they passed.
SPECIAL RULE NO. 6.—Trains 13, 14, 15 and 16 will take their date at SILVER BOW and GARRISON.
SPECIAL RULE NO. 7.—Trains 1, 2, 11 and 12 will take their date at SILVER BOW and BUTTE.
SPECIAL RULE NO. 8.—Trains 3, 4, 5, 6, 9 and 10 will take their date at EAGLE ROCK and BUTTE.
SPECIAL RULE NO. 9.—Trains will not exceed schedule time except by special order.

SPECIAL RULE NO. 10.—Passenger Trains must positively reduce speed over all switches to Ten (10) Miles per hour, and Freight Trains to Six (6) Miles per hour.
SPECIAL RULE NO. 11.—South Bound Trains will look out carefully for helping Engines running ahead MONIDA to CAMAS.
SPECIAL RULE NO. 12.—Engines running without trains, or backing pulling trains, will carry one Red Light at night, on rear of tank.
SPECIAL RULE NO. 13.—Engines helping trains carrying signals will duplicate the signals while helping the train. Conductors will notify Engineers of helping engines on their trains of any orders they may have.
SPECIAL RULE NO. 14.—All trains, or engines without trains, will register at SILVER BOW.
SPECIAL RULE NO. 15.—Trains must come to a full stop within 300 feet of SILVER BOW JUNCTION SWITCH.
SPECIAL RULE NO. 16.—The line from SILVER BOW to DEER LODGE will be known as the Deer

* Trains do not stop except on signal.

Oregon Short Line train at the old bridge at American Falls, about 1905. The old town of American Falls is behind the bridge. The original power plant, on the left in shadow, was built in 1902. These are the original American Falls in about their natural state, except to the east of the river. Abe Lillibridge collection, Idaho State University.

Wreck of Pacific class (4-6-2) engine from passenger train #5 near Pescadero, between Montpelier and Georgetown, 1918. The engine ran out of track during construction of the double track mainline. Clifford Peake collection, Bannock County Historical Society.

Union Pacific Railway timetable, (September, 1883). Eagle Rock to Butte; from Beal (1957).

or the Bureau and the dispute festered for ten years until the Act of September 1, 1888, was passed, ratifying the treaty of May 27, 1887.

The Idaho headquarters of U & N was established at Eagle Rock (Idaho Falls) and by 1880 the tracks had been extended up Beaver Canyon to the Continental Divide at Monida Pass. By December, 1881 service was instituted to Butte, Montana. Garrison, Montana was reached in 1882 but this portion of the right of way was later leased to Northern Pacific.

The Planning of the Oregon Short Line

In 1881, Union Pacific finally announced plans to construct a main line across Idaho toward the Pacific coast. Potential revenues in Idaho had not increased but a threat of competition from the west prompted the changed attitude. A new subsidiary, the Oregon Short Line Railway Company, was established to construct a broad gauge line from Granger, Wyoming through Idaho to a junction in Huntington, Oregon with the Oregon Railroad and Navigation Company. The proposed route would enter the Fort Hall Indian Reservation just west of Bancroft and pass through the Reservation in an east-west direction to the western border near Bannock Creek, west of Pocatello.

The new road sought permission under the Fort Bridger Treaty for its right of way but it did not yet have sufficient corporate structure to handle the negotiations required with the Indians and the Federal government. Both Utah & Northern and Oregon Short Line were subsidiaries of Union Pacific so Utah & Northern was instructed to obtain the necessary right of way.

The Act of Congress providing for Oregon Short Line did not mention the Fort Hall Indian Reservation either, but Utah & Northern did not raise any objection to the procedure and the terms of the Fort Bridger Treaty were complied with fully. The Railway Company sought a 100 foot wide right of way, with 20 acre station grounds approximately every 10 miles, except at Pocatello Junction, where it sought 200 additional feet of right of way and 40 acres for station grounds, totaling 772 acres. A gathering of the adult males on the Reservation agreed to the sale for $7.77 an acre, or $6,000.00. The Treaty was ratified by the Act of July 23, 1882, and shortly thereafter payment of this sum was made by Utah & Northern to the Treasurer of the United States on behalf of the Fort Hall Indians. On the next day, Utah & Northern transferred to Oregon Short Line all of its right, title and interest in the lands for $6,001.00.

The Founding of Pocatello

When the Oregon Short Line survey maps were prepared in 1881, there was no community named Pocatello. There had been a wagon freight station in the vicinity but no one lived in the area. Railroad records give no hint as to why the name Pocatello was selected, although it probably adopted the name of the freight station, named after Shoshoni Chief Pocatello, who lived in the general area. In the treaty negotiations the junction site was identified as "Pocatilla." The location map filed by Oregon Short Line identifies the location as "Pocatello Junction." However, there was at first no junction between the Oregon Short Line and the narrow gauge Utah & Northern Railway Company. This was built in 1882.

Chief Pocatello

In 1859, Col. Frederick W. Lander reported the first meeting with Chief Po-ca-ta-ro or the "White Plume," an independent, aggressive leader of a band of Northwestern Shoshoni that ranged across the Hudspeth Cutoff and the Oregon-California Trails, from the Raft River on the west to Bannock Creek and the Portneuf River on the east (Madsen, 1986). Pocatello was an important figure in the late 19th century, born in about 1815 in the Grouse Creek area of northwestern Utah, southwest of Oakley, Idaho. It was probably his band that made the attacks on wagon trains at Massacre Rocks in August 1862. The name Pocatello has no Indian significance and is apparently a phonetic attempt to express an Indian word. The Shoshoni language does not contain an "L" sound. The chief apparently referred to himself as "Tonaioza," meaning "Buffalo Robe." Other Indians had various names for him, but none was Pocatello. Apparently the name was a white man's label, without meaning. One cannot deny that the word has a nice ring to it.

Many fables have been suggested for the meaning of the name but none has been established as authentic. Especially offensive is the suggestion that the Chief would beg for food in Pocatello, asking for "pork and tallow," which became corrupted into the name Pocatello. The suggestion has no basis in fact and is impossible since the Chief's name predated the settlement of the town. Furthermore it is (typically) demeaning and insulting to the Chief and the tribe.

Tender on steam engine pushing Oregon Short Line snowplow on the Victor Branch, 1920s. Clifford Peake collection, Bannock County Historical Society Collection.

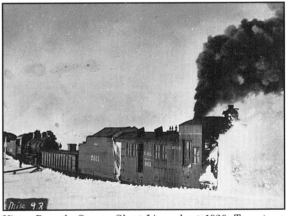

Victor Branch, Oregon Short Line, about 1920. Two steam engines (one backwards) push rotary snow plow. The rear engine will pull the entire train out after the snow has been removed. Clifford Peake collection, Bannock County Historical Society.

Some make the claim that Pocatello is the only town in the United States to have the name, whatever significance that may have. There are many towns which fit that condition. No doubt the residents of Pocatalico, West Virginia, make the same claim.

Construction of the Oregon Short Line

Oregon Short Line began construction of its standard-gauge line shortly after the road was organized in 1881. In Idaho, the roadbed was built in both directions from Pocatello but track was laid from east to west. By early summer in 1882, construction gangs from the Utah & Northern had built the roadbed past American Falls out into the desert north of the Snake River and a major broad-gauge bridge over the Snake was being finished. Because U & N crews had only narrow-gauge equipment, the tracks were at first narrow-gauge, but after Oregon Short Line track-laying crews arrived, the gauge was widened.

By the end of 1882, the tracks had reached Shoshone, where progress halted while the first branch line in Idaho was constructed north to Hailey to access the booming silver, lead, and zinc mines.

Oregon Short Line continued building west in 1883, and by November, 1884, crossed the new bridge over the Snake River at Huntington, Oregon, to connect Idaho and the east with Oregon and the Pacific slope. Rail service brought considerable growth and prosperity to Idaho leading to statehood on July 3, 1890.

Communities which the rails bypassed often closed doors and moved to the new line, except Boise City. To the great consternation of capital residents, Oregon Short Line followed a route 20 miles to the west, because to build into Boise would have involved a steep grade which the railroad wished to avoid. Instead, it built a branch from Nampa to Boise, not at all satisfying residents of what was then Idaho's 4th largest city (behind Rexburg, Moscow and Pocatello). This situation was not "corrected" until 1925.

Realignment of Right of Way in the Portneuf Canyon

Utah & Northern had discovered that from Oneida, as Arimo was known then, to Blackrock, west of Inkom, the water table of Marsh Creek was so high that frequent flooding interfered with train operations. It was decided in 1882 to shift the right of way to higher ground and to utilize the new Oregon Short Line roadbed from McCammon to Pocatello. A three track configuration resulted. Broad, or standard gauge, was fixed by law at 4 feet 8 1/2 inches; the narrow-gauge utilized by Utah & Northern was 3 feet wide, so standard-gauge trains used the two outer rails while the narrow-gauge ran on the interior rail and one outer rail. This configuration was extended to Pocatello and through-out the yards there and the original narrow-gauge line through the east side of what later became Pocatello was abandoned.

The Ramsey Transfer and the Widening of the Narrow Gauge

Having two different gauges of track utilize the same facilities created operating problems. To avoid having to physically transfer the ladings between cars of the different gauges, a device was constructed at Pocatello known as the Ramsey Transfer where incoming cars of either gauge were jacked up and wheels of the other gauge put under the cars. While this speeded up the process of transferring freight between the gauges, it was still necessary to keep a large force of workers to transload freight between cars.

The difference in gauges created a bottleneck in the growing freight business. Most of the freight destined for Montana came into Pocatello on the broad-gauge Oregon Short Line and southbound freight from Montana went out on the broad-gauge. The gauge from Pocatello to Butte was widened on July 25, 1887, although the accepted version of the story (Beal, 1957; 1980) has the widening taking place on Sunday, July 24, 1887 (Pioneer Day).

Pacific Hotel and Passenger Station between the tracks in Pocatello, looking northeast, in the 1880s. Telegraph, railway agency and waiting room are on the right (south) end of building. Waitresses, maids, and other hotel employees are assembled on the station platform. The dining room was at the far (north) end. The Pacific Hotel was built in 1883 and the Mansard Roof was added in about 1887. The track has 3 rails, indicating that both narrow- and broad-gauge trains stopped here. This was true until 1890. Clifford Peake collection, Bannock County Historical Society.

A Blackfoot, Idaho Newspaper, *The Idaho News*, in its July 30, 1887 edition carries an account by a reporter who boarded the first train over the new broad-gauge road, in company with Superintendent Robert Blickensderfer and many other railroad officials. Engineer G. Orum was at the throttle. Everything had been made ready for the change and at first dawn on Monday, July 25th, the signal was given and track crews began to re-lay the tracks. So as to avoid interrupting service as much as possible, extra crews had been brought in from the Oregon Short Line and the southern division of Utah & Northern. No mention is made in the newspaper account of any private citizens being used or of anyone being paid extra for the work.

Work was completed before the end of the day and only one train was delayed. The entire 245 mile road from Pocatello to Silver Bow, Montana, a few miles west of Butte, had been widened to standard-gauge. Utah & Northern went into Butte over leased track which did not require widening.

The narrow-gauge tracks to the south were not widened until 1890, when a new alignment through Cache Valley permitted the entire road to be standard-gauge. With this change, Preston became the end of the Cache Valley Branch and the main line passed along the west side of Cache Valley and down the Bear River canyon at Cutler Narrows to Brigham City.

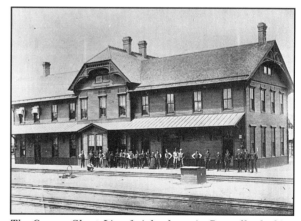

The Oregon Short Line freight depot in Pocatello, looking northeast, 1885. This structure was north of the Pacific Hotel, also between the tracks. The men standing in front of the station are probably railroad office workers. The Oregon Short Line offices were in this building. Note the three rail arrangement to accommodate narrow- and standard-gauge trains. Bannock County Historical Society Collection.

Demise of Eagle Rock

As east-west traffic increased, Oregon Short Line became the dominant road. Utah & Northern was having labor troubles. A wind storm in 1886 that destroyed the roundhouse in Eagle Rock was utilized as the excuse for moving the headquarters to Pocatello. The facilities at Eagle Rock were closed and in July and August, 1887, everything which could be put on flat cars was moved to Pocatello. When most of its adult population left town (the number of residents was reduced from about 2,000 to 400), Eagle Rock nearly disappeared. The remaining citizens reorganized the community, adopting the new name of Idaho Falls by referendum in 1890. Now in the late 20th century, with huge Federal expenditures and employment at the Idaho National Engineering Laboratory, Idaho Falls vies with Pocatello for the place as Idaho's second city.

Enlargement of the Pocatello Townsite

Soon after its founding in 1882, the forty acre terminal grounds at Pocatello became very crowded. Oregon Short Line made Pocatello a main terminal and built a round house, shop facilities and a coaling station. Also, between the tracks, in the center of the operation, were constructed the Pacific Hotel and the freight depot.

A row of permanent houses lined "Company Row" along the west right-of-way boundary, but many employees could not find a place to live on railway property.

Because Pocatello Junction had been carved out of the Indian Reservation, there was no private land around the station grounds and anyone who lived off the right-of-way was a trespasser on the Reservation. Frequently Agency police tore down or burned structures on the Reservation. Nonetheless, as early as 1885, many of the local businesses and the homes of the people who ran them were outside the right-of-way, in trespass on the Reservation. The rest of the white man's activities were in trespass on the reservation. There were no saloons on the reservation (this would have been a violation of the Indian Intercourse Act), but there was a bar in the Pacific House Hotel on Oregon Short Line-owned property, opened in 1883.

An order was issued by the Secretary of the Interior in late 1885 to clear the land once and for all of the parties "unlawfully and improperly" on the Reservation. Implementation of this order was delayed time and again because there was a need for the workers and the services provided and nowhere else for them to go.

View looking south at the Ramsey Transfer apparatus, (in center of photo, with men working, to the right of the second main line) Pocatello, Idaho, (June, 1886). To the right is "Company Row" along North Harrison Ave. Beyond it is the quartzite hill on the southwest side of the Portneuf River, on the Fort Hall Indian Reservation. The Ramsey Transfer involved jacking railcars up and placing wheels of different gauges under them. Note the mainlines have three rails. The freight house is to the left, with the Pacific Hotel (without Mansard Roof) behind it. Abe Lillibridge collection, Idaho State University.

Monument on Idaho State University campus, in front of the Liberal Arts Building, showing standard-gauge and narrow-gauge rails. Monument was erected in 1963 during the Idaho Territory Centennial celebration, and lies on the original narrow-gauge right-of-way, (June, 1992).

One shipper from Omaha, in a letter to his old Civil War buddy L.Q.C. Lamar, Secretary of the Interior, observed that maybe there were trespassers not on the right-of-way, but as anyone who had been to Pocatello knew, the buildings

"are on a barren waste utterly valueless to Indians or anyone else—except to hold a few building up."

Even the Federal justice of the peace assigned to maintain law and order in the area lived on the Reservation and was a trespasser, although he did hold court in a box car on the right-of-way.

In the fall of 1886, a petition signed by 41 persons, mainly railway employees, was sent to the Bureau of Indian Affairs seeking permission for them to stay on Reservation land until Congress could provide more space. In warm weather, they said, it was agreeable to live in tents wherever they could pitch them but now, with winter at hand, they needed houses to protect themselves "from the awful cold of the Idaho winter." In 1887, a report was sent to the Secretary f the Interior that Pocatello's popultation was then around 1,500 persons and a list was furnished of 60 buildings or structures built on Reservation land. The list included laundries, carpenter shops, butcher shops, the house of the justice of the peace, barber shops, a wholesale grocery, Keeney's stable, a barn, blacksmith's shop, warehouses, restaurants and a number of residences. Interestingly, no churches were included.

In order to give validity to the efforts of the justice of the peace, requests for exception to the order to clear all trespassers from the Reservation were made.

The Indian Agent wrote the Commissioner of Indian Affairs that the Justice of the Peace was young, sober, industrious and a good citizen. Furthermore:

"When it is remembered that Pocatello, though having but small space, is doing its best to reach Metropolitan in size and its 1,500 inhabitants are quite cosmopolitan in character, a dire and absolute necessity will at once be seen in the interest of 'law and order' that someone have jurisdiction in police affairs among those who are located there . . . "

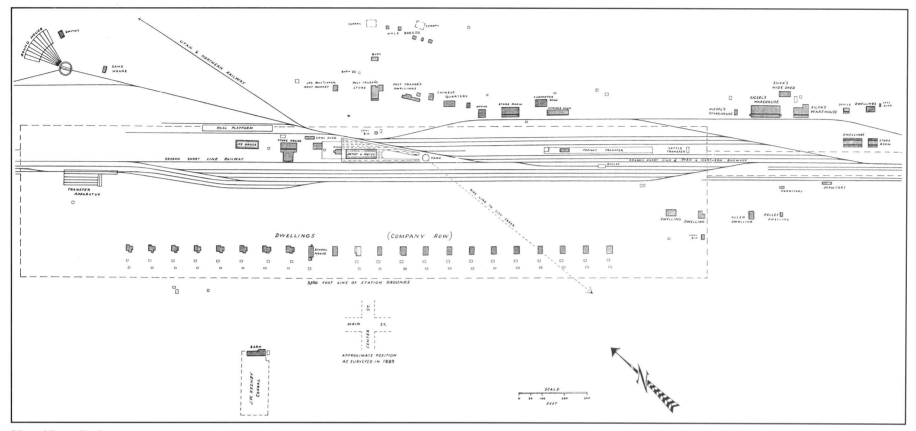

Map of Pocatello Junction, 1885, sketch from Wrigley, (1942, Fig. 14). Note water pipeline to City Creek and ethnic businesses east of the tracks and south of Center Street. The Warehouse District had also become established, both on and off the Indian Reservation.

Throughout this period of tension between the Railway, the employees, the Indians and the Department of the Interior, the correspondence among the various parties seemed to assume that only Utah & Northern was involved. It is seldom mentioned that Oregon Short Line was the operator of the railway and the employer of the trespassers and that its business was what had brought these people and businesses to the area. Perhaps the illegality of Utah & Northern's right-of-way on the Reservation and the continuing dispute over its failure to pay compensation therefor exacerbated the dispute. But things were rapidly reaching the condition where a solution had to be found. Conditions were made even worse in 1887 when Utah & Northern moved its headquarters from Eagle Rock to Pocatello Junction. Some houses were moved onto the right-of-way, even further reducing the available space.

In May, 1887, a treaty was signed ceding additional right-of-way to the railroads and setting aside 1,840 acres for a townsite. The treaty was ratified on September 1, 1888, finally legitimizing what Oregon Short Line had begun in 1882, when it called its Reservation home Pocatello Junction. The townsite was surveyed and divided into lots which were sold at public auction in 1891.

Merger of the Two Railroads

Ultimately, the two railroads combined and in 1889 became the Oregon Short Line & Utah Northern Railway Company. The new combined railroad, along with the parent Union Pacific Railway Company, fell on hard times and both entered receivership in 1893, emerging under the presidency of Edward R. Harriman in 1897 as Union Pacific Railroad Company and Oregon Short Line Railroad Company, respectively.

Establishment of Eastern Idaho Counties

The new village of Pocatello did not remain in Bingham County for long. The 1893 Legislature of the State of Idaho created Bannock County, with Pocatello as the county seat. All of eastern Idaho had started out as Oneida County when Idaho territory was established in 1863; later, Bingham County was cut out of it. Later, Bingham gave up land for Bannock, Bonneville, Madison, Jefferson and Fremont Counties and a part of Power County, while Bannock and Oneida furnished land when Caribou County was established. After World War II, an additional amount of Bannock County was attached to Caribou County.

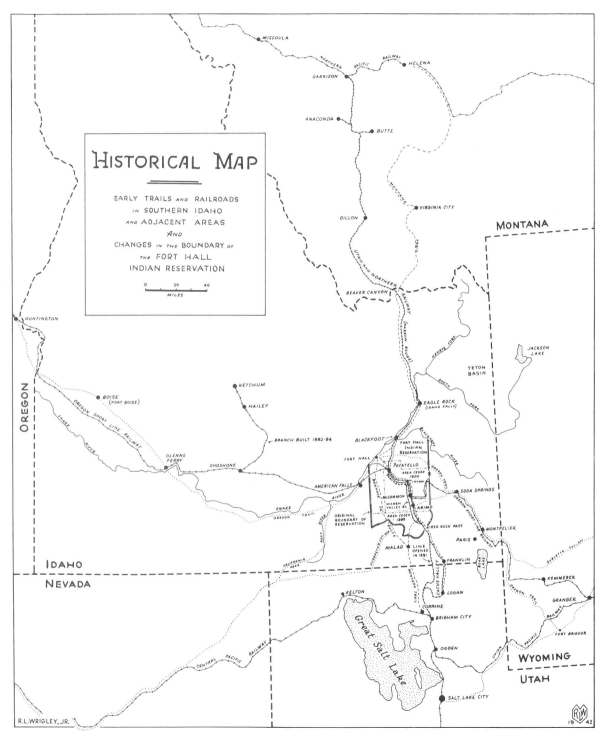

HISTORICAL MAP

EARLY TRAILS AND RAILROADS
IN SOUTHERN IDAHO
AND ADJACENT AREAS
AND
CHANGES IN THE BOUNDARY OF
THE FORT HALL
INDIAN RESERVATION

0   20   40
MILES

Historical Map showing early trails and railroads in southern Idaho and adjacent areas and changes in the boundary of the Fort Hall Indian Reservation (from Wrigley, 1942, Fig. 13.)

Russell Yardley, Tie Bucker, Union Pacific Timber Treating Plant (Tie Plant), Pocatello, Idaho, ca. 1940. Men were paid on a piece work basis, about 2 cents per tie. Ties weighed between 110 and 200 pounds each. A days work was 400 ties when they were available. Thus one worker handled, on average, 30 tons of ties per day, for $8.00. These wages were not bad for the depression era. Photo courtesy of Elmer Yardley via F.W. Dykes

View of Pocatello roundhouse, taken from coal tipple, by Cook Photo, late 1920s. The roundhouse is at its largest extent, with 49 stalls. Each stall had a chimney for the locomotive smoke. The Union Pacific heating plant (power house) chimney, still standing though unused, is on the left. The turntable in the center is still in use. Yellowstone Avenue is in the distant right. Clifford Peake collection, Bannock County Historical Society.

Pocatello coal tipple (shortly after it was built in 1913), where steam engines were refueled. This huge structure held coal mainly brought from Union Pacific mines near Kemmerer. The lead engine is a 4-6-2 Pacific. Bannock County Historical Society Collection.

Two railroad engines at the University of Idaho, Southern Branch Museum, 1942. Number 11, a 2-8-0 Consolidation, was the last narrow gauge engine to run south from Pocatello in 1890. These priceless engines, gifts of the Union Pacific, were cut up for war-time scrap metal at the insistence of Governor Chase Clark within weeks after this picture was taken. The scrap was never used in the World War II war effort. Clifford Peake collection, Bannock County Historical Society.

	SECOND CLASS		FIRST CLASS					Distance from Salt Lake	WESTWARD—Salt Lake and Butte—EASTWARD.	Distance from Butte	FIRST CLASS				SECOND CLASS		
		277 Montana Time Freight	**31** Salt Lake-Portland Express	**13** Idaho Express	**9** Butte and Portland Express	**1** Salt Lake Butte Express			Time Table No. 176. November 8, 1914.		**2** Butte-Salt Lake Express	**10** Butte-Salt Lake Express	**14** Portland-Salt Lake Express	**32** Portland-Salt Lake Express	**278** Utah Time Freight		
		Leave Daily	Leave Daily	Leave Daily	Leave Daily	Leave Daily		STATIONS		Arrive Daily	Arrive Daily	Arrive Daily	Arrive Daily	Arrive Daily		
		7.00 PM	12.30 AM	8.00 AM	2.05 PM	11.45 PM	0.0	SALT LAKE	433.3	8.05 AM	10.00 PM	4.35 PM	10.15 AM	7.35 AM		
		9.25	1.45	9.15	3.20	1.10 AM	36.3	OGDEN	397.0	7.00	9.00	3.40	9.15	5.40		
		10.25 PM	2.29	10.00	3.57	1.55	57.4	BRIGHAM	375.9	6.05	8.10	2.45	8.25	3.50		
		12.30 AM	3.20	11.00 AM	4.45	3.00	85.2	CACHE JCT.	348.2	5.15	7.10	1.55	7.25	1.45 AM		
		4.30	5.35	1.10 PM	6.30	5.20	147.6	McCAMMON	285.6	3.35	5.05	12.10 PM	5.35	10.00 PM		
		5.30 / 6.30	6.15 AM	1.50 / 2.05	7.10 / 8.08	8.00 / 8.45	170.4	Arr. POCATELLO Lv. Lv. Arr.	262.9	2.55 / 3.10	4.25 / 4.15	11.35 / 11.15 AM	4.50 AM	8.30 / 8.30		
		8.05		2.55	8.58	7.33	194.4	BLACKFOOT	238.9	1.55	3.25	10.23		4.50		
		9.45 AM		3.55	9.53 PM	8.33 AM	220.8	IDAHO FALLS	212.5	1.05 AM	2.35 PM	9.25		2.40 PM		
					6.05 PM		271.8	Arr. ASHTON Lv.				7.15 AM				
							327.9	Arr. YELLOWSTONE Lv.	319.6							
		7.00 PM			2.05 AM	12.20 PM	316.2	LIMA	117.1	9.55	11.35			7.30 AM		
		4.45 PM			6.45 AM	4.55 PM	433.3	BUTTE	00	5.05 PM	7.00 AM			7.40 PM		
		Arrive Daily	Arrive Daily	Arrive Daily	Arrive Daily	Arrive Daily		(433.3)		Leave Daily	Leave Daily	Leave Daily	Leave Daily	Leave Daily		
		(33.45)	(5.40)	(10.05)	(16.40)	(17.10)		Time over District		(16.00)	(15.00)	(9.20)	(5.25)	(35.55)		
		12.4	31.2	27.0	26.0	25.5		Average speed per hour		26.8	28.5	19.5	32.4	13.1		

December, 1914 Union Pacific timetable of the Salt Lake to Butte route.

Population of Ten Largest Idaho Cities in 1890 and 1990

	1890			**1990**	
Rank	**Name**	**Population**	**Rank**	**Name**	**Population**
1.	Rexburg	2,967	1.	Boise	125,738
2.	Moscow	2,861	2.	Pocatello	46,080
3.	Pocatello	2,330	3.	Idaho Falls	43,929
4.	Boise	2,311	4.	Nampa	28,365
5.	Eagle Rock	1,588	5.	Lewiston	28,082
6.	Preston	1,504	6.	Twin Falls	27,591
7.	Franklin	1,330	7.	Coeur d'Alene	24,563
8.	Dayton	1,230	8.	Moscow	18,519
9.	Montpelier	1,174	9.	Caldwell	18,400
10.	Blackfoot	1,174	10.	Rexburg	14,302

Population Trends

Prior to the arrival of rail service, Idaho appeared to be going backwards. A special census in 1863, during the gold rush in northern Idaho, gave the new territory a population of 32,342. At that time Idaho included all the later territory of Montana and most of Wyoming. Excluding those areas, Idaho had a population of 20,116. Seven years later in 1870, after the gold fever had subsided, the territory's population was only 14,999. This does not include the 1,925 Mormons in the Bear Lake area who claimed they were in Utah Territory and were counted with the Utah census, even though they were living in Idaho north of the 42nd Parallel (Hatzenbuehler, 1994). Adding them plus Mormons in Cache Valley counted with Utah brings the corrected 1870 population to 17,804 (Idaho State Historical Society, 1976). After the arrival of the railroad, the 1890 population of the new State of Idaho was 88,548 and by 1900, it had increased 100% to 161,772. Obviously, the coming of rail service was the vital factor in the growth of Idaho.

When the State of Idaho was created on July 3, 1890, most of the population was in the eastern or southern parts, along the rights of way of the Oregon Short Line & Utah Northern Railway Company. The ten largest towns according to the 1890 census were, in order, Rexburg, Moscow, Pocatello, Boise, Eagle Rock, Preston, Franklin, Dayton, Montpelier and Blackfoot. All of these communities had 1,000 people or more, Rexburg, the largest, had 2,967 souls. Five of these towns were Mormon farming communities in southeast Idaho, most of whose inhabitants were at the time disenfranchised because of the anti-polygamy Idaho Test Oath. Only one other Idaho community, Hailey, exceeded 1,000 persons and it was on the first branch line of Oregon Short Line. This reflects the agricultural nature of the new state and the influence of its railroads. One hundred years later the first had become last, Rexburg was now 10th in size. One town in the first 10, Twin Falls, had not even existed in 1890 and the second town in 1890, Moscow, was now 8th.

Best Narrow-Gauge Reference
The best single reference on the Utah and Northern, containing exquisite photographs, journals and time tables is Colorado Rail Annual No. 15, The Idaho-Montana Issue, published in 1981.

References

Beal, Merrill D., 1957, The Story of the Utah Northern Railroad: Idaho Yesterdays v. 1 no. 2, p. 16-23.

Beal, Merrill D., 1980, The Utah & Northern Railroad: Pocatello, Idaho, The Idaho State University Press, 81 p.

Colorado Railroad Museum, 1981, Colorado Rail Annual No. 15, Idaho-Montana Issue, Colorado Railroad Historical Foundation, P.O. Box 10, Golden, Colorado, 80401, 215 p.

Gittins, H. Leigh, 1976, Idaho's Gold Road: Moscow, Idaho, The University Press of Idaho, 165 p.

Gittins, H. Leigh, 1983, Pocatello Portrait: The Early Years, 1878 to 1928: Moscow, Idaho, The University Press of Idaho, 224 p.

Hatzenbuehler, Ron, 1994, Idaho migration and settlement: *in* Idaho and the American West, Boise, Idaho Humanities Council, p. 14-15.

Howard, Minnie, 1928, Early life and times of the First Congregational Church of Pocatello: Pocatello, Idaho, Written for the dedication of the new church extension, November 11, 1928, The First Congregational Church, 65 p.

Harstad, P.T., editor, 1972, Reminiscences of Oscar Sonnenkalb, Idaho Surveyor and Pioneer: Pocatello, Idaho, The Idaho State University Press, 66 p.

Idaho State Historical Society, 1976, Idaho, An Illustrated History: Boise, 250 p.

Madsen, B.D., 1986, Chief Pocatello: The "White Plume": Salt Lake City, University of Utah Press, 142 p.

Photograph taken in 1911 of locomotive shop crew, Pocatello. Abe Lillibridge, who became professor of Engineering at Idaho State University, is sitting in the cluster at the lower right, about three rows back, He has the number "1" on his head. Eli Oboler Library, Idaho State University.

CHICAGO to PORTLAND and SEATTLE via Omaha and Denver

Table D Condensed Schedules All Trains Daily	Domeliner City of Portland 105 Daily Example	City of Portland—Park Special 106-47 Summer Season Example	Park Special Portland Rose 48-17 Summer Season Example	Trains 7-17 Daily Example
C. M. St. P. & P.				
Lv Chicago (C.S.T.)	● **3.00** SUN	**3.00** SUN		**7.30** SUN
Ar Omaha	**11.15** "	**11.15** SUN		**7.30** MON
Union Pacific				
Lv **Omaha**	**11.35** SUN	**11.35** SUN		10.45 MON
" Fremont	▣ " MON	▣ " MON		11.35 "
" Columbus	12.49 "	12.49 "		**12.29** "
" Grand Island	1.50 "	1.50 "		1.50 "
" Kearney	2.25 "	2.25 "		2.32 "
Ar North Platte (C.S.T.)	**3.50** "	**3.50** "		**4.30** "
Lv North Platte (M.S.T.)	2.55 "	2.55 "		**3.45** "
Lv Sterling	**5.05** "	**5.05** "		Ar Cheyenne
" La Salle	**6.30** "	**6.30** "		**8.15** MON
Ar **Denver**	**7.40** "	**7.40** "		Lv Cheyenne
Lv **Denver**	**8.05** "	**8.05** "		**9.20** MON
" Laramie	10.55 "	10.55 "		10.55 MON
" Rawlins	**12.50** "	**12.50** "		1.05 TUE
" Rock Springs	f **2.37** "	f **2.37** "		**3.05** "
Ar Green River	**3.05** "	**3.05** "		**3.35** "
Lv Green River	**3.15** "	**3.15** "		**4.30** "
" Kemmerer	f **4.27** "	f **4.27** "		**6.01** "
" Montpelier	**5.45** "	**5.45** "		**7.55** "
Ar **Pocatello**	**7.25** MON	**7.25** MON		10.10 TUE
Ar **Ashton** ▪		▪ **5.45** TUE		
Ar **Victor** ▪		▪ **7.30**		
Lv **Victor** ▪			▪ **8.15** MON	
Lv **Ashton** ▪			▪ 10.20	
Lv **Pocatello**	→ **7.35** MON		10.50 TUE	10.50 TUE
" Minidoka	▣ **8.25** "		12.01 "	12.01 "
Ar **Shoshone**	9.11 MON		1.00 "	1.00 TUE
Lv Shoshone	♦ 9.15 MON		♦ 1.10 TUE	♦ 1.10 TUE
Ar **Sun Valley** (Ketchum)	♦ 11.15 MON		♦ 3.10 TUE	♦ 3.10 TUE
Lv **Sun Valley** (Ketchum)	♦ **7.00** MON		♦ 10.55 TUE	♦ 10.55 TUE
Ar Shoshone	♦ **9.00** MON		♦ **12.55** TUE	♦ **12.55** TUE
Lv **Shoshone**	→ 9.11 MON		1.00 "	1.00 TUE
" Glenns Ferry	10.05 "		2.25 "	2.25 "
" Boise	11.20 "		**4.05** "	**4.05** "
" Nampa	11.43 "		**4.40** "	**4.40** "
" Ontario	... TUE		**5.43** "	**5.43** "
Ar Huntington (M.S.T.)	**1.15** "		**6.50** "	**6.50** "
Lv Huntington (P.S.T.)	12.16 "		**6.00** "	**6.00** "
" Baker	**1.30** "		**7.22** "	**7.22** "
" La Grande	**2.40** "		**8.40** "	**8.40** "
Lv Pendleton	**4.45** "		11.00	11.00 "
Ar Hinkle	**5.30** TUE		11.55 TUE	11.55 TUE
" Arlington			1.02 WED	1.02 WED
" The Dalles	**7.05** TUE		2.30 "	2.30 "
" Hood River	f **7.33** "		3.17 "	3.17 "
Ar **Portland**	**9.00** "		**5.00** WED	**5.00** "
Lv **Portland**	✗ **9.30** TUE		✗ **9.30** WED	✗ **9.30** WED
Ar Tacoma	✗ **12.27** "		✗ **12.27** "	✗ **12.27** "
Ar **Seattle** (P.S.T.)	✗ **1.30** TUE		✗ **1.30** WED	✗ **1.30** WED

Equipment for Page 8

NO. 105— *Domeliner* CITY OF PORTLAND—DAILY
C. M. St. P. & P. to Omaha; No. 457 Portland-Seattle.

Radio and Recorded Musical Programs

Dome Lounge Car.......Chicago to Portland.
Streamlined Sleeping Cars.Chicago to Portland—10 Roomettes, 6 Double Bedrooms. (Two cars).
Chicago to Portland—11 Double Bedrooms.
Reclining Seat—
Leg Rest Coaches......Omaha to Portland—all seats reserved.
Dome Coach.............Chicago to Portland—36 leg rest seats reserved; dome seats not reserved.
Dome Dining Car........Chicago to Portland—Club and a la carte service.
Coffee Shop-Lounge Car....Chicago to Portland—Moderately priced meals and lounge for coach passengers. (Operates approx. June 15 to Sept. 2nd.)

NO. 105-47—CITY OF PORTLAND—PARK SPECIAL—DAILY (See Note ▪)
C. M. St. P. & P. No. 105 to Omaha; U. P. No. 105 to Pocatello; No. 47 to Victor.

Club Lounge Service.......Chicago to Victor.
Streamlined Sleeping Cars..Chicago to Pocatello—Bedrooms, Roomettes, Pocatello to Victor—10 Roomettes, 6 Double Bedrooms (from Salt Lake).
Reclining Seat Coaches.....Chicago to Pocatello—reserved seats. Pocatello to Victor—seats not reserved. Omaha to Pocatello—reserved seats.
Dome Dining Car........Chicago to Pocatello.
Coffee Shop-Lounge Car....Chicago to Pocatello—moderately priced meals and lounge for coach passengers.

No. 7-17—Daily
C. M. St. P. & P. No. 19 to Omaha; U. P. No. 7 to Green River; No. 17 to Portland.
Reclining Seat Coaches....Chicago and Omaha to Portland—requires car to car change at Omaha and Cheyenne. Seats not reserved.
Cafe Lounge Car.........Omaha to Cheyenne; Green River to La Grande—moderately priced meal service.
(See Table F for sleeping car equipment Train 17).

NO. 48-17—PARK SPECIAL—PORTLAND ROSE—DAILY (See Note ▪)
No. 48 to Pocatello; No. 17 to Portland.
Club Lounge Service.......Victor to Portland.
Streamlined Sleeping Car...Pocatello to Portland—6 Sections, 6 Roomettes, 4 Double Bedrooms (occupancy at Portland until 7:30 a.m.). Victor to Pocatello—10 Roomettes, 6 Double Bedrooms (to Salt Lake).
Reclining Seat Coaches.....Victor to Pocatello; Pocatello to Portland—seats not reserved.
Cafe Lounge Car.........Pocatello to La Grande—Moderately priced meal service.

Footnotes for Page 8

▪ Ashton, Idaho is western gateway to Yellowstone National Park. Victor, Idaho is southern gateway to Grand Teton and Yellowstone National Parks. Trains 47 and 48 serve Ashton and Victor during summer season June 16 through August 21.
▣ Conditional stop; see Table 1 or 20.
♦ Motor Bus. This service is provided passengers arriving or departing Shoshone and holding through rail tickets to and from Sun Valley or Ketchum, Idaho.
● Limited handling of checked baggage on Train 105; consult agent.
✗ Daily train No. 457.
(C.S.T.) Central Standard time. (M.S.T.) Mountain Standard time. (P.S.T.) Pacific Standard time.
(f) Stops only on signal.
Time from 12.01 midnight to 12.00 noon shown in light face type.
Time from 12.01 noon to 12.00 midnight shown in heavy face type.

Union Pacific Steam Engine 8444, a 4-8-4 Northern, on special passenger train, Pocatello yards. The engine is maintained for special occasions. Its original number was 844, and this number has now been restored, (June, 1989).

Special UP Passenger train just east of Lava Hot Springs, (June, 1989)

Union Pacific Railroad timetable, January 27, 1969.

Pocatello Railroad Station and Union Pacific Special Passenger Train from Benton Street Bridge, looking north, (June, 1989).

Union Pacific class 9,000 locomotive, "Union Pacific" Series (4-12-2), 1933. Photograph taken by Fred E. Dykes from the front yard of the Dykes' home near the old Kraft Cheese Plant, looking east at the Union Pacific mainline. This is the same engine pictured on p. 183. The U.P. tie plant storage yard is in the background. Ties were stored for a year or two to dry out, then run through the mill and then boiled in creosote. U.S. Highway 30 to American Falls is between the locomotive and the tie storage yard. Photo used courtesy of Fred W. Dykes.

Union Pacific Railroad timetable, January 27, 1969.

PORTLAND and SEATTLE to CHICAGO via Denver and Omaha

Table **D** Condensed Schedules All Trains Daily	Domeliner City of Portland 106 Daily Example	Park Special —City of Los Angeles— 48-36-104 Summer Season Example	Portland Rose Park Special 18-47 Summer Season Example	Trains 18-8 Daily Example
Union Pacific				
Lv **Seattle** (P.S.T.)	‡ 8.05 SUN		⚹ 5.00 SUN	⚹ 5.00 SUN
" Tacoma	‡ 9.01 "		⚹ 6.02 "	⚹ 6.02 "
Ar Portland	‡ 12.20 SUN		⚹ 9.15 SUN	⚹ 9.15 SUN
Lv **Portland**	12.30 SUN		9.45 SUN	9.45 SUN
" Hood River	f 1.44 "		11.09 "	11.09 "
" The Dalles	2.15 "		11.55 SUN	11.55 SUN
" Arlington			1.02 MON	1.02 MON
" Hinkle	3.56 "		2.20 "	2.20 "
" Pendleton	4.31 "		3.20 "	3.20 "
" La Grande	6.45 "		6.05 "	6.05 "
" Baker	7.45 "		7.25 "	7.25 "
Ar Huntington (P.S.T.)	9.05 "		8.50 "	8.50 "
Lv Huntington (M.S.T.)	10.06 "		10.00 "	10.00 "
" Ontario	▣ "		10.55 "	10.55 "
" Nampa	11.25 "		12.05 "	12.05 "
" Boise	11.50 SUN		12.35 "	12.35 "
" Glenns Ferry	1.05 MON		2.15 "	2.15 "
Ar **Shoshone**	1.57 MON		3.30 MON	3.30 MON
Lv Shoshone	♦ 2.00 MON		♦ 3.35 MON	♦ 3.35 MON
Ar **Sun Valley** (Ketchum)	♦ 4.00 MON		♦ 5.35 MON	♦ 5.35 MON
Lv **Sun Valley** (Ketchum)	♦11.50 SUN		♦ 1.25 MON	♦ 1.25 MON
Ar Shoshone	♦ 1.50 MON		♦ 3.25 MON	♦ 3.25 MON
Lv **Shoshone**	1.57 MON		3.30 MON	3.30 MON
" Minidoka	▣ 2.40 "		4.20 "	4 20 "
Ar **Pocatello**	3.40 MON		5.35 MON	5.35 MON
Ar **Ashton** ■		Via Ogden	■ 5.45 TUE	■ 5.45 TUE
Ar **Victor** ■			■ 7.30 "	■ 7.30 "
Lv **Victor** ■			■ 8.15 SUN	
Lv **Ashton** ■			■10.20 "	
Lv **Pocatello**	3.55 MON			6.15 MON
" Montpelier	5.40 "			8.30 "
" Kemmerer	f 7.05 "			10.10 "
Ar Green River	8.25 "	12.40 MON		11.30 MON
Lv Green River	8.35 "	12.50 "		12.50 TUE
" Rock Springs	f 8.55 "	1.10 "		1.12 "
" Rawlins	10.46 "	3.01 "		3.30 "
" Laramie	12.32 "	4.55 "		5.40 "
Ar **Denver**	3.30 "			Ar Cheyenne
Lv **Denver**	3.50 "	Via		7.00 TUE
Lv LaSalle	4.38 "	Cheyenne		Lv Cheyenne
" Sterling	6.03 "			7.50 TUE
Ar North Platte (M.S.T.)	8.20 "	9.50 "		11.55 "
Lv North Platte (C.S.T.)	9.25 "	10.55 MON		1.05 "
" Kearney	10.42 "	TUE		2.55 "
" Grand Island	11.25 MON	12.55 "		4.00 "
" Columbus	12.18 TUE	"		5.06 "
" Fremont	▣ "	▣ "		6.04 "
Ar **Omaha**	1.40 TUE	3. 10 TUE		7.00 TUE
C. M. St. P. & P.				
Lv **Omaha**	2.00 TUE	3.40 TUE		8.00 TUE
Ar **Chicago** (C.S.T.)	10.15 TUE	11.59 TUE		8.50 WED

Equipment for Page 9

NO. 106— *Domeliner* **CITY OF PORTLAND—Daily**
C. M. St. P. & P. east of Omaha; No. 460 Seattle-Portland.
Radio and Recorded Musical Programs

Dome Lounge Car........Portland to Chicago.
Streamlined Sleeping Cars.Portland to Chicago—10 Roomettes, 6 Double Bedrooms. (Two cars).
Portland to Chicago—11 Double Bedrooms.

Reclining Seat—
Leg Rest Coaches......Portland to Chicago—all seats reserved.
Portland to Omaha—all seats reserved. (Occupancy until 6:30 a.m.)
Dome Coach...............Portland to Chicago—36 leg rest seats reserved; dome seats not reserved.
Dome Dining Car........Portland to Chicago—Club and a la carte service.
Coffee Shop-Lounge Car....Portland to Chicago—Moderately priced meals and lounge for coach passengers. (Operates approx. June 15 to Sept. 2nd).

NO. 48-36-104—PARK SPECIAL—CITY OF LOS ANGELES— DAILY (See Note ■)
No. 48 to Pocatello; No. 36 to Ogden; No. 104 to Chicago; C. M. St. P. & P.east of Omaha

Club Lounge Service.......Victor to Chicago.
Streamlined Sleeping Car...Victor to Ogden—10 Roomettes, 6 Double Bedrooms.
Ogden to Chicago—Bedrooms, Roomettes, Compartments Drawing rooms.
Reclining Seat Coaches.....Victor to Ogden—seats not reserved.
Ogden to Chicago—reserved seats (on Train 104).
Ogden to Omaha—reserved seats (on Train 104). (Occupancy until 6:30 a.m.)
Dome Dining Car........Ogden to Chicago.
Coffee Shop Lounge Car....Ogden to Chicago—moderately priced meals and lounge for coach passengers (on Train 104).

NO. 18-8—Daily
No. 18 to Green River; No. 8 to Omaha; C. M. St. P. & P. No. 20 to Chicago.

Reclining Seat Coaches....Portland to Omaha and Chicago—requires car to car change at Cheyenne and Omaha Seats not reserved.
Cafe Lounge Car.........La Grande to Green River; Cheyenne to Omaha— moderately priced meal service.

(See Table F for sleeping car equipment Train 18.)

NO. 18-47—PORTLAND ROSE—PARK SPECIAL—DAILY (See Note ■)
No. 18 to Pocatello; No. 47 to Victor.

Club Lounge Service.......Portland to Victor.
Streamlined Sleeping Car...Portland to Pocatello—6 Sections, 6 Roomettes, 4 Double Bedrooms.
Pocatello to Victor—10 Roomettes, 6 Double Bedrooms (from Salt Lake).
Reclining Seat Coaches.....Portland to Pocatello; Pocatello to Victor—seats not reserved.
Cafe Lounge Car.........La Grande to Pocatello—Moderately priced meal service.

Footnotes for Page 9

■ Ashton, Idaho is western gateway to Yellowstone National Park. Victor, Idaho is southern gateway to Grand Teton and Yellowstone National Parks. Trains 47 and 48 serve Ashton and Victor during summer season June 16 through August 21.

▣ Conditional stop; see Table 2 or 20. (f) Stops only on signal.

♦ Motor Bus. This service is provided passengers arriving or departing Shoshone and holding through rail tickets to and from Sun Valley or Ketchum, Idaho.

● Limited handling of checked baggage on Train 106; consult agent.

‡ Daily Train No. 460. ⚹ Daily Train No. 458.
(C.S.T.) Central Standard time. (M.S.T.) Mountain Standard time.
(P.S.T.) Pacific Standard time.
Time from 12.01 midnight to 12.00 noon shown in light face type.
Time from 12.01 noon to 12.00 midnight shown in heavy face type.

We solicit your kind consideration and cooperation . . . .

PLEASE DON'T BE A " *NO SHOW*." (A "no show" is the person who reserves coach or Pullman accommodations in advance and then fails to cancel out when his plans change.)

So that we may serve you better, please be sure to cancel reservations promptly when it is found you will not use the space you have reserved.

We can then serve you and others better by not having any space go unused.

Pocatello railroad yards, looking southwest, winter late 1920s. In the foreground is part of the roundhouse. The chimneys are to carry off the engine smoke. The long building in the right middle distance is the Stores Department. The large black structure in the right center is the coal tipple, built in 1913. Kinport Peak is directly above it. Cars of coal on the right are to supply the tipple. To the left of the coal tipple is the steeple of St. Andrew's Church and across Arthur Street is the second Pocatello High School. In the center are at least 30 stored steam engines. The Caboose ("crummy") servicing area is to the left. At the left is the Center Street viaduct. In the middle distance is the Bannock Hotel, and the Carlsen (Spaulding) Building to its right. In the haze, to the left of the Bannock Hotel, is the Pocatello water reservoir system, originally operated by James Murray, with Lombardy poplars on the edge of the open reservoir. Photograph by Cook Photography, Bannock County Historical Society Collection.

View from the Center Street viaduct of passenger depot, downtown Pocatello and the Bannock Range, looking southwest, late 1920s. Note covered passenger waiting shed in front of depot. An icing car services a diner in a string of passenger cars, removed from a passenger train that terminated at Pocatello. Baggage and mail cars are the second and third from the front of the string. Two business cars of railroad officials stand just north of the depot. The houses north of the depot are on Company Row, east of South Harrison Ave. To the right of the Fargo-Wilson Wells building (light-colored, center of picture) is the Benson Hotel; the Kasiska Building, and the Telephone Building to the left of the Nicollet (Whitman) Hotel. The Bannock Hotel tower is at right distance. The Yellowstone Hotel is the large three-section building to the left of Fargo's. Note stairs leading up onto the viaduct on right edge of view. Photograph by Cook Photography, Bannock County Historical Society Collection.

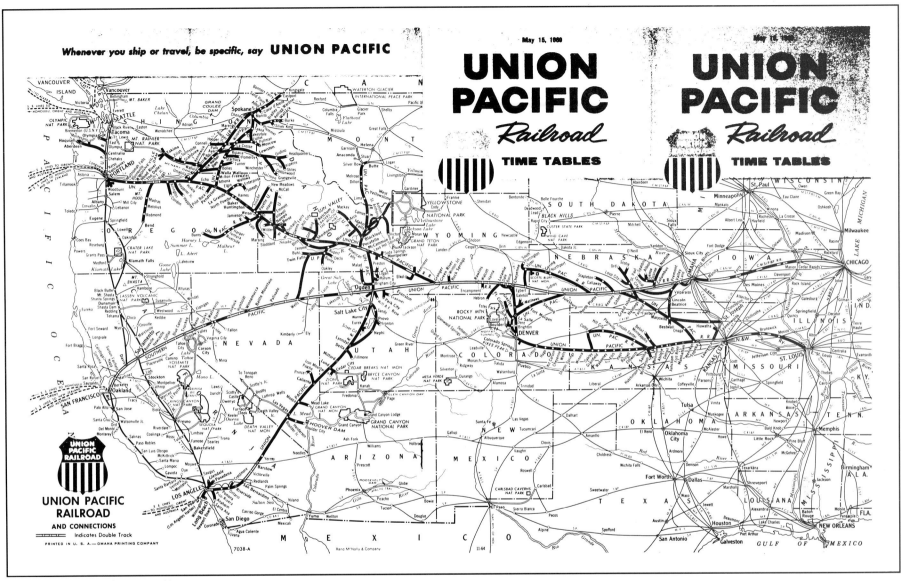

Map of Union Pacific System, 1969.

Milner Dam, the fount of the Magic Valley, looking north, (July, 1989). The dam was begun in 1904 and finished in 1905. Note the dam is in the middle of a scabland swath cleaned of soil by the Lake Bonneville Flood. The Oregon Trail passed along the south side of the Snake River here and ruts are preserved in a Bureau of Land Management recreation site. The Twin Falls Branch of the Union Pacific Railroad runs south of the river. From north to south the arteries of Snake River water to irrigate the Magic Valley are the Milner-Gooding Canal, the North Side Canal, the Snake River in its canyon, the South Side Main or Twin Falls Canal, and heading south directly at the camera, the Milner Low Lift Main Canal. This was near the point where the Wilson Price Hunt Party in 1811 got into trouble in navigating the Snake River by boat. A few miles downstream, at Caldron Lynn, they gave up their river journey and set off on foot, headed for Fort Astoria.

Water in Idaho

One of the most important features of life in the intermountain area of the United States is water. Both because there is so little of it available and because water for agricultural uses must be stored in reservoirs or obtained from underground sources, the subject of water occupies the attention of many people. In water-short years, there is a real concern that there will not be enough to go around and that crops may suffer. Climatic patterns are cyclical. There are both drought years and wet years when winter snowfall has been adequate and spring rains have soaked into fields and watersheds. Water is a matter of constant concern.

Idaho contains parts of three major drainage basins: the Salmon River and other tributaries of the Columbia in the mountainous northern part, the Bear River and Great Salt Lake in the southeast, and the Snake River, which is the lifeblood of the agriculture in southern Idaho. Northern Idaho has a wetter climate and the need for water storage is much less essential. In the south, the weather is warmer and drier. Water storage is absolutely necessary.

The fur trappers were little bothered with water resources. As long as beaver could build dams in the forested areas, trappers were mainly unconcerned with how much moisture fell during the year.

As the Pioneers of the Oregon and California Trails passed through southern Idaho, they were appalled by the dust, the lack of water and the obvious hostility of the land. They hurried past, expressing doubt that the vast desert wilderness would ever support civilization, much less irrigated agriculture. It is wonderful irony how wrong they were.

State law mandates that the slogan "Famous Potatoes" appear on standard Idaho automobile license plates.

Mormon settlements and the use of water

Early Mormon Pioneers, led by Brigham Young, changed the desolate deserts of the valleys of the intermountain west into green, productive farmland. The construction of canal systems, which in the Lake Bonneville basin took advantage of existing shoreline benches on the edges of valleys to feed water to the former lake bottoms below, allowed mixed farming in mountain valleys which had formerly supported only sagebrush and grasses.

As Mormon settlers moved into southern Idaho in the 1860s, it was obvious that the land had to be irrigated for farming to be feasible. Irrigation canals were built in Cache and Malad Valleys soon after settlement. Much of the country too high or too rugged to irrigate became grazing land.

In the early 20th century, the determined efforts of the Last Chance Canal Company to bring irrigation water to the Grace area in Gem Valley were opposed by the Utah Power and Light Company, which sought the water for hydroelectric generation. The historic Dietrich Decree of 1919 awarded water rights to the Mormon farmers who had filed on it first. One of the primary tenets of Western water law (first in time is first in right) had been established (McCarthy, 1987).

> "since the Mormon farmers from Utah . . . had pushed ahead into the agricultural lands of Southern Idaho, irrigation commenced to be introduced, and I must give my fullest regard and admiration to the skill and the perseverance of these first irrigators and re-clamationists, who were teaching new settlers how the desert lands could be made blooming like the rose . . . The reclamation of the upper Snake River valleys, in its first work almost solely performed by the Mormons, is one of the examples of their wonderful ability as colonizers of a good deal of the western country. As our early Pioneers they were strong and patient and with firm belief in the protection of a divine power to enable them to endure the hardships and sufferings attendant upon the early settlement of what are now the prettiest, the richest and the most promising valleys of Idaho."
> Oscar Sonnenkalb (*in* Harstad, 1972, p. 8, 15-16).

Oneida Narrows Reservoir, north of Preston, looking southeast from high above the west shore. The dam is at the narrow constriction in the distance. The rocks here belong to the Late Proterozoic and Cambrian Brigham Group, (August, 1985).

Irrigation of the Snake River System

North of the Mormon country, there were limited attempts to establish irrigation systems. Rev. Henry Spaulding at the Lapwai Mission, up the Clearwater River from Lewiston, developed some irrigation during the 1830s and 40s as he tried to turn the Nez Perce of the area into farmers. The first Mormon settlement in Idaho, in 1855 at Fort Limhi along the East Fork of the Salmon River, built an irrigation system.

Through the sagebrush desert of much of southern Idaho, the Snake River flowed full of water along treeless plains, adjacent to vast fields of fertile soil which were unproductive because the nearby waters could not be diverted. The Snake drains a huge area which usually has heavy snows in the winter and from which a number of tributaries flow.

Flume and arched support carrying water for the Last Chance Canal across Bear River northeast of Grace, (August, 1991).

Last Chance Canal at its headgate along the Bear River northeast of Grace, (August, 1991).

Sprinkler irrigation against the summer sun, Star Valley, Wyoming, (June, 1977).

Sign protesting Idaho Department of Water Resources policies in the lower Big Lost River drainage, (June, 1995). During drought years in 1993 and 1994 the water table dropped in this area because there was not enough recharge to keep up with irrigation withdrawal of both surface and ground water. Hundreds of cottonwood trees along newly dry watercourses died.

An area several hundred miles long north of the Snake River between Henry's Fork in eastern Idaho to the Malad River (the continuation of the Wood River) at Hagerman Valley contains almost no surface streams that persist as far as the Snake. Extensive lava flows block the pre-existing drainage channels. In these areas are large underground water supplies contained within the Snake River Plain Aquifer.

Snake River Plain Aquifer

The Snake River Plain Aquifer underlies about 10,000 square miles of eastern Idaho. Its annual recharge and discharge is estimated at 8 million acre-feet, and its storage capacity is estimated at 200 million acre-feet, enough to cover the entire state of Idaho with 4 feet of water. The aquifer is recharged by precipitation that falls on the ranges to the north and south and flows into rivers whose discharge is absorbed into porous sediment. Recharge by irrigation water is another important source for the aquifer.

More than 3 million acres of land on the Snake River Plain were irrigated in 1980, of which 1 million were supplied by ground water and 2 million by surface water from canals (Whitehead, 1986).

Snake River Plain Aquifer		
Source	**Annual Recharge**	**Annual Outflow**
Irrigation diversions	5.1	
Valley underflow	1.5	
Precipitation	0.8	
River seepage	1.3	
Total	**8.7**	
Pumping for irrigation		1.6
Springs and river gains		7.1
Total in millions of acre-feet		**8.7**

Estimated annual water budget for the Snake River Plain Aquifer (from Hackett and others, 1986). Numbers are in millions of acre-feet, that is enough water to cover a million acres one foot deep.

The Growth of Agricultural Idaho

In the 1870s, economic growth in southern Idaho awaited several things. A reliable and adequate transportation system, needed to carry produce to market and to bring back machinery and equipment and the people to operate them, arrived in the early 1880s with the railroads. The territory grew and became a state; the state grew and towns began to proliferate along the rail lines. Vast areas of southern Idaho lay unused and unoccupied, however, because of a lack of water. Irrigation projects were needed.

Early Irrigation Failures

Although visionary engineers like Arthur Foote, who surveyed and attempted to start canal systems in the Boise Valley in the 1880s, saw the potential in irrigated agriculture in Idaho, large irrigation systems on the Snake River Plain were stymied by lack of investor capital through the 1890s. Although the Mormon Pioneers had made the desert bloom in their corner of the state, central and western Idaho remained the territory of cattle and sheep grazers who neither needed irrigation nor welcomed the fences and restrictions which came with building of farms.

The Carey Act, named after a Wyoming senator, was passed by Congress in 1894 to stimulate state and private cooperation to develop canal systems. The Act gave western states up to a million acres of Federal land if the land could be irrigated or reclaimed. Idaho contains 3/5 of all land reclaimed under the Carey Act.

> Arthur DeWint Foote was a mining engineer who saw the great potential for irrigation in the Boise Valley as early as 1881. His visionary schemes, backed by determination and hard work, but not by outside investment, all came to naught. His story is painted in his wife's memoirs (Foote, 1972; Paul, 1975), and documented in historical fiction in the exquisite book "Angle of Repose" by Wallace Stegner.
>
> "He was not foolish or mistaken. He was premature. His clock was set on Pioneer time. He met trains that had not yet arrived, he waited on platforms that hadn't yet been built, beside tracks that might never be laid. Like many another Western Pioneer, he had heard the clock of history strike, and counted the strokes wrong. Hope was always out ahead of fact, possibility obscured the outlines of reality." (Stegner, 1971, p. 382).

Farm workers pause from labor of "bucking spuds"—hand picking up and sacking potatoes, fall, mid 1930s, on the Snake River Plain probably between Blackfoot and American Falls. The tractor-pulled potato-digger (right) scooped up soil and patatoes. On the left is a similar but horse-drawn plow. Potato sacks were attached to one's belt, and drawn between the legs as the harvester leaned over and tossed potatoes into the sacks. This was hard work. Potato prices were controlled by outside forces, and so the farmer found himself the victim of external economics. The situation is not much different today. Before the development of controlled atmosphere insulated buildings where potatoes are now stored in bulk, potatoes were stored in dug-out cellars, waiting for the best price on the market. A hay derrick is in the right background, with the haystack in the center. The hay was not baled, but piled in great piles, which were gradually moved to the feeding areas where livestock was kept. Note the well-dressed woman leaning on her shiny car in the left background. She has not been harvesting with the rest of the crew. Photograph by Cook Photography, Bannock County Historical Society Collection.

Ira Burton Perrine

In 19th century America, a few lucky men of vision found rich fields for their dreams. And so it was on the Snake River Plain. The water was available, running deep in the Snake River Canyon, but means did not exist for getting the waters onto the lands. A man of vision, I.B. Perrine moved from his native Indiana to southern Idaho in the late 1800s and began farming operations in the canyon of the Snake River just downstream from Shoshone Falls at Blue Lakes. Perrine planned an irrigation project that would cover 500,000 acres by taking water from the Snake River at a point then known as "The Cedars." In 1900, Perrine incorporated the Twin Falls Land and Water Company, filed notice with the State of Idaho for the diversion of water on both the north and south sides of the Snake River, contracted with the State of Idaho to develop 270,000 acres under the new Carey Act which set up procedures for private enterprise to develop irrigated tracts, and began to sell land and water rights.

A dam to effect the diversion of the waters was completed by 1905 and named for Stanley Milner, a business man from Salt Lake City, who loaned $30,000 towards the project. Water was sent first to the Twin Falls Tract on the south side of the Snake River through a canal 10 feet deep and 80 feet wide at the bottom and 120 feet at the top. Later canals were built on the north side of the Snake to irrigate the 185,000 acre North Side Tract (Lovin, 1985). The Magic Valley was born.

Minidoka Project

Above Milner Dam, the first Federal water project under the National Reclamation Act of 1902 established Minidoka Dam which watered 120,000 acres on both sides of the Snake. Finished in 1907, lands were irrigated around the new communities of Heyburn, Paul, Acequia and Rupert.

The Twin Falls project, North Side Project, and Minidoka Dam were the first examples in the United States of irrigation waters provided by the U. S. Reclamation Service being merged with private and state water resources to develop huge irrigated tracts.

As part of the Minidoka Project, Jackson Lake Dam was constructed in 1905 on the Snake River opposite the Grand Teton at Moran, Wyoming. Originally a small log dam, which was washed out by high water two years later, it was rebuilt several times more before being built as a concrete structure in 1916. This dam had to be strengthened in the late 1980s because of structural weakness and concern about earthquake damage. In order to be assured of water in dry years, the North Side Tract secured access to 322,000 acre-feet of water stored behind Jackson Lake Dam.

American Falls Dam

The American Falls Project of the Bureau of Reclamation, successor to the Reclamation Service, built in the 1910s and 1920s, assured late-season water for small cooperatives on the upper Snake, the thousands of farmers in the Twin Falls and North Side Projects and the Minidoka Project. It, too, was partly a brain-child of I.B. Perrine. The project required cooperation by federal, state and local governments, private interests and both corporate and individual proprietorships.

In later years expansion of the American Falls Project required the removal of the town of American Falls to higher ground because a new dam would flood the old town. This large concrete structure created a reservoir of 1.7 million acre-feet, to bring into cultivation an additional 115,000 acres in the vicinity of Gooding and provided supplemental water for over one million acres above and below the facility. Construction began in 1925, and the gates were closed upon completion in October, 1926. The reservoir first reached its maximum storage size on July 1, 1927.

Irrigation of the Snake River System

Other dams and projects utilizing tributary waters of the Snake or the main stream itself have been installed throughout southern Idaho (Idaho Yesterdays, 1986). Upstream from Idaho Falls, Palisades Dam and Reservoir were finished in 1959. This is a major facility used as a balancing source of stored water to maintain stream flows and provide late-season irrigation. In addition to projects on every irrigable acre along the Bear River and its tributaries, irrigation systems exist on the Teton River east of Rexburg, the Blackfoot River (which provides water via the Fort Hall Canal to the east side of Pocatello), the Portneuf River in Marsh Valley, Goose Creek south of Burley, Raft River, and Salmon Falls Creek which rises in Nevada and flows into the Snake west of Buhl. Farther north and west in Idaho are Arrowrock and Lucky Peak Dams on the Boise River (which were Arthur Foote's ideas) and the large Dworshak Dam and Reservoir on a fork of the Clearwater River above Lewiston.

With so many structures and systems involved with storing and utilizing water in agricultural pursuits, it is little wonder that the weather and the moisture it brings are matters of continual interest to southern Idahoans. It is little short of a miracle to compare the Magic Valley near Twin Falls today with the same place one hundred years ago. The desert has been made to bloom.

Idaho and the Great Depression

Leonard Arrington, later Professor of History at Utah State University, wrote about farming near Twin Falls during the Depression.

Perhaps a word of personal recollection may not be inappropriate. My father—a farmer east of Twin Falls—decided that 1929 was a good year to expand his farming acreage, and after much soul-searching he finally purchased a tract of sixty acres of rich apple orchard land, paying $300 per acre. He planned to raise potatoes, and Grade A potatoes in 1929 were selling for $1.50 per bushel. At such a price, and considering his big family of boys, he could envision paying for the land within a few years. But in 1930 when he harvested the first crop, potatoes were selling for only 75 cents a hundred. In 1931 the land yielded well, but potatoes were down to 50 cents per hundred. In 1932, as the Depression continued to deepen, run-of-the-field "spuds" brought 10 cents per sack. I was 15 years old at the time, and while helping to load several truckloads of these ten-cent "spuds", I asked my father, "What do you suppose people will pay for these potatoes in grocery stores?" My father said he didn't know, but why didn't I find out?

Under my father's direction I prepared ten letters which were placed in representative sacks on different truckloads. The letters indicated where the potatoes were produced, mentioned the ten-cent price per sack, included a self-addressed envelope, and asked the final purchaser to reply what he had paid. As I recall, we received five replies from the ten we had enclosed in the sacks. All of the replies were from California, and the price paid by the ultimate purchaser had varied from a low of $1.50 per sack to a high of $2.15 per sack . . . . How my father ever held on to the land and made the payments I was never able to find out. My mother said it was by the labor of her boys, but that may have been her way of making us feel important . . . .

There were persons in our neighborhood who had made similar investments who did not have the boys to do the work nor wives who could manage to "get along" on virtually no income. Sometime during the winter of 1932-33 a family acquaintance was foreclosed by his creditor, and a sheriff's sale ordered for a certain Monday. All the farmers in his neighborhood gathered together on Sunday evening and agreed upon a plan to help their friend. They would attend the sale and refuse to bid against each other. The next day, as the auctioneer went through his accustomed chant, a splendid team of horse sold for $1.50 . . . Prices of other animals and equipment ran from a low of 50 cents to a high of $3.00. The farmers duly paid the sums they had bid, received the items purchased, and promptly turned them back to the farmer who had been foreclosed."

(Arrington, (1969), *in* Etulain and Marley, 1974, p. 131).

The Swan Falls Controversy

Idahoans, with the greatest per capita water consumption in the U.S., have over-used their water. A greater volume of water has been appropriated in water rights than is available at sustainable yields from both surface and ground water sources. A process of adjudication of all Snake River basin water rights was begun in 1977 with a lawsuit by Idaho Power Company to protect its hydropower water right at its Swan Falls Dam south of Boise. The resolution of this issue will be complex and will affect the economic future of Idaho. Many voices now say that in-stream flow, water quality, and tourist dollars should also be protected from depletion of water for irrigation. Such opinions were absolutely heretical when Idaho water policy was formulated.

Irrigated farming is expensive, and the United States Taxpayers, over the last 100 years, have paid the bill. Although farmers might resent the assertion, irrigation in Idaho has been heavily subsidized. Indeed, so are many crops. One Magic Valley farmer is alleged to have said, about the total cost of irrigated farming," The only cash crop that would bear the true cost of the water is marijuana."

The Teton Dam Disaster, June 5, 1976

One Idaho reclamation project failed, spectacularly and tragically. The Teton Dam, built on the Teton River 3 miles upstream from Newdale, was designed to provide irrigation water to farms in the Upper Valley of the Snake River, north and east of Rexburg.

The possibilities of a dam on the Teton River were discussed as early at 1904. The Teton Dam was authorized in 1964, and the construction contract was awarded in December, 1971. The dam was finished in November, 1975. Filling began on October 3, 1975, and continued until the dam failed on June 5, 1976. At that time, the reservoir was 302 feet deep, with its surface at 5302 feet elevation, 3.3 feet below the spillway. Leaks below the dam were first noticed on June 3, 1976, but were not considered cause for alarm. However, starting at 7:00 a.m. on June 5th, dam personnel noted leaks both in the abutment rock at the north bank of the river at the base of the dam and about 100 feet from the top of the dam. These leaks worsened and

About 10:45 a.m. June 5, 1976. Flow of muddy water is increasing from dam. Two D-8 Caterpillar Dozers were sent in (from top) to fill hole at elevation 5,200 ft. All photos are from U.S. Bureau of Reclamation.

About 11:20 a.m. Dozers are lost in hole.

by mid-morning warnings were sent out that the dam might fail. Failure occurred at 11:50 am. Fourteen persons died in the flood. Property damage was estimated at $400 million to $1 billion.

The Independent Panel to Review Cause of Teton Dam Failure reported on December 31, 1976, that the dam failed because of a combination of geological factors and design decisions. Additional allegations of improper construction procedures were also expressed.

Dam crest breaching. 11:55 a.m. June 5, 1976

Late afternoon June 5, 1976

The Federal Government paid almost all of the damage claims and the area was rebuilt, often in much better condition than prior to the flood. One of those afflicted, whose sense of humor remained intact, commented: "We weren't flooded; we were just over-irrigated." (Arrington, 1986, p. 11)

Early afternoon, June 5, 1976

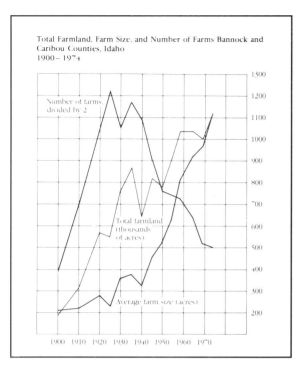

Chart of total farmland, farm size, and number of farms in Bannock and Caribou Counties, Idaho 1900-1974.

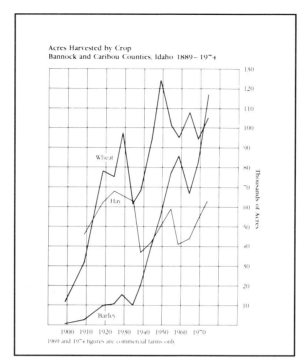

Chart showing acres harvested by crop, Bannock and Caribou Counties, Idaho 1889-1974.

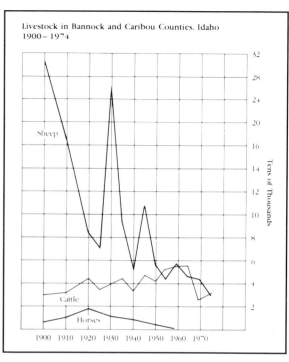

Chart of livestock in Bannock and Caribou Counties, 1900 to 1974. All charts from the Chesterfield Foundation (1982).

Agriculture Today

As is true across the United States, farms in Idaho are getting larger and fewer. The political dominance of farmers over the Idaho legislature is waning. Family farms, especially dryland ones, are under severe economic pressure. Sheep grazing, once a vital part of the Idaho economy, is almost a thing of the past. Several charts, shown above, from the Chesterfield Foundation's documentation of life in northern Gem Valley, illustrate these trends.

References

Arrington, Leonard J., 1969, Idaho and The Great Depression: Idaho Yesterdays, v. 13, Summer, 1969, p. 2-8, reprinted *in* Etulain, R.W., and Marley, B.W., editors, 1974 (3rd printing, 1984), The Idaho Heritage: A collection of historical essays: Pocatello, Idaho, The Idaho State University Press, p. 129-133.

Arrington, Leonard, 1986, Irrigation in the Snake River Valley: Idaho Yesterdays, v. 30, nos. 1-2, p. 3-11.

Etulain, R.W., and Marley, B.W., editors, 1974 (3rd printing, 1984), The Idaho Heritage: A collection of historical essays: Pocatello, Idaho, Idaho State University Press, 230 p.

Foote, Mary Hallock, 1972, A Victorian Gentlewoman in the Far West, edited by Rodman W. Paul: San Marino, California, The Huntington Library, 416 p.

Hackett, W.R., Pelton, J., and Brockway, C., 1986, Geohydrologic story of the eastern Snake River Plain and the Idaho National Engineering Laboratory: Idaho Falls, Idaho: U.S. Department of Energy, Idaho Operations Office, Idaho National Engineering Laboratory, 32 p.

Harstad, P.T., editor, 1972, Reminiscences of Oscar Sonnenkalb, Idaho Surveyor and Pioneer: Pocatello, Idaho, The Idaho State University Press, 66 p.

Idaho Yesterdays, 1986, Special Issue: Irrigation in Idaho, v. 30, no. 1-2, 76 p.

Lovin, Hugh T., 1985, Free Enterprise and large-scale reclamation on the Twin Falls-North Side Tract, 1907-1930, Idaho Yesterdays, v. 29, no. 1, p. 2-14.

McCarthy, Max R., 1987, The Last Chance Canal Company: Provo, Utah: Brigham Young University, Charles Redd Center for Western Studies Monographs in Western History, no. 16, 131 p.

Paul, Rodman W., 1975, When culture came to Boise: Mary Hallock Foote in Idaho: Idaho Yesterdays, v. 20, no. 2, p. 212.

Peterson, F. Ross, 1994, Water and Agriculture: The Idaho Story: *in* Idaho and the American West, Boise, Idaho, Idaho Humanities Council, p. 21-26.

Reisner, Marc, 1986, Cadillac Desert: New York, New York, Penguin Books, 582 p.

Stegner, Wallace, 1971 (reprinted 1992), Angle of Repose: New York, Penguin Books, 569 p.

The Chesterfield Foundation, Inc. 1982, Chesterfield: Mormon outpost in Idaho: The Chesterfield Foundation Inc, Rural Route, Bancroft Idaho, 83217.

Whitehead, R.L., 1986, Geohydrologic framework of the Snake River Plain, Idaho and eastern Oregon: U.S. Geological Survey Hydrologic Investigations Atlas HA-681, scale 1:1,000,000.

Southeastern Idaho

Bear Lake Valley

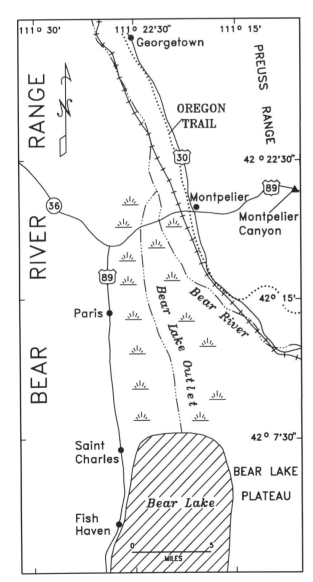

The Oregon Trail in Bear Lake Valley

The Oregon Trail entered Bear Lake Valley near present Montpelier and followed the valley of the meandering Bear River. Travelers remarked on the abundant flowers, berry bushes and mosquitoes on this stretch of trail, in distinct contrast to the dry and windy sagebrush plains of Wyoming.

Osborne Russell comes to Bear Lake Valley

On the 2nd of July, 1834, Osborne Russell, travelling with Nathaniel Wyeth's band of trappers left Ham's Fork, Wyoming, crossed a high range of hills (the Preuss Range), and

"fell on to a stream called Bear River which emptied into the Big Salt Lake. This is a beautiful country. The river which is about 20 yards wide runs through large fertile bottoms bordered by rolling ridges which gradually ascend on each side to the high ranges of dark and lofty mountains upon whose tops the snow remains nearly the year round. We travelled down this river northwest about 15 miles and encamped opposite a lake of fresh water about 60 miles in circumference which outlets into the river on the west side." Haines (1965, p. 3).

Bear Lake and Bear River

The Bear River was named in 1818 by Donald Mackenzie and a party of trappers. Bear Lake is shallow, about 20 feet deep at most, but it overlies up to ten thousand feet of lake and marsh deposits. The lake at the south end is fed by streams from the nearby mountains, and not by the Bear River, which flows north of Bear Lake, and into which the Lake formerly drained. Today water is pumped out of the lake through a series of canals controlled by Utah Power and Light Company and several irrigation companies.

Bear Lake, looking east toward Bear Lake fault scarp and Bear Lake Plateau. Fault line scarp is plainly visible on the steep front of the hills on the east side of the lake, (October, 1985).

Early Settlement of Paris

Charles C. Rich and a group of Mormon settlers founded Paris on Sept. 26, 1863. A young man named Frederick Perris surveyed the town and left for California. The town was named after him, and the incorrect spelling was used. Robert Price, one of the leaders in Paris after 1870, built a sawmill at the mouth of Paris Canyon, designed to provide building material for all the settlements in the Bear Lake region.

Utah or Idaho?

Unfortunately for the early Mormon settlers, the newly formed communities of Paris, Saint Charles and the country around the north end of Bear Lake were not in Utah, but in Idaho. Nonetheless, the 1,925 residents of Bear Lake County were included with the Utah Territorial census of 1870. The location of the boundary was in dispute until it was surveyed in 1872. Bear Lake County was established in 1875 with Paris as county seat, broken out of what had been Oneida County. For several years in the 1880s, C.C. Rich served in the Utah legislature and his son in the Idaho legislature, though they both lived in Paris.

Montpelier railway station, (March, 1992).

Montpelier

Montpelier (elevation 5,920) was founded in 1864 as a Mormon farming community, comfortable with its remoteness. The west-building Oregon Short Line reached the community in 1882, and for a while there were two Montpeliers, one the established Mormon community, the other the largely Gentile railroad outsiders, regarding each other with suspicion. The railroad built a repair shop and a roundhouse and the town served until recently as a railroad division point. Farnworth (1993) relates stories of Montpelier and the Oregon Short Line. At the time of statehood in 1890 Montpelier was the 9th largest city in Idaho.

The population of railroad workers was separate from the Mormon settlers of Bear Lake County, who farmed the western and southern ends of the lake and established the county seat at Paris. In the late 1800s and early 1900s, the road from Paris to Montpelier was often impassible due to washouts and mud. In 1911, the railroad company built a branch line to Paris to serve the farming area but motor vehicles and World War II brought its demise in 1943. World War II also brought a large airfield out on the flat marshy country north of Bear Lake, but it is almost totally unused now.

Geology

Bear Lake Valley is topographically high, (near 6,000 feet) and has long cold winters and short summers. The valley is a fault-bounded basin, or graben, with normal faults on both the east and west sides. The largest fault borders the east side of Bear Lake, and has been dropping the valley downward and tilting it eastward with respect to the Bear Lake plateau for perhaps 10 million years. Total displacement on this fault is close to 10,000 feet.

The mountains of the Preuss and Aspen Ranges to the northeast of the Bear Lake Valley belong to the Meade thrust plate of the Idaho-Wyoming thrust belt. This is the area that contains the rich phosphate deposits of the Permian Phosphoria Formation, deposited in a nutrient-rich warm sea about 250 million years ago. Mining of the Phosphoria Formation has been and will be a major influence on the economy of not only the Bear Lake area, but much of southeast Idaho.

The Bear River Range on the west of the Bear Lake Valley contains Lower Paleozoic and Late Proterozoic rocks of the Paris thrust plate. The Paris thrust extends along the east side of the Bear River Range and places these older rocks over younger Paleozoic rocks of the Meade thrust plate.

Paris Tabernacle, designed by John Young (son of Brigham) and built between 1884 and 1889, (March, 1992).

Historical marker and statue at the Paris Tabernacle. Text reads "Charles Coulson Rich, 1809-1883. Pioneer builder of the west. Major-general of the Nauvoo Legion. Alderman of the city of Nauvoo in the time of Joseph Smith. Pioneer of Utah, 1847. Chairman of the first committee to organize civil government in the Rocky Mountains. Colonizer of San Bernardino Valley, California in 1851. First mayor of San Bernardino city. Member of the Utah territorial legislature for many years. Colonizer of Bear Lake Valley, 1863, where he lived and died. Husband of six wives and father of fifty children. Friend of the Indians, humanitarian. Apostle of the Church of Jesus Christ of Latter-Day-Saints, thirty four years. One of God's noblemen." This monument erected by the citizens of Bear Lake Valley, the Utah Pioneer trails and landmarks association and his descendants, (May, 1991).

Phosphate Mining History

Underground phosphate mining began in Georgetown Canyon in the early 1900s and a phosphate processing plant was built in 1957. Open pit mining began in 1958. An avalanche destroyed many of the facilities and the processing operations were moved to Conda, north of Soda Springs, in 1964.

The oldest phosphate mine in Idaho is the Waterloo Mine in Montpelier Canyon, about 3 miles east of the city of Montpelier. Mining began in 1907 and the mine was closed in 1929. The property was reopened from 1945 to 1958.

Underground mining of phosphate began in the Slight Canyon area north of Paris in 1920.

December, 1914 Oregon Short Line Timetable for the Paris and Bear River (Grace) Branches. The Paris branch is now abandoned.

References

Armstrong, F.C., and Oriel, S.S., 1965, Tectonic development of the Idaho-Wyoming thrust belt: American Association of Petroleum Geologists Bulletin, v. 49, p. 1847-1866.

Arrington, L.J., 1974, Charles C. Rich: Mormon General and Western Frontiersman: Provo, Utah, Brigham Young University Press, 386 p.

Evans, J.H., 1936, Charles Coulson Rich: Pioneer Builder of the West: New York, Macmillan Co., 400 p.

Farnworth, Jo Ann, 1993, Montpelier and the Oregon Short Line: Montpelier, Idaho, 85 p.

Haines, Aubrey L., editor, 1965, Osborne Russell's Journal of a Trapper: University of Nebraska Press, Lincoln and London, 191 p.

Hale, L.A., editor, 1967, Anatomy of the Western Phosphate Field: Salt Lake City, Intermountain Association of Geologists, 15th Annual Field Conference Guidebook, 287 p.

Kerns, G.L., and Kerns. R.L., Jr., editors, 1985, Orogenic patterns and stratigraphy of north-central Utah and southeastern Idaho: Utah Geological Association Publication 14, 329 p.

Mansfield, G.R., 1927, Geography, geology and mineral resources of part of southeastern Idaho, with descriptions of Carboniferous and Triassic fossils, by G.H. Girty: U.S. Geological Survey Professional Paper 152, 453 p.

Oriel, S.S., and Platt, L. B., 1980, Geologic map of the Preston 1° x 2° quadrangle, southeastern Idaho and western Wyoming: U.S. Geological Survey Miscellaneous Investigations Map I-1127, scale 1:250,000.

Poulsen, E.J., 1962, Robert Price: Salt Lake City, Granite Publishing Company, 179p.

Reitzes, L.B., 1981, Paris: A Look at Idaho Architecture: Boise, Idaho State Historical Preservation Office, 104 p.

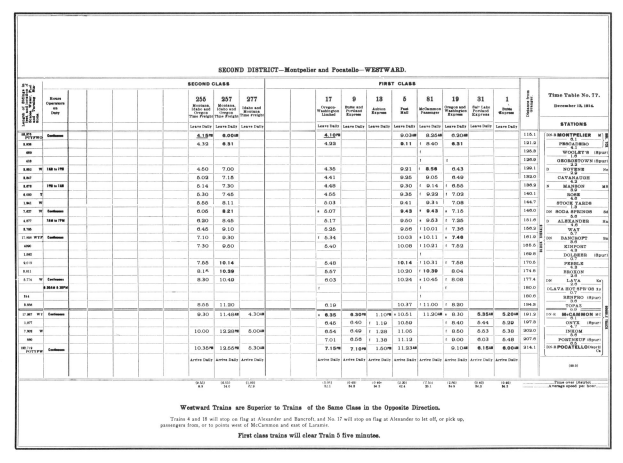

December, 1914 Oregon Short Line Timetable, Westbound trains, Montpelier to Pocatello. This was the main line of the Overland Route of the Union Pacific.

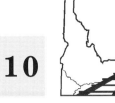

10 Soda Springs Area

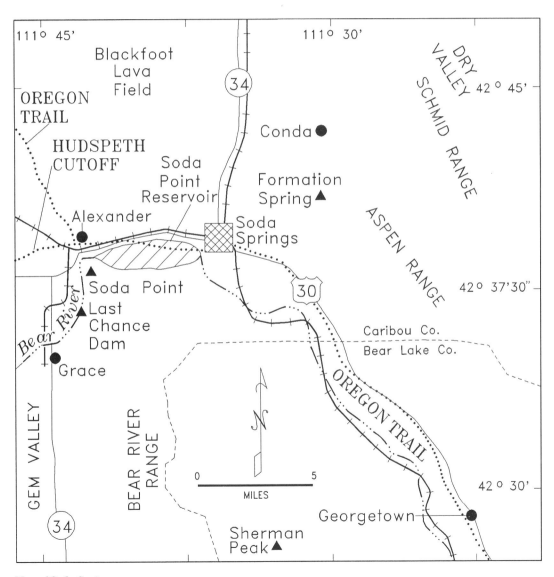

Map of Soda Springs area

Oregon Trail

Soda Springs was a well-known landmark on the Oregon Trail which passed along the Bear River and turned northwest at Soda Point (Sheep Rock). Ruts can be seen in many places along the Bear River, including on the north side of Soda Point Reservoir in the Soda Springs golf course and in the Historic Park area just west of town. The mineral springs were remarkable to the early Pioneers. Steamboat Springs emitted sounds similar to a steam-powered boat and were mentioned by most of those who kept journals. It is now covered most of the year by the waters of the reservoir.

Sheep Rock

"We travelled down the (Bear) river and on the 9th (July, 1834) encamped at a place called the Sheep Rock so called from a point of the mountain terminating at the river bank in a perpendicular high rock: the river curves around the foot of this rock and forms a half circle which brings its course to the S.W. from whence it runs in the same direction to the Salt Lake about 80 miles distant. The (Mountain) Sheep occupy this prominent elevation, which overlooks the surrounding country to a great extent, at all seasons of the year." Osborne Russell, Journal of a Trapper. (Haines, 1965, editor, p. 3-4).

Settling of Soda Springs by Morrisites

Soda Springs was settled in May 1863, by a group of refugees (Morrisites; followers of Joseph Morris) fleeing from the Mormon-controlled Utah Territory. Morris, who was convinced that he was a prophet, had organized a communal settlement near the present site of Ogden and was preaching in open defiance of Brigham Young. Morrisites were active participants in the millennial dreams of nineteenth century America. They expected the imminent Second Advent of Christ and expected to take a leading role in the society that would be established after the second coming and that would last 1000 years.

Soda Point or Sheep Rock, looking east. Soda Point reservoir and city of Soda Springs are in the background. The Bear River here makes almost a 180° bend and flows southward into a canyon cut in Pleistocene basalt. Also at this point the Oregon Trail headed northwest while the Hudspeth Cutoff headed straight west across Gem Valley, (June, 1992).

Aerial view of Soda Springs, looking southeast, (June, 1992). Geyser is on the extreme right middle side of photo, one block west of Main Street, which runs diagonally through the right foreground of photo. Idan-ha' hotel stood east of Main Street, just north of the railroad tracks and west of the grain elevator. Soda Creek in foreground.

In June 1862, a Mormon territorial posse attacked the Morrisite settlement in Ogden. Joseph Morris was killed. The remnants of the movement, after their leaders were pardoned by the Utah territorial governor, realized they needed to flee.

In May 1863, two wagon trains, including 160 Morrisites, left Salt Lake City, led by Colonel Patrick E. Connor. In January, 1863 Connor had commanded the California militia which had perpetrated the massacre of Shoshoni Indians north of Preston at Battle Creek on Bear River. Connor was antagonistic to Indians and intended to subdue them, open the area to settlement, and to counter the expansion of the Mormons, who were viewed by him as disloyal to the Union cause during the Civil War.

U.S. Militia troops under Connor established a post at Soda Springs, on May 20, 1863. Morristown was built on the north bank of the Bear River about a mile below the present townsite of Soda Springs. It is now under Soda Point Reservoir.

> A teenage Morrisite, Emma Thompson Just, described the trip to Soda Springs in May 1863. The letter reflects both the seductive beauty of an Idaho springtime and the naivete of the Morrisite clan:
> "The hillsides were so green and flower-covered and the river was so deep and blue. The mountains are not so steep and rugged as they were at Ogden, but it is a beautiful spot. The Creator must have designed it just for this little band: logs to build our houses; firewood to keep us warm; health giving (mineral) waters to drink, streams full of fish and mountains full of game" (*in* Morgan, 1987).

But the climate at 5,800 feet, 1,600 feet above the Salt Lake Valley, was more severe than anticipated and agricultural productivity was low. Frosts during summer nights repeatedly killed crops. The settlement disbanded within 2 years. Most of the Morrisites became discouraged and left. Some of those who remained spearheaded the anti-Mormon movement in Idaho a decade later. The gravestone on p. 90 is for two who stayed in Soda Springs.

View looking east along Oregon Trail and U.S. Highway 30 just west of Soda Springs. Soda Point (Alexander) Reservoir is on the right, and was the original site of the 1863 Morrisite settlement of Soda Springs. Union Pacific Railroad is just out of the view to the left. Oregon Trail followed a route just north (left) of the reservoir. Prominent scar between Oregon Trail and the Highway is a natural gas pipeline, (June, 1992).

Mormon Colonization

In 1869, Brigham Young invested in 650 acres of land, including part of the present Soda Springs townsite. In June 1870, Young and a contingent of Mormons visited Soda Springs with an eye toward colonization. A lodging house for Young and his family was built overnight by 20 volunteers from Paris. Gold was discovered at Carriboo Mountain, north of Soda Springs, later that year. The first permanent Mormon settlers arrived in Soda Springs in the spring of 1871. Also in 1871, the Utah-Northern Railroad Company, a project of the Mormon church, was started north from Brigham City, headed for Soda Springs by way of Franklin, and ultimately to the mines near Butte, Montana.

A Wild Frontier Town

By the time Oregon Short Line Railroad Company reached Soda Springs in 1882, the town was a wild frontier community. It served as the railhead for a huge area of mountains and forest to the north, over which ranged miners starting in 1870, cattlemen starting in the 1880s, and sheepherders starting in the 1890s.

Steamboat Spring, just south of the Cedar View Country Club, west of Soda Springs, October, 1990. This spring, which formerly made a noise like a rushing steamboat engine, is usually covered with the waters of Soda Point Reservoir. The original Morrisite settlement of Soda Springs was north of the Bear River, to the left of this photograph.

North side of the Soda Springs village, north of the railroad tracks, 1890. Photo was taken looking south from the north end of Main St. Johnny Woodale collection, Horsley Municipal Library, Soda Springs.

Soda Point or Alexander Reservoir, covered with ice, (March, 1990). The snow-covered Aspen Range is in the background.

The Kackley Family

Doctor Ellis Kackley, fresh out of the University of Tennessee Medical School, came to Soda Springs in 1898, resolved to become "The Best Damn Doctor in the West". Many would say he succeeded (Carney, 1990). He, his wife, Ida Sarver Kackley, and son, Evan, served the area for over 50 years, performing feats of frontier medicine by using ingenuity and common sense. He and Evan built the first Soda Springs hospital in 1925 to 1927. The hospital doubled in size to 40 beds in 1932. Ellis delivered over 4,000 babies.

Ellis Kackley died in November 1943, when Evan was in the Pacific during World War II. Twenty-five hundred people attended his funeral, which was held in the Soda Springs High School. His two large dogs created a commotion at the wake. Evan said his father would have enjoyed knowing that the dogs were still in control.

Butch Cassidy's Gang

Butch Cassidy and his band of outlaws frequented the Soda Springs area in the late 1890s, and had a camp in Star Valley, Wyoming. They, like some Mormon polygamists, found refuge in this isolated valley. Cassidy's gang robbed the Montpelier Bank of $16,500 on August 13, 1896, and escaped up Montpelier Canyon. An unmounted pack horse carried the loot out from under the nose of the posse.

On June 2, 1899, Cassidy's Gang robbed the Overland Flyer of the Union Pacific Railroad. Later that summer Dr. Kackley was asked to treat a wounded member of the gang that was holed up near Freedom, Wyoming. Both Kackley and Cassidy sympathized with underdogs and did not like the big corporations. Kackley brought the injured man to Soda Springs under cover of darkness and housed him close to the railroad. Another of the Cassidy Gang was disguised as a woman and took care of the injured man until he recovered.

Geology of the Soda Springs Area

Soda Springs is located near the trace of the Paris thrust fault, which separates the older, Late Proterozoic and Lower Paleozoic rocks of the Bear River Range from the younger Paleozoic rocks of the Preuss Range north and east of town. These younger rocks, belonging to the Meade thrust plate, contain the Permian Phosphoria Formation which is so important to the economy of the Soda Springs area.

Phosphate Mining

Phosphate mining began in the Soda Springs area in 1920 with an underground mine at Conda, named for the owner, Anaconda Copper Co. The Conda mine and townsite was officially abandoned on August 31, 1984.

Today the phosphate industry is the largest employer in the Soda Springs area, with several open-pit mines

Idan-ha' Hotel in Soda Springs about 1899, looking north across the Oregon Short Line. The luxurious hotel opened August 12, 1887. The elaborate gabled structure, built for railroad visitors to the bubbling springs, was furnished in French Provincial. It burned down June 7, 1921, suffering the same fate as most large frame buildings built in Idaho in the late 1800s. An exploding still (1921 was during Prohibition) was supposedly the cause of the fire. The Caribou Hotel, another old Soda Springs landmark, burned in 1923. Photo from Abe Lillibridge collection, Idaho State University.

north and east of Soda Springs and large chemical processing plants on the north edge of town.

Reserves are large and demand is constant. Unlike the silver mining business, phosphate mining will be a strong industry for the foreseeable future. According to the Idaho Geological Survey, in 1990, Idaho's annual revenue from phosphate mining and processing was nearly $600 million. Silver mining produced about $70 million.

Anyone who has travelled U.S. Highway 30 through Soda Springs on a cloudy night will remember the ghostly red glow reflected off the bottoms of low clouds hanging above the molten slag piles near the Monsanto Chemical Plant north of the city.

Mineral Springs

The mineral springs in the Soda Springs area are charged with sulphur dioxide, calcium carbonate, and sodium silicate, products of their long journey through Paleozoic limestone bedrock. Formation Springs, northeast of town, has a large travertine terrace deposit.

References

Carney, Ellen, 1990, Ellis Kackley, Best Damn Doctor in the West: Bend, Oregon, Maverick Publications, 283 p.

Carney, Ellen, 1992, The Oregon Trail: Ruts, Rogues and Reminiscences: Wayan, Idaho, Traildust Publishing Co., 332 p.

Haines, Aubrey L., editor, 1965, Osborne Russell's Journal of a Trapper: University of Nebraska Press, Lincoln, Nebraska, 191 p.

Johnson, Elaine S. and Carney, Ellen, 1990, The Mountain: Cariboo and other gold camps in Idaho: Bend, Oregon, Maverick Publications, 245 p.

Abandoned townsite of Conda, looking north, (May, 1992). The streets remain but the houses have been removed. One of the open pits of the abandoned Conda Mine is to the right of the industrial buildings. The buildings served until 1991 as a loading facility for phosphate ore brought by slurry pipeline from the new Simplot mine at Smoky Canyon, about 30 miles east. The Conda mine began as an underground mine run by the Anaconda Copper Company, and was last operated by the J.R. Simplot Company. The dry tailings pond from the mine is behind the railroad tracks. The railroad cars are probably in storage.

The Ballard Phosphate mine north of Soda Springs, operated by NuWest Industries, (October, 1992).

Monsanto elemental phosphorous plant north of Soda Springs. View looks east toward the Conda Mine. Highway 34 and the Union Pacific Railroad are just east of the plant, (May, 1992).

The municipally regulated geyser in Soda Springs looking south. Under normal conditions the geyser is allowed to erupt about every half hour, (March, 1996).

Warm waters of Hooper Spring, north of Soda Springs. The waters are naturally carbonated and are allegedly tasty for making root beer. In the 1890s the Idan-ha' Natural Mineral Water Company shipped bottled water from the Soda Springs area all over the world, (October, 1989).

Caribou Mountain Area

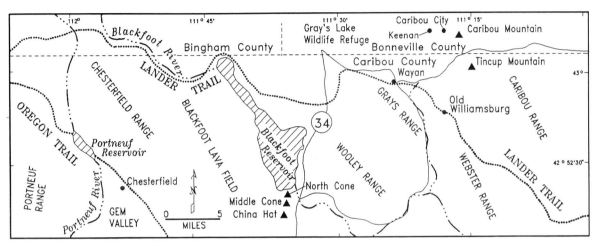

Map of Caribou Mountain and Grays Lake area

Grays Lake and Blackfoot Lava Field

Volcanic activity of the Blackfoot Lava field over the last million years has produced the large flat area north of Soda Springs. Rivers here wander slowly through marshes, as if they were wondering which way to escape the basin.

Grays Lake has been an enclosed catchment area for water for at least a million years and contains a valuable record of pollen for the changing climates of Pleistocene time.

Lander Trail

The Lander Trail, named after F.W. Lander, who supervised its construction, went through the Grays Lake Valley. In the 1860s it became known as the Old Salt Road when salt was brought from Stump Creek to Montana, Boise and the west.

An admirer of the Lander Trail wrote
"for four years the party has toiled—leveled mountains, bridged rivers, sunk tanks, and fought the Indians, and the result of their labors stands forth the model emigrant route of America."

The Lander Trail was shorter than the Oregon Trail from South Pass to Fort Hall, but the hardships often extended the duration of the journey. Spring rains often made the trail impassable.

Caribou Mountain and Grays Lake basin from the west, (July, 1992). The mountain is held up by granite stock intruded in Eocene time, about 45 million years ago. Gold in placer deposits eroded from veins around the stock has lured prospectors to the area for over 100 years.

West-East geological cross section of Caribou Mountain—Grays Lake area from Mabey (1979, p. 10), used by permission.

Discovery of Gold on Caribou Mountain

Gold was discovered on Mt. Pisgah (now Caribou Mountain) in 1870 by Jesse Fairchilds or "Cariboo Jack", an itinerant miner who gained his name in the Cariboo Mining District of British Columbia. A typical western gold rush followed. Two good-sized towns, Carriboo City and Keenan, grew up close to each other on the mountain, which looms above Grays Lake Valley to elevation 9,803 feet. Both cities were deserted after a few years but mining has continued sporadically to the present. About one million dollars of gold was taken from the area, mainly by placer methods, with the associated ditches and pipelines to supply water to the mines. Two hand-dug ditches, with a length of about 7 miles, rimmed Caribou Mountain.

John Codman, describing events on August 5 and 6, 1874, Idaho Yesterdays, 1976, v. 19, no. 4, p. 19-20.

"The gulch (at Carriboo) is away back in the pine forest, and the sight is very romantic. The placer miners were at their work, and near by among the trees several log-cabins, tastily decorated with spruce boughs, and some very spruce young women too, the wives and daughters of the miners around them."

After ascending five hundred feet we came to patches of snow. Above them it was beautifully green with pines and grass, and just where gold was "struck," halfway to the summit, there was a great, wide, grassy lawn, looking as if it had been laid out by a landscape-gardener. On the edge of this, among the pines, were the huts of the prospectors, made of bark and pine boughs, and having a very tasty appearance.

We were on the highest peak of the range, and looked down upon lesser mountains of snowy summits, and over them all beyond the valleys near us, into valleys in the far distance, tracing the Snake and Blackfoot Rivers for at least a hundred miles . . . The extent was so great that even the beauties and grandeur of the Yosemite were eclipsed by the magnificent panorama. If I was asked what miners lived upon I should answer, "Whiskey and hope."

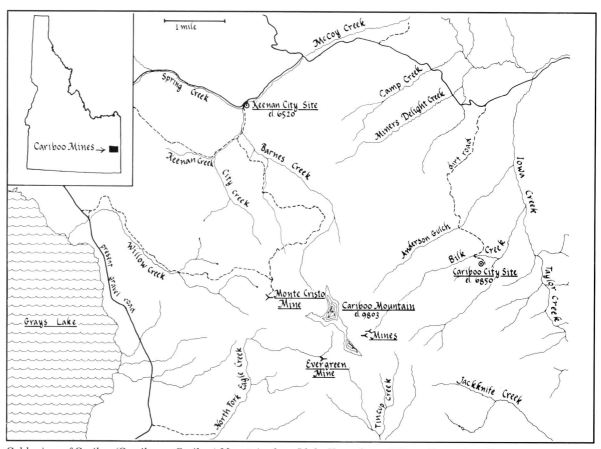

Gold mines of Cariboo (Carriboo or Caribou) Mountain, from Idaho Yesterdays, 1976, v. 19, no. 4, p. 10.

China Hat, a rhyolite dome, intruded about 100,000 years ago in the Blackfoot Lava Field north of Soda Springs. Immediately beyond China Hat is China Cap, and North Cone is to the north of it. Both of these are also rhyolite domes. View looks north to the Blackfoot Reservoir and Pelican Mountain. The town of Henry is just out of the photo in the right distance, (May, 1992).

Report of Gustavus C. Doane's Military Expedition from Star Valley to Carriboo Mountain, December 16-22, 1876:

December 16th. We were moving at the break of day. Weather bitterly cold. Were obliged to build fires whenever we stopped to rest to prevent our feet from freezing. The snow was knee deep on level ground and crusted so that the leader on the trail had to break through at every footstep. We alternated at this labor. Could not make over a mile an hour. About noon we reached an ice bound creek which empties into the Snake from the Southeast (sic, southwest actually), the river channel having turned northward. This creek (McCoy Creek) showed signs of placer washings and we followed it.

Idaho Yesterdays, 1976, v. 19, no. 4, p. 25.

Chinese Miners

Chinese miners came to Carriboo in 1872 and were not excluded from the camp as they were in other Idaho mining camps. They were most numerous about 1880, and were generally acknowledged as being more skilled at mining than the Caucasians. The Chinese miners fled Carriboo in 1885 after a number of Chinese massacres in the west. In 1870 Chinese were the largest ethnic group in Idaho. Of the 4,269 Chinese, 3,853 were working as miners. That same year there were only 2,719 white miners in Idaho.

Freight to the Carriboo Mines

Until 1871, freight traffic for the Carriboo mines came from Corinne, Utah, through Ross Fork (Fort Hall) and north of Grays Lake along the McCoy Creek drainage. From 1877 to 1878, Oxford was the railroad stop nearest the mines and in 1878, a stage road was established from Oxford through Soda Springs to the Carriboo Mining Region.

In 1878, the U & N railway reached Oneida (Arimo). In 1882 the first Oregon Short Line railway train passed through Soda Springs and the town became the major center to supply the Carriboo Mines.

Old Williamsburg

Williamsburg, now almost totally abandoned, had in the 1870s, three dairies, a boarding house, saloon, school, post office and a summer tent city which included two prostitute tents. Today it is the site of management of the Kackley Ranches.

Photograph of L to R, Jack Rucker, Lois Kackley, Leigh Gittens, "Doc" Evan Kackley, Chilton Phoenix at the Kackley home, Old Williamsburg, (July, 1991).

Demise of the Name Carriboo

In 1907, the U.S. Forest Service created Caribou National Forest, changing the name from Carriboo (or Cariboo) over the protests of the locals. The residents correctly pointed out that no Caribou had ever lived in the area. The incorrect spelling persists today, in the name of the National Forest and the County surrounding Soda Springs.

Polygamists in Star Valley, Wyoming

Many of the original settlers of Freedom, Wyoming were Mormon polygamists who refused to give up their wives and families when Idaho and Utah enforced the Edmonds Anti-polygamy act of 1882, but Wyoming refused to do so. The name Star Valley comes from Starvation (Starve) Valley, a name the area gained during bitter winters in the late 1880s. Many cattle were lost in the severe winter of 1889. There were over 40 inches of snow in two days and nights in March.

Cattle, Sheep, and Cranes

By 1875, large cattle herds were grazed in the Grays Lake area or passed through the area. Sheep became common in the 1890s. By 1894, 50,000 sheep summered north of Soda Springs. By the early 1900s that number had increased to over a million. Today much of the Grays Lake wetland area is part of a National Wildlife Refuge, and provides nesting sites for Sandhill and Whooping Cranes.

Aerial view looking east, upstream in Blackfoot River Canyon west of Blackfoot Reservoir. The river occupies a narrow canyon cut in a Pleistocene lava flow which was erupted from the Blackfoot Lava Field. The lava flow filled the former river valley, (April, 1987).

Sheep grazing was the largest cash agricultural crop in Idaho in the early 1900s. Photo taken near Wayan in July, 1978.

References

Anonymous, 1976, Gold Mines of Cariboo Mountain, Idaho Yesterdays, v. 19 no. 4, p. 10-15.

Carney, Ellen, 1992, The Oregon Trail: Ruts, Rogues, and Reminiscences: Wayan, Idaho, Traildust Publishing Co., 332 p.

Codman, John, reprinted 1976, A Trip to Cariboo Mountain: Idaho Yesterdays, v. 19, no. 4, p. 18-24.

Derig, Betty, 1972, Celestials in the Diggings: Idaho Yesterdays, v. 16, no. 3, p. 2-23.

Fiesinger, D.W., Perkins, W.D. and Puchy, B.J., 1982, Mineralogy and Petrology of Tertiary-Quaternary Volcanic Rocks in Caribou County, Idaho, *in* Bonnichsen, Bill, and Breckenridge, R.M., editors, Cenozoic Geology of Idaho: Idaho Bureau of Mines and Geology Bulletin 26, p. 465-488.

Johnson, Elaine S. and Carney, Ellen, The Mountain: Cariboo and other Gold Camps in Idaho, 1990, Maverick Publications, Inc. P.O. Box 5007, Bend Oregon, 97708, 245 p.

Mabey, Don, 1979, The Bend of Bear River. Bountiful, Utah, Horizon Publishers and Distributors, 136 p.

Gravestone of Caribou Jack, Soda Springs Cemetery, (September, 1995).

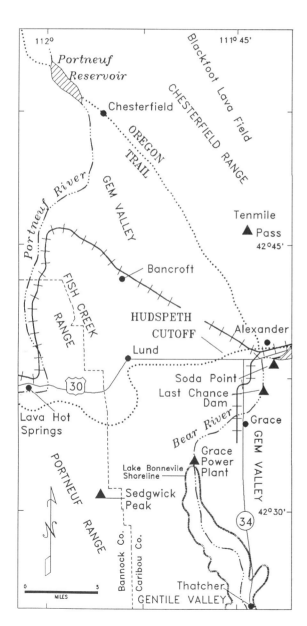

Map of the Gem Valley area.

Gem Valley and Gentile Valley

The first settlers of the area between the Portneuf and Bear River Ranges (Gem Valley) were non-Mormons (Gentiles) who homesteaded in the southern end of the valley in the 1860s. The west side of the Bear River became known as Gentile Valley by 1875. The first three Mormon families settled in 1871 with impetus from Brigham Young, who was planning on the Utah-Northern Railroad Company coming through the southern end of the valley on the way to Soda Springs.

> Oscar Sonnenkalb wrote, concerning Gentile Valley in the 1880s, that:
>
> "nature had blessed it with all the features for the development of a prosperous and self supporting farming district. Deep and fertile soil in the level bottom lands, and on the lower mountain benches numerous spring branches flowing down from the mountain chains which on both sides of the long stretching valley gave protection against heavy wind storms of the inclement winter weather in these high altitudes of the Rockies, also rich pasturage on the foot hills and mountain sides, and numerous shade giving parks and copses of aspen and pine timber for animals to lie down and rest during the hot summer days, invited the settlers to engage in all the branches of a healthy farming industry, the raising of grain and hay, in dairying and stock breeding." *in* Harstad, editor, (1972, p. 15).

Aerial view looking south at Grace, (May, 1992). The Utah Power and Light Company dam is in the left foreground, with the flume on an elevated trestle crossing under the highway to the right. Bear River occupies canyon cut in Pleistocene basalt. The East Branch of the Last Chance Canal winds east of town in the center left of the view.

City of Grace

The first bridge across Bear River north of the present site of Grace was built in 1893, and the city was established shortly thereafter. Farming on the surrounding country was dependent upon irrigation efforts of the Last Chance Canal Company, which proceeded slowly and with great effort. In 1913, the Oregon Short Line completed the Grace Branch Line. In 1915, the village of Grace was incorporated. The village was named after the wife of the land agent in Blackfoot.

Last Chance Canal

Attempts to get water to the Grace area were unsuccessful between 1895 and 1902. Although the Bear River ran just to the north, it was deep in a basalt canyon, and the water was inaccessible. Furthermore, Gem Valley's winters were harsh, and wooden flumes for canals using water from Bear River were repeatedly destroyed by winter snows. On March 4, 1897 the Last Chance Irrigation Co. filed for Bear River water and a dam site was selected a mile and half below Soda Point (Sheep Rock). Construction started in 1898. The canal was opened in 1902-1904 and today provides water for farmland both north and south of Bear River on the upland around Grace.

The Last Chance Canal was built without federal assistance and without outside capital by local farmers, who worked cooperatively in the best spirit of the Mormon settlers. To provide footings for the dam, the farmers built log cribs of timber and rocks which they set on the ice-covered river in the winter. They hauled huge timbers 60 feet in length.

> Fred Cooper who served as secretary of the Last Chance Canal Co. from 1928 to 1961 said:
>
> "It can be said of the men who organized this company and carried out the work ... that they were willing to make the sacrifice necessary without murmur of discouragement, always forging ahead and helping one another in common endeavor."

In June 1917, the Utah Power and Light Co. brought suit against Last Chance Canal Co. to get a decree on waters of Bear River and Bear Lake. Litigation of the suit lasted for three years until the Canal Company won the case with the Dietrich Decree of June 1920. This case adjudicated Bear River water for the first time.

Grace Power Plant

In 1906, L.L. Nunn and his Telluride Power Company moved in from Colorado and began construction of the a major hydroelectric plant on the Bear River, taking advantage of the 500 foot drop in the elevation of the Bear River between Sheep Point and the floor of the canyon west of Grace. In 1908, they finished a dam north of Grace above the elevation of the Lake Bonneville shoreline, with the power plant a few miles down the valley and 525 feet lower, on what had been the lake floor. At that time the plant was the largest hydroelectric station west of Omaha. At first the electricity was for use in the mining districts of Bingham, Utah and Eureka, Nevada; it was not sold to local customers.

The Telluride Power Company eventually became the Utah Power and Light Company. In 1915, the Grace plant was the biggest station on the newly integrated Utah Power and Light system.

Last Chance Canal Dam historical marker, (August, 1991).

Lake Thatcher and the Gem Valley Volcanic Field

Bear River makes nearly a 180° bend around Soda Point and runs south into southern Gem Valley and Cache Valley (Mabey, 1979). However, as hypothesized in the 1963 Ph.D. dissertation of geologist Robert C. Bright, a native of Preston, the river's course prior to about a million years ago was probably north to near Chesterfield and then down the present Portneuf River canyon past Lava Hot Springs and to the Snake River west of Pocatello. At this time, Gem Valley drained to the north, much as Bear Lake Valley does today.

At times in the last million years the outlet of the ancestral Bear River became dammed and a lake, named Lake Thatcher, formed in Gem Valley. Volcanic activity of the Gem Valley volcanic field produced

basalt lava flows which filled the north end of the valley, damming up the former Bear River course and forcing the river to turn south. The highest shoreline of Lake Thatcher was established at about 5445 feet elevation, after the lake was restricted to the southern part of the valley. Sediments deposited in Lake Thatcher underlie the farming country south of Grace and are recognized in water wells drilled as far north as Chesterfield. At its thickest point the Thatcher Formation is about 590 feet thick.

Some lava flows in northern Gem Valley were sourced from the Blackfoot lava field to the east. The lava flowed westward over the Chesterfield Range through Ten Mile Pass. Other main sources for lava flows were a fissure system that runs along the east side of the Gem Valley. The largest known lava tube is now an ice cave about 800 feet east of the cinder cone at Niter, south of Grace. About 600,000 years ago two basalt lava flows from northern Gem Valley ran down the course of the Portneuf River to Pocatello to form the Basalt of Portneuf Valley.

After Lake Thatcher occupied southern Gem Valley for perhaps several hundred thousand years, the Bear River drainage was captured, in Oneida Narrows, by south-flowing tributaries to Strawberry Creek and the Lake Bonneville basin. After Lake Thatcher drained southward into Cache Valley, the input of water from the Bear River plus a time of generally greater precipitation (a pluvial interval), caused Lake Bonne-

Aerial view looking east at the Utah Power and Light power plant on the Bear River west of Grace. The penstock and pressure relief tower are at the top of the hill, about 300 feet above the elevation of the plant at the river's edge. The town of Grace is in the background, (May, 1992).

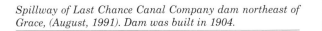

Spillway of Last Chance Canal Company dam northeast of Grace, (August, 1991). Dam was built in 1904.

Aerial view looking north at Alexander Crater, a cinder cone on the Oregon Trail in Gem Valley. The Chesterfield Range is in the background, (September, 1984).

ville to grow in the Great Salt Lake basin. The high level of Lake Bonneville, about 5,140 feet, reached into Gem Valley about 20,000 to 14,500 years ago. The shoreline was located just south of the site of the Grace Power Plant.

Chesterfield–Mormon Outpost in Idaho

Chester Call, a Mormon bishop from Bountiful, Utah, established a ranch near Chesterfield in 1879. Call convinced many of his relatives and friends to move to the new settlement.

Oscar Sonnenkalb wrote of Chester Call that he was:

"one of the sturdy farmers who had emigrated from Utah to Idaho, had promoted all the colonization of this part of Oneida County, and helped the settlers who had followed him to find good land and water sources to start their new farms. He was the genuine type of the jolly old Pioneer, full of enterprise, practical and resourceful in overcoming the many difficulties and hardships . . . " *in* Harstad, editor, (1972, p. 19).

Early settlers came to the Chesterfield area in 1881 and 1882 and built crude dugout shelters along the bottom land of the Portneuf River. The community was dealt a major setback in 1882, when the Oregon Short Line was built through Bancroft to the south, but the proponents of Chesterfield refused to believe this would doom their town.

Mormon Church authorities from Cache Valley visited Chesterfield in November, 1883, and advised that a townsite be laid out on high ground east of the Portneuf River flood plain. The townsite was a mile long and ¾ mile wide, and was divided into 10 acre blocks that would then be subdivided into four equal lots of 2.5 acres. The settlers followed the pattern of Salt Lake City and laid out a city with streets ninety-nine feet wide, with sixteen foot sidewalks at each side. The streets of Chesterfield were wider than the boulevards of New York.

The site was named Chesterfield in memory of Chesterfield, England, and to honor Chester Call. Some families chose homesites in the village, but many did not. Prosperity came slowly, if at all.

Most of the buildings of Chesterfield were built between 1884 and 1904. By the mid-1890s 50 families had moved into the village. A kiln was built east of town to fire the bricks used to build new church buildings. By 1900, Chesterfield had 418 people on its ward records. A few brick homes were built, the pride of the community. The agricultural Depression of the 1920s and 1930s was the final blow to the city of Chesterfield.

Aerial view looking north at the Chesterfield townsite. The ambitious town plat was never fully subscribed and houses were not built on many of the possible sites. The Moses and Mary Vashti Call Muir house is at the lower right. The Chesterfield Range is in the background, (May, 1992).

Near Grace
by Harald Wyndham

The log house abandoned at the edge of a thousand acres.
Potato farmland stretching all the way to Bancroft.
Driving past, I feel a poem forming.
Something about the hard life of the pioneers.
Windows broken, sagging roof and walls.
Something about dying and returning to earth.
Distance exists first in the imagination.
Stand in a snowfield under a washed-out moon.

in Wyndham, editor, (1986), Famous Potatoes

Moses and Mary Vashti Call Muir house, Chesterfield, (April, 1996). This is the oldest brick house in the Chesterfield area, built in 1888. In Mormon style of the time, it has two front doors.

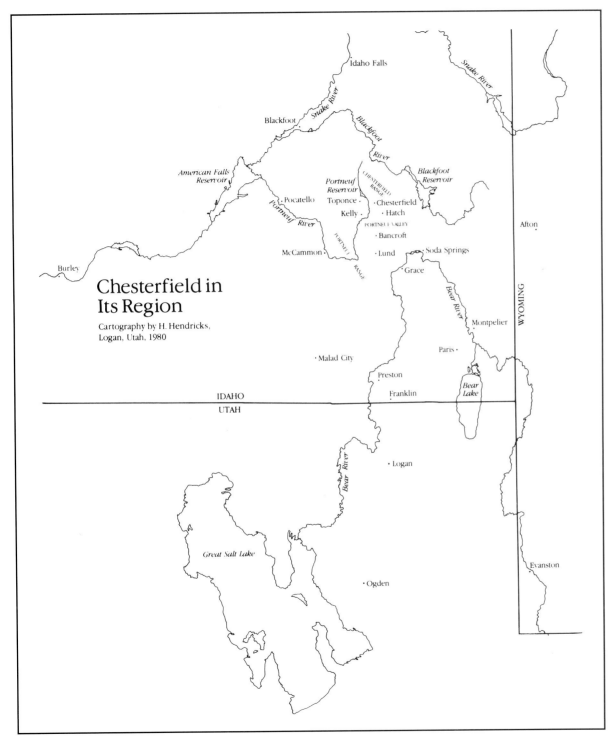

Chesterfield in Its Region

Cartography by H. Hendricks,
Logan, Utah, 1980

Mormon Families in Chesterfield

Chesterfield, though today largely a ghost town, lives on in the spirit of the descendents of its Pioneers. The Chesterfield Foundation is dedicated to preserving the Chesterfield heritage, and has published the exquisite book "Chesterfield: A Mormon Outpost in Idaho."

Most Mormon farm families in the Chesterfield area were monogamous, though there were some polygamous households. Large families were considered an asset in Chesterfield, as in most Mormon communities; 8 or 10 children was a small family. Sixteen children was normal. Boys married at age 18 or 19 and girls at 16 or 17.

The history of Chesterfield's residents is a cycle of dreams and hard work to plow the sagebrush, followed by tragedy with the loss of land, crops, and livestock. Then the process would start over again, usually somewhere else. Chesterfield was always a cold and dry place. The farmers tired of watching summer storms pour a deluge on Gentile Valley to the south and miss their land. The knowledge that the Snake River Valley to the north was well watered through irrigation further disillusioned them. Most early settlers, including church leaders, eventually sold out and moved away.

> Nathan James Barlow recorded the leaving of Judson Tolman, a polygamous Mormon Bishop, and his family. Tolman had been for three decades one of the pillars of the community.
>
> "It was a beautiful morning of that day of November 8, 1908, when we left Chesterfield, Idaho. The sky was blue and the day bright, giving no indication of the anxiety and confusion in the breasts of Father and Mother . . . One may well imagine that our departure from Chesterfield–leaving friends, relatives and most of the worldly goods we had enjoyed–would leave Mother with intense bitterness. Fortunately it did not do so . . . Mother and Father carried their burden without a murmur." (The Chesterfield Foundation (1982, p. 17).

Map of Chesterfield and its region from The Chesterfield Foundation (1982), used by permission.

The diary of Wanda Katie Whitworth, born in 1905, and who lived on a ranch about eight miles from Chesterfield, is quoted in Swetnam (1991, p. 61).

There was ever so much to be done to make a decent living for our family. Many long, hard late hours were spent by everyone. We made our own butter, cottage cheese, dried fruit, and I bottled everything such as peaches, pears, cherries, raspberries, pickles, relishes, beets, jams, jellies, etc. It was always such a special thrill for me to go down to the basement at the end of the summer to see all my work, some 700-800 quarts of bottled fruit filled for our winter storage, labeled and washed, simply a beautiful sight.

Chesterfield LDS church and meeting house, dedicated August 23, 1892. Photo taken October, 1988.

Farming in the Chesterfield area today mainly consists of large dry farms and ranches, operated by a few hardy survivors.

"Once a man with an hundred and sixty acres of land and a dozen cows could make a good living. Now it takes at least a thousand acres, and thousands of dollars worth of machinery. The young fellows with nothing but muscles and ambition have had to go elsewhere to make a living. The land belongs to a few men. When I go back, except for a dozen or so old friends, I find myself among strangers." Frank C. Robertson, former Chesterfield farmer, (The Chesterfield Foundation, 1982, p. 18).

References

Harstad, P.T., 1972, Reminiscences of Oscar Sonnenkalb, Idaho Surveyor and Pioneer: Pocatello, Idaho, The Idaho State University Press, 66 p.

Mabey, Don, 1979, The Bend of Bear River: Bountiful, Utah, Horizon Publishers and Distributors, 136 p.

McCarthy, Max R., 1987, The Last Chance Canal Company: Provo, Utah, Brigham Young University: Charles Redd Center for Western Studies, Monograph no. 16, 131 p.

Swetnam, Susan Hendricks, 1991, Lives of the Saints in Southeast Idaho: Moscow, Idaho, The University of Idaho Press, 188 p.

The Chesterfield Foundation, Inc.: Chesterfield: Mormon outpost in Idaho: 1982, The Chesterfield Foundation Inc., Rural route, Bancroft Idaho, 83217.

In particular the articles by:

F. Ross Peterson, Chesterfield: A Picture from the past, p. 7-20; and

Paul L. Anderson: An Idaho variation on the City of Zion, p. 71-78.

Wyndham, Harald, editor, 1986, Famous Potatoes: southeast Idaho Poetry: Blue Scarab Press, 242 S. 8th Street, Pocatello, Idaho, 83201, 64 p.

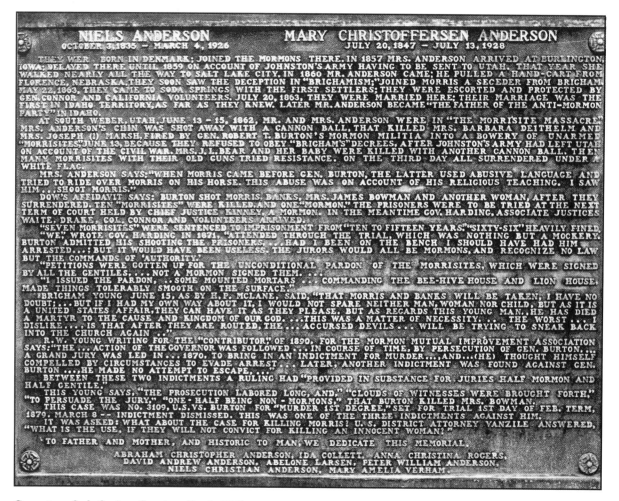

Gravestone, Soda Springs Cemetary (April, 1996)

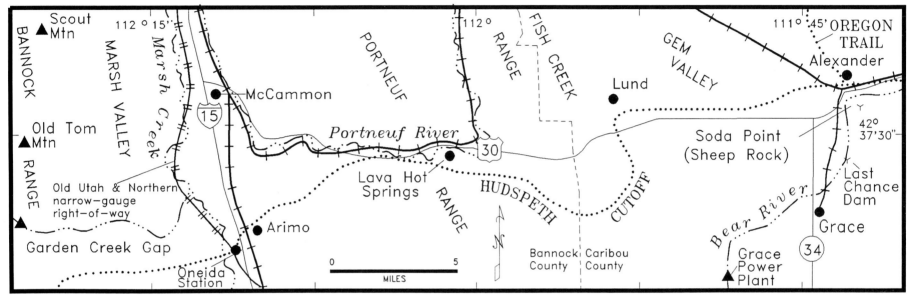

Map of Lava Hot Springs area.

Hudspeth Cutoff

The Hudspeth Cutoff, after climbing high over the Portneuf Range south of the Portneuf River, wound down through Henderson Canyon and what is now the Lava Hot Springs golf course, to the river at a hill of Silurian dolomite known as Island Butte. The river formerly passed south of the Butte, but now flows only on the north side except in large floods. The dry channel can be seen from Highway 30. The Cutoff then headed up a small canyon south of the river and down into what became the rail station of Oneida and now is Arimo. From there it struck out west across Marsh Valley, crossing the Bannock Range south of Garden Creek Gap. Although this part of the Cutoff gained and lost considerable elevation, it was, at least, well-watered. The same cannot be said for the Cutoff west of the Bannock Range.

Mountain Man Bob Dempsey

Bob Dempsey, one of the last of the mountain men in southeastern Idaho, had a permanent camp west of Lava Hot Springs, where Dempsey Creek flows into the Portneuf. From 1851 to 1861, he trapped the mountains south of Lava, and effectively kept other trappers out. When the Hudson's Bay Company ceased operations in southeastern Idaho, Dempsey moved north to the Montana gold fields. Until 1915, the town of Lava Hot Springs was known as Dempsey, Idaho.

Lava Hot Springs railroad depot, about 1920. The depot is now used, in two pieces, as a farmhouse and a shed, north of U.S. Highway 30 west of Lava Hot Springs. Clifford Peake collection, Bannock County Historical Society.

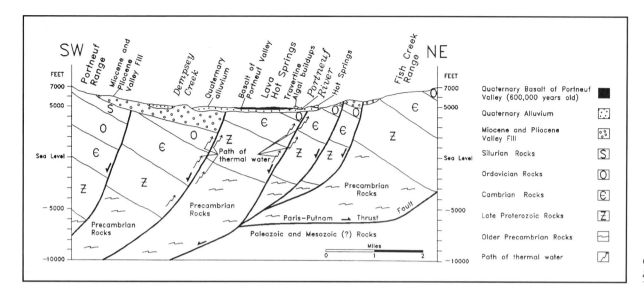

Generalized west-east geologic cross-section of the Lava Hot Springs area.

Lava Hot Springs and the Portneuf River

Lava Hot Springs was deeded to the state in 1902 to provide a health and recreation facility. The Lava Hot Springs area contains several hot springs which occur along a north-south normal fault southwest of town and an east-west normal fault which follows the Portneuf River canyon. The clear waters in gravel-bottomed pools at the state-operated resort make for a wonderful, relaxing visit. The east end of the pools are just as hot as a person can bear.

After the train depot was constructed in 1902-1905 the hot springs were accessible to the western traveler. The state built a natatorium in 1918 and now oversees operation of the swimming pools and hot baths through the Lava Hot Springs Foundation. The South Bannock County Historical Center located in the former Bank of Idaho building in Lava Hot Springs acts to preserve the heritage of the area.

On cold winter nights, when the steam of the hot springs reduces visibility to a few feet, people of all ages talk and play in perceived anonymity. Yet the city of Lava Hot Springs has been slow to take off as a recreational development. It has been for the last 30 years a quaint, tattered place, very much small-town southeast Idaho.

Ligertown, a ramshackle compound where dozens of lions, "ligers" (lion-tiger crosses), and hybrid wolves were kept (October, 1995). In September 1995 some animals attacked the owners and escaped. Several were shot and the owners were charged with numerous violations. The compound was destroyed in April, 1996.

Postcard of Lava Hot Springs, looking south from U.S. Highway 30, 1942. Abe Lillibridge collection, Idaho State University.

References

Boag, P.G., compiler, 1992, Trails, Trappers, Trains, and Travelers: The Economic Development of Southern Bannock County as influenced by transportation: South Bannock County Historical Center, Lava Hot Springs, Idaho 83246, 17 p.

Kerns, G.L., and Kerns. R.L., Jr., editors, 1985, Orogenic patterns and stratigraphy of north-central Utah and southeastern Idaho: Utah Geological Association Publication 14, 329 p.

Schwarze, D.M., 1960, Geology of the Lava Hot Springs area, Idaho: Occasional Papers of the Idaho State College Museum, Pocatello, Number 4, 51 p.

South Bannock Historical Center, 1990, A Century of Transition, 1890-1990, Pocatello, Idaho State University Press, 32 p.

Osborne Russell Kills a Grizzly in the Portneuf River Bottoms

On the 20th of August (1834) we started again to hunt meat: we left Fort Hall and traveled about 6 miles where we discovered a Grizzly Bear digging and eating roots in a piece of marshy ground near a large bunch of willows. My partner approached within 100 years and shot him through the left shoulder; he gave a hideous growl and sprang into the thicket. My partner then said "let him go he is a dangerous varmint" but not being acquainted with the nature of these animals I determined on making another trial.... We walked round the bunch of willows ... when we heard a sullen growl about 10 ft from us, which was instantly followed by a spring of the bear toward us; his enormous jaws extended and eyes flashing fire. Oh Heavens! was ever anything so hideous? We... took to our heels ... he turned and bounded toward me—I could go no further without jumping into a large quagmire which hemmed me in on three sides, I was obliged to turn about and face him. He came within about 10 paces of me then suddenly stopped and raised his ponderous body erect, his mouth wide open, gazing at me with a beastly laugh, at the moment I pulled trigger and I knew not what else to do and hardly knew that I did this but it accidentally happened that my Rifle was pointed towards the Bear when I pulled and the ball piercing his heart, he gave one bound from me, uttered a deathly howl and fell dead. *(modified from Haines, ed, 1965, p. 6-8. That this happened on the Portneuf is the opinion of H. Hilbert.)*

Haystack Mountain after a New Year's blizzard, (1982), looking east from near McCammon.

Waterfalls along the Portneuf River west of Lava Hot Springs, (January 1984). The falls cascade down terraces of algally deposited travertine, and the calcium carbonate deposits of hot springs.

On the Portneuf
by Harald Wyndham

Late September, down by Whiskey Mike's.
From where I sit by a sharp bend in the river,
my line curving fifty yards downstream,
I can see Haystack veined with its first snow
and sunlight pouring bright as molten steel
out of the cloudless blue.

Shirtsleeve weather,
no mosquitoes or flies. Just the heavy drift
of clear green water running the riffle of rocks
and bits of watercress tumbling under the surface
where long strands of algae like wavering beards
wait to snag my hook somewhere downstream.

The water fills my thinking, pulling me apart
into the gentle and disconnected noises, willow leaves

blowing against each other, burbles and splashes,
the sun broken into jagged bits on the water,
so that I relax completely, even the desire
for enormous trout smoothed out and washed away...

A golden eagle circles overhead.
On wide wings
he enters my imagination, dominant, representing
all that Idaho has come to mean:
freedom, clear waters,
wild places, fragrance of aspen and sage, silver
rainbows laid in a creel of grass . . .

Thirteen years.
I have been here all my life.

in Wyndham, editor, (1986), Famous Potatoes

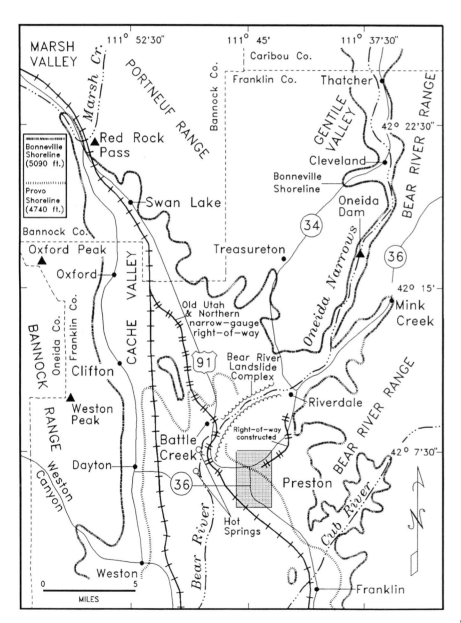

Map of Cache Valley area.

Geography

About half of Cache Valley is geographically in Idaho, but 80% of its people live in Utah. Logan, at the southern end of the valley, site of Utah State University and a Mormon Tabernacle, has historically been the center of commerce. The solidly Mormon agricultural towns of Preston and Franklin on the east side of the Bear River, and Oxford, Clifton, Dayton, and Weston, west of the river, are geographically and economically closer to Logan than to the Idaho towns of Malad City, Montpelier or Pocatello. This area was settled by Mormons who thought they were living in Utah Territory, and even in the 1990s, some Preston area residents see themselves as part of Utah, feeling that they have little in common with the politicians in Boise who collect and spend their tax money.

Geologically, Cache Valley is a graben, bounded by normal faults on both the east and west sides. On the east side is the Bear River Range, which passes into the Portneuf Range on the north side of the Bear River across the canyon at Oneida Narrows. These ranges contain mainly Late Proterozoic and Paleozoic bedrock

View looking northeast at town of Swan Lake and Lake Bonneville shorelines. The Bonneville level is at the bench at the top of the wheat field to the left of the grain elevator. The Provo level is near the base of the grain elevator, (June, 1995).

Early summer scene of the Bear River and the southern Bannock Range, Cache Valley, Idaho, taken looking west from northwest of Preston. Weston Mountain is the high ridge in right background. The lower ridge, cut by two steep canyons, is composed of the Late Proterozoic Pocatello Formation. The West Cache normal fault runs north-south near the base of the mountains.

This part of Cache Valley is mantled with several hundred feet of fine sands and silts deposited in lakes, the latest of which was Lake Bonneville. The Bonneville shoreline (5,090 feet) is a short way up the slope of the mountain. The Provo shoreline (4,740 feet) is the prominent horizontal line at the base of the mountains. The conspicuous terraces between the Provo shoreline and the present Bear River level (4,450 feet) were formed as Bear River incised the lacustrine sands and silts as the level of Great Salt Lake fell, (June, 1984).

Osborne Russell's Journey from Fort Hall to Cache Valley, March, 1835.

"On March 25th we left the Fort and travelled about six miles southeast and encamped on a stream (called Portneuf) running into the Snake River about twelve miles below the Fort. The next day we followed up this stream in an easterly direction about 15 miles. Here we found the snow very deep. From this point (in Marsh Valley) we took a south course in the direction of Bear River. Our animals were so poor and the travelling so bad that we had to make short marches. We reached Bear River on the first day of April. The place where we struck Bear River is called Cache Valley, so called from its having formerly been a place of deposit for the fur traders. The country on the north and west side of the river is somewhat broken and uneven. It is covered with wild sage. The snow had disappeared only upon the south sides of the hills. On the south and east sides of the river lay the valley but it appeared very white and the river nearly overflowed its banks insomuch as it was a very difficult crossing.

"The next morning I took a walk up a smooth spur of the mountain to look at the country. This valley commences about 30 miles below the Soda Springs. The river, running west of south, enters the valley through a deep cut in the high hill. After winding its way through the north and west borders of the valley it turns due west and runs through a deep canyon of perpendicular rocks on its way to the Salt Lake.

"The valley is nearly surrounded by high and rugged mountains from which flow large numbers of small streams crossing the valley and emptying into the river. There are large quantities of Beaver and Otter living in these streams but the melting snow raises the water so high that our trappers made but slow progress in catching them." (Haines, 1965, p. 9)

(limestone and quartzite) above the Paris thrust fault, which is exposed on the east side of the Bear River Range. West of Cache Valley are the Bannock and Malad Ranges and the Wellsville Mountains in Utah, underlain by the same Paleozoic formations as well as Late Proterozoic strata beneath, including the Brigham Group and the Pocatello Formation.

Lake Bonneville

Cache Valley was filled with the northeastern arm of Lake Bonneville, and the lake flooded to the north through Red Rock Pass into Marsh Creek, the Portneuf River, and Snake River. The unconsolidated sands and silts deposited on the floor of Lake Bonneville form the surface of Cache Valley, and, when irrigated, make excellent agricultural soil. A network of canals, the trademark of lands settled by Mormon Pioneers, provide water to much of the valley.

1863 Bear River Massacre

California Volunteers from Camp Floyd, south of Salt Lake City, annihilated between 240 and 300 Shoshoni Indians at the mouth of Battle Creek, north of Preston on a frigid morning, January 29, 1863. Only 23 soldiers were killed. The attack was led by Colonel Patrick E. Connor. Although the Mormon settlers had asked Connor for help, the attack was also motivated by Connor's desire to open the Bear River area to settlement by non-Mormons. Five months after the attack Connor led the Morrisites to Soda Springs. A decade of Indian skirmishes followed the Massacre, but the patterns of Native American hunting and settlement were effectively disrupted forever by this attack (Madsen, 1985).

Bear River Massacre Historical Marker, updated in the 1980s to the generally accepted account of the incident.

1932 monument that paints the Bear River Massacre in a rather different light from the modern view.

1953 monument; its emphasis is in keeping with the 1932 monument.

Mount Smart, west of Franklin, looking northeast from Highway 91. Franklin cemetery is in the foreground. Cemeteries for Mormon settlements were generally constructed out of town (possibly for sanitary reasons or to provide a central location for several villages), and trees planted around them. The Bonneville shoreline is near the top of the hill. The Provo shoreline is at the prominent bench just at the level of the top of the trees, (September, 1986).

Bear River Range and city of Franklin, Idaho's oldest town, looking southeast from just west of Cub River. The Provo shoreline is obvious below the uneven bare hills. The Bonneville shoreline is less prominent, 400 feet above, on the steep face of the bare hills. High Creek is the prominent canyon in the background. The base of the mountains are underlain by east-dipping Late Proterozoic and Cambrian Brigham Group; Paleozoic limestone forms the summits, (June, 1992).

Franklin

Franklin was the first settlement in Idaho, established by Mormon Pioneers in 1860. Clifton, Weston, and Dayton were established in 1864, 1865, and 1867.

Lorenzo Hill Hatch was Bishop of Franklin from 1863 to 1875. His son was bishop from 1875 to 1907. He came west with the 1846 migration from Nauvoo, Illinois. Hatch married plural wives and was the father of twelve sons and twelve daughters. At the time of his death in 1900 he had 170 grandchildren and 32 great grandchildren.

Home of L.H. Hatch in Franklin, built 1874. Hatch was a prominent Mormon bishop, polygamist, and political leader. House stands next to the ZCMI Co-op, (June, 1992).

Utah & Northern Railway grade just north of Preston. The grade is the raised embankment dotted with sagebrush in the foreground. View looks west across the Bear River toward the south end of the Bannock Range near Dayton, Clifton and Oxford, (April, 1996).

Utah-Northern Railroad

The Utah-Northern Railroad Company, a cooperative project of the Mormon Church and local farmers, reached Franklin in 1874 and the Bear River at Battle Creek in 1876, but the company ran out of money. Utah-Northern shops had been built at Battle Creek, just south of the Bear River, at the site of Connor's Massacre.

The roadbed for the Utah-Northern Railroad, headed north to Soda Springs, was built toward Riverdale and Oneida Narrows, but tracks were never laid. It is still plainly visible near Johnson Reservoir north of Preston.

When construction was begun again (by the reorganized Utah & Northern Railway), the route headed north through Red Rock Pass to Marsh Valley and Pocatello.

Raised roadbed of Utah-Northern Railroad at Johnson Reservoir north of Preston. Rails were never laid. The route was rejected after the reorganization of the Utah & Northern Railway in favor of a route across the Bear River and up Battle Creek, (August, 1992).

Preston

Preston (originally called "Worm Creek' when it was founded in 1874), was located where it is because ground water, though alkaline, was shallow on the west banks of Worm Creek. In 1880, the name Worm Creek was changed to Preston, honoring Bishop Wm. B. Preston of Logan. Mormon leaders had, thankfully, objected to the word "worm." In 1881, the Cub River and Worm Creek irrigation system began. It was the first of several canal systems that would bring water to Cache Valley. In 1888, the townsite of Preston was surveyed and platted.

Nellie Parkinson, whose husband was the bishop of the Preston ward, describes conditions in 1884:

"At that time Preston was a desert sand ridge. Not a spear of anything green was to be seen and the few families were in desperate poverty . . . The wind would blow a gale and carry the sand ridge north in the morning and in the afternoon would blow it all back to the south again to be ready for the next morning's blow. We set out some poplar trees and planted them 6 feet deep. I watered them every day, with the soapsuds from washing. These were the very first trees on the flat." (Hart, 1973)

Site of Utah & Northern Railway grade climbing up Battle Creek north of the Bear River in Cache Valley. The narrow gauge grade followed the steep unimproved road in the foreground, (August, 1992).

In 1890, the Oregon Short Line & Utah & Northern Railway laid standard gauge railroad tracks to replace the old narrow gauge line, and the main line was moved to the west side of the valley. Preston became the terminus of the branch line from Logan.

The first water system for Preston was in 1912, to replace the alkaline wells. In 1913 Oneida County was divided; Preston became the county seat of Franklin County.

In 1914, a building boom began. Many of the brick buildings of downtown date from this era. The demand during World War I for agricultural products brought a real time of prosperity to Cache Valley from 1915 to 1921. The 1920 population of Preston was 3,235, approximately the same as 1970, and only 500 less than 1990.

Logan Rapid Transit System

The Logan Rapid Transit system, consisting of inter-urban trolleys connecting Logan to Ogden and northern Cache Valley, was organized in 1910 and reached Preston in 1915. The first timetable showed 16 trolleys daily, with the trip from Ogden to Preston taking $3\frac{1}{2}$ hours. The line was discontinued in 1947 and the material sold for scrap.

West Cache and Twin Lakes Canals.

In 1899, the West Cache Canal, designed to water 17,200 acres on the west side of Bear River, was begun. The Twin Lakes Canal was begun in 1902 by enthusiastic farmers who were advised that the project would take 5 years and cost $282,000. Instead it took 20 years and cost $1,500,000.

Squaw Hot Springs building west of Preston. Building was vacant at the time of this photograph (June, 1992). It had been used in the past ten years as a greenhouse and a pig farm. Large travertine-coated open well flows water at 84°centigrade.

Hot Springs

Natural hot springs exist along the Bear River at several locations north and west of Preston. The water is emitted along the trace of the normal fault which bounds the east side of Clifton Hill or Little Mountain east of Twin Lakes Reservoir. Commercial hot springs were operated at Old Bridge Porte just south of Battle Creek and at Riverview—Sunset—Del Rio Hot Springs half a mile downstream. Presently a hot springs complex at Riverdale is operated as a swimming pool.

Wide canyon of Bear River, looking east from the old grade of Highway 91, cut in unconsolidated sands and silts deposited in Lake Bonneville. The landslide shown in the upper photo on p. 99 is directly across the tree-lined course of the Bear River. Bear River Range in the background, (June, 1992).

Bear River Landslide Complex

Active rotational landslides exist on both banks of the Bear River north and west of Preston. These landslides represent response of unconsolidated Lake Bonneville silts, sands, and clays to the lowering of the base level of the Bear River after the drying up of the remnants of Lake Bonneville about 14,000 years ago. Installation of irrigation systems in the country both east and west of the river resulted in major landslides in the 1910s. Wet cycles of several years of duration with higher than normal rainfall have triggered periods of landsliding since then. The last period of active

Headwall scarp of "Highway slide" which cuts the old alignment of U.S. Highway 91 north of the Bear River and Preston, (August, 1983).

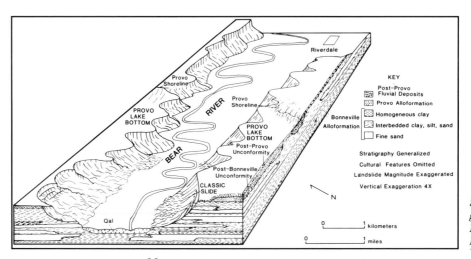

Schematic view showing geologic setting of Bear River Landslide Complex, from Link and others (1987).

earth movement was in 1983-86. In 1993, the grade of U.S. Highway 91 was reconstructed to the west, away from the face of the hill, to avoid its former grade over a headwall scarp of one of these landslides.

Scar of landslide along the south bank of the Bear River. Photo taken in May, 1983. Trace of old farm road can be seen across the earthflow. Arcuate scars of former landslides can be seen to the right of the active flow.

Oxford Mountain and Oxford Basin looking west from central Cache Valley near the railroad siding at Oxford. The Lake Bonneville shoreline forms the straight bench (LBS). The dark cliffs behind Oxford basin are underlain by Late Proterozoic rocks of the Pocatello Formation. The rocks at the top of the mountain belong to the Brigham Group, and dip eastward above a flat younger-over-older fault, (October, 1978).

Oxford

Oxford was settled in 1864. With completion of the Utah & Northern, the town became a mixed Mormon-Gentile community and aspired to replace Malad City as county seat of Oneida County. Oxford obtained the public land office in 1879 and a newspaper, the Idaho Enterprise, in 1880. Oscar Sonnenkalb lived there from 1881 to 1889.

Oneida County, in the 1880s, embraced 13 of the present counties of southeastern Idaho, extending 180 miles south to north from the Utah border to Montana, and about 100 miles east to west from the Wyoming border. The County Seat of this vast territory was first at Soda Springs, but in 1866, was moved to Malad City. However, as Malad City was far from the railroad, more than half of the county-officers resided and had offices in Oxford, on the narrow gauge railway.

> **Sonnenkalb (p. 10) related**
> "there were several saloons, grocery stores, also a newspaper edited by Colonel Straight who, with the famous imagination of the western promoter, predicted a wonderful growth of our village into a second Chicago with the Oxford slough representing Michigan Lake." (in Harstad, editor, 1972, p. 10.)

Oxford in 1880 had bright prospects. The settlement was near the Utah & Northern Railway , but the mile and a half distance separating Oxford Station from the business and residential area insured residents that they would not suffer the liabilities of a railroad town.

In 1884 Oxford became the headquarters for the Oneida Stake of the Church of Jesus Christ of Latter Day Saints in southern Idaho. It became a storm center for the political movement which disenfranchised the Idaho Mormons the next year. The headquarters of the Oneida Stake were removed from Oxford in September 1886, to allay the persistent prejudice and opposition of the anti-Mormon party, who had also made its headquarters at Oxford.

However, in 1885, Oxford had suffered a great setback. A politically-motivated change of the site of the U.S. Land Office moved personnel from Oxford to Blackfoot. Further, the creation of Bingham County in 1885 reduced Oneida County to the territory west of the Bannock Range. Business drifted north to Blackfoot and Eagle Rock. The decline of Oxford was partly an anti-Mormon move by Idaho politicians led by Fred T. Dubois, who was a resident of Blackfoot.

References

Arrington, L.J., and Jensen, Richard, 1973, Lorenzo Hill Hatch: Pioneer Bishop of Franklin: Idaho Yesterdays, v. 17, no. 2, p. 2-8.

Bjorklund, L.J., and McGreevy, L.J., 1971, Ground-water resources of Cache Valley, Utah and Idaho: Utah Department of Natural Resources, Technical Publication 36, 72 p.

Dion, N.P., 1969, Hydrologic reconnaissance of the Bear River basin in southeastern Idaho: Idaho Department of Reclamation, Water Information Bulletin 13, 65 p.

Harstad, P.T., 1972, Reminiscences of Oscar Sonnenkalb, Idaho Surveyor and Pioneer: Pocatello, Idaho, Idaho State University Press, 66 p.

Hart, Newell, 1973 (reprinted 1986), Hometown Album: Preston, Idaho, Cache Valley Newsletter Publishing Co.

Kerns, G.L., and Kerns, R.L., Jr., editors, 1985, Orogenic patterns and stratigraphy of north-central Utah and Southeastern Idaho: Utah Geological Association Publication 14, 329.

Link, P.K., Mahoney, J.B., McCalpin, J., Henkelman, J.J., and Smith, B.L., 1987, Field trip roadlog for the Bear River Landslide Complex: in Robinson, Lee, editor, Proceedings of the 23rd Symposium on Engineering Geology and Soils Engineering, Logan, Utah, 334-352 p.

Madsen, B.D., 1985, The Shoshoni Frontier and the Bear River Massacre: University of Utah Press, Salt Lake City.

McCarthy, Max R., 1987, The Last Chance Canal Company: Provo, Utah, Brigham Young University Charles Redd Center for Western Studies, Monograph no. 16, 131p.

Ricks, J.E., ed., 1956, The History of a Valley: Cache Valley, Utah-Idaho: Logan, Utah, Cache Valley Centennial Commission, 504 p.

Late spring (1992) afternoon south of Red Rock Pass. The prominent bench in the background is the alluvial fan surface incised by the Lake Bonneville Flood. Uneven country just across the railroad track is scabland where bedrock was scoured and jostled by the flood.

Malad Valley and Country to the West

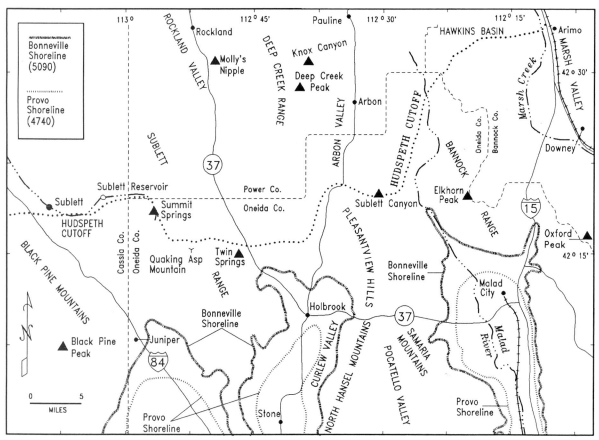

Map of Malad Valley and country to the west.

Hudspeth Cutoff

West from Marsh Valley the Hudspeth Cutoff crossed the Bannock Range, Blue Spring Hills, Deep Creek Range, and Sublett Range before reaching the Raft River Valley and joining with the California Trail near present-day Malta. Twin Springs, between present-day Rockland and Holbrook was one of the few reliable water supplies.

Pioneers chose the Hudspeth Cutoff in the great rush of 1849, when, sheeplike, they sought a more direct route to California. It is estimated that from June 20 to August 31, 1849, 250 wagons a day (an estimated

Malad Valley and Samaria Mountain, looking west from Interstate 15, south of Malad City, (November, 1984).

16,000 to 25,000 people) travelled this route, even though it was unproven, more difficult, and as it turned out, did not save any time. The Pioneers were desperate to get to California first. About 45,000 travelled it in 1850 and 50,000 in 1852. The cutoff had a life of perhaps 10 years since few went that way after 1859, as the California gold fields played out. Arthur Hope's book "The Hudspeth Cutoff, Idaho's Legacy of Wheels" is a detailed account of the route.

Empty Country

The vast area from Malad City west to the Raft River Valley is mainly empty. There are few paved roads, and no gas stations. This is dry, sparsely settled country. Although much of it was homesteaded near the turn of the century, most of the farm houses were abandoned in the 1930s and the land is now divided into thousand-acre dry farms. The mountains are not high enough to catch significant winter snows and the streams in the valleys are small and unreliable. Extensive irrigation systems are not feasible. However, if most of these hardy farmers, who remain here, were given the choice, they would live nowhere else.

The Name "Malad"

Osborne Russell, fur trapper, wrote of his movements in March, 1842, in his last spring before he left Idaho for the Willamette Valley of Oregon.

> "The next day we travelled south about fifteen miles through a low defile and the day following we crossed the divide (Malad Summit) and fell onto a stream called "Malade" or sick river, which empties into Bear River about ten miles from the mouth. This stream takes its name from the beaver which inhabit it living on poison roots. Those who eat their meat in a few hours become sick at the stomach and the whole system is filled with cramps and severe pains. I have never known or heard of a person dying with this disease." (Haines, 1965, p. 124)

The original name of the Big Wood River in south-central Idaho also was Malade, for the same reason.

Jensen Pass over the Deep Creek Range from southern Arbon Valley, (June, 1990). This is where the Hudspeth Cutoff crossed into the Holbrook area. Lorenzo Sawyer wrote about the country along the Hudspeth Cutoff thusly: "The mountains in this region seem piled up in the most wild and romantic confusion."

Geology of the Malad Area

The Wasatch fault runs along the east side of Malad Valley, and there are several active faults in the area to the south and west. Malad Valley is thus a half-graben, with the sedimentary valley fill generally tilted east.

The Bannock, Deep Creek, and Sublett Ranges as well as the Samaria and North Hansel Mountains are underlain by Paleozoic rocks, mainly limestones. These mountains are generally good fossil hunting country, with horn corals, brachiopods and gastropods easy to find if one knows the right place and is prepared to walk. There are several areas of limestone caverns. Air escaping from these caves on northern Samaria Mountain sometimes causes the mountain to "moan" in early spring.

Lake Bonneville extended north into the southern parts of Malad, Curlew and Juniper Valleys. Its shorelines can be seen if one looks closely, usually near the top of the level of plowed fields. They are generally more prominent in the southern parts of the valleys, closer to the Utah border.

Settlement and Brigham Young's Placement of the Utah Border

The first colonization of the Malad Valley, by Mormon cattlemen, was in the early 1850s. The settlers were recalled to Salt Lake City with the coming of the federal army of occupation (Johnston's army) to Utah in 1857-58. The first permanent settlement was in 1863. Malad City was settled mainly by Mormon converts from Wales.

Brigham Young came through the Malad Valley in 1855. Acting on the basis of astronomical observations by Orson Pratt, he marked the boundary line between Oregon and Utah territories as 108 miles from Salt Lake City, near the present town of Woodruff, Idaho. Although this placement was very close to correct, many Mormon settlers in Malad, Cache, and Bear Lake Valleys claimed that they were actually in Utah. The matter was not settled until the U.S. Government survey of 1872.

Early Malad City and Oneida County

Malad City grew up as a composite community in which Mormons, Gentiles, and Mormon apostates (the Josephites) dwelt without much friction. Soda Springs was the first county seat of Oneida County, which in the early 1860s included all of southeastern Idaho. Transportation from the Malad Valley to Soda Springs was difficult and the county seat was moved to Malad City in 1866. This move quieted hostilities between Malad Valley Mormons, who thought (or hoped) they were actually in Utah, and Gentiles. Oxford (in Cache Valley), served as the Federal Land Office until 1885, and many Oneida County officials lived there.

The Gold Road

In the early 1860s, two overland stage routes operated from Utah to the Snake River Plain and the mines in Montana. Both came north to Malad City. The Bannock Road split off up the Malad River and crossed into Arbon Valley to the mouth of Bannock Creek, and then north and east along the south bank of the Snake River. The more-used Portneuf Road, operated by stages owned by Ben Holladay, went over Malad Summit and to Marsh Valley, along the road followed by Interstate Highway 15 today. Holladay sold the Portneuf Road to William Murphy. In April 1870 Murphy was fatally shot in Malad City, by a deputy sheriff, after a dispute with county commissioners about how much he could charge. Leigh Gittins' book "Idaho's Gold Road" is a rich source of this history.

Josephites

In 1866 a splinter group of Mormons, led by one of the sons of Joseph Smith, came to Malad City, seeking a community far enough away from Salt Lake City not to cause friction but close enough to allow missionary work. They formed the Josephites, the Reorganized Church of Jesus Christ of Latter Day Saints, which still exists.

Indian Settlement at Washakie

After the Bear River Massacre in 1863, the Shoshoni Indians, with help of the LDS church, made a permanent settlement in Malad Valley. Chief Sagwitch, wounded at the massacre, lived to join the LDS church and is buried at Washakie 2 miles west of the Malad River south of Malad City.

Holbrook

The Holbrook valley, only fifteen miles west of Malad City, but drier and less hospitable, was settled in 1878, 30 years after the Pioneers entered the Salt Lake Valley. But the big rush of homesteading did not come until about 1895. The main growth was 1901-1907.

Holbrook did not get electricity until 1946. Today its homesteads are largely abandoned. Dry farming for grain and cattle grazing are the primary agricultural activities.

References

Beus, S.S., 1968, Paleozoic stratigraphy of Samaria Mountain, Idaho-Utah: American Association of Petroleum Geologists Bulletin, v. 52, p.782-808.

Eliason, Carol, and Hubbard, Mary, 1987, Holbrook and surrounding areas history book 1878-1987: Holbrook, Idaho, 491 p.

Gittins, H. Leigh, 1976, Idaho's Gold Road: Moscow, Idaho, The University Press of Idaho, 165 p.

Haines, A.L., ed., 1965, Osborne Russell's Journal of a Trapper: University of Nebraska Press, p. 124.

Harstad, P.T., editor, 1972, Reminiscences of Oscar Sonnenkalb, Idaho Surveyor and Pioneer: Pocatello, Idaho, The Idaho State University Press, 66 p.

Hope, A.C., 1990, Hudspeth Cutoff, Idaho's legacy of Wheels: Idaho Falls, Idaho, Bookshelf Bindery and Press, P.O. Box 2204, Idaho Falls, Idaho, 222 p.

Howell, Glade F., 1960, Early history of Malad Valley: M.A. Thesis, Department of History, Brigham Young University, 130 p.

Kerns, G.L., and Kerns, R.L., Jr., editors, 1985, Orogenic patterns and stratigraphy of north-central Utah and southeastern Idaho: Utah Geological Association Publication 14, 328 p.

Link, P.K., and Smith, L.H., 1992, Late Proterozoic and Early Cambrian stratigraphy, paleobiology, and tectonics: Northern Utah and southeastern Idaho: *in* Wilson, J.R., editor, Field Guide to Geologic Excursions in Utah and Adjacent Areas of Nevada, Idaho, and Wyoming: Utah Geological Survey Miscellaneous Publication 92-3, p. 461-481.

Garden Creek Gap, looking west from west of Arimo. Garden Creek meanders through the narrow defile cut in hard east-dipping quartzite of the Scout Mountain Member of the Late Proterozoic Pocatello Formation. The stream is superposed, that is, it established its course on a cover of valley fill above the present level of the quartzite ridge. Vegetated stripes near the top of the slope north of the gap are normal faults, dropping the rocks down to the east, toward Marsh Valley, (August, 1982).
Near here in July, 1994 supermodel Niki Taylor married Matthew Martinez, a McCammon man. Super-supermodel Cindy Crawford was among the wedding guests.

Grain elevator east of Twin Springs, along the Hudspeth Cutoff, (June, 1992).

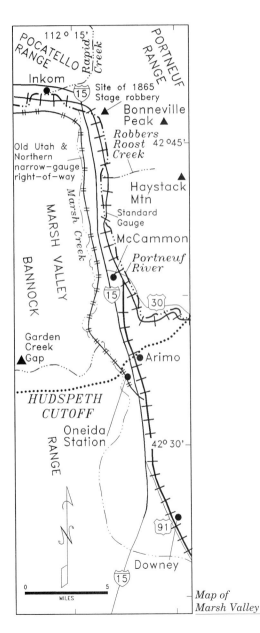

Map of Marsh Valley

Geography and History of Drainage

Marsh Valley, bordered on the east by the Portneuf Range and on the west by the Bannock Range, is the primary access to the Snake River Plain from the south. As the area was, after 1867, part of the Fort Hall Indian Reservation, legitimate settlement of the southern part was delayed until after 1889 when the land south of McCammon was excised from the reservation. Euro-American settlement of northern Marsh Valley began with the Land Run of 1902.

The Portneuf Range contains east-dipping Lower Paleozoic and Late Proterozoic rocks and the Bannock Range contains the same sequence, repeated across a normal fault that bounds the east side of Marsh Valley. The Basalt of Portneuf Valley is at the surface at the north end of Marsh Valley, having been erupted from the Bancroft area about 600,000 years ago.

The north end of Marsh Valley today contains an example of "inverted topography" with the lava flows filling the middle of the valley and the rivers confined to the sides. The Portneuf River is on the east and Marsh Creek, the main path of the Lake Bonneville Flood, is on the west. At the time of eruption of the lava flow, the center of the valley was lowest, and thus the term "inverted topography."

Geophysical surveys indicate that there is as much as 10,000 feet of valley fill underneath Downey, and that over the last few million years, drainage in Marsh Valley was primarily to the south, perhaps into a lake basin which periodically had an outlet to the Bonneville Basin. The prominent pediment surfaces seen below Scout Mountain and Mount Bonneville were established during this time of southward drainage and are graded to a base level several hundred feet above the present valley floor.

After establishment of the throughgoing drainage of the ancestral Bear River, the base level fell and the pediments were incised. Garden Creek which had been flowing east on deposits of gravel and sand began cutting down and encountered the bedrock ridge at Garden Creek Gap. It continued downcutting, resulting in the superposed canyon seen today.

Osborne Russell's thoughts on leaving southeastern Idaho for the Willamette Valley of Oregon in 1842.

"In July 1842, I ascended to the top of Ross Mountain (probably Mt. Bonneville in the Portneuf Range) on which the snows remain till the latter part of August. I sat down under a pine and took a last farewell view of a country over which I had travelled so often under such a variety of circumstances. The recollections of the past connected with the scenery now spread out before me put me somewhat in a poetical humor, and for the first time I attempted to frame my thoughts into rhyme.

In the year 1836 large bands of buffalo could be seen in almost every little valley on the small branches of the Portneuf River. But now the only traces which could be seen were the scattered bones of those that had been killed. Their trails which had been made in former years deeply indented in the earth were overgrown with grass and weeds. The trappers often remarked to each other as they rode over these lonely plains that it was time for the white man to leave the mountains as beaver and game had nearly disappeared." (Haines, 1965, p. 123-125).

Henry O. Harkness and early McCammon

Henry O. Harkness took over the operation of William Murphy's stagecoach service between Corinne, Utah and the Montana gold mines in 1870 and set up operations at the toll bridge over the Portneuf River at what is now McCammon (named for the man who negotiated purchase of the right of way for the Oregon Short Line Railway across the Fort Hall Indian Reservation). Harkness was an archetypal American entrepreneur of the late 19th century and a testimony to the power of the American Dream. In 1871, he married Murphy's widow Catherine, who had inherited her husband's property rights to land on the Fort Hall Indian Reservation.

In 1874, Harkness turned to ranching and purchased land at Oxford, just south of the border of the Fort Hall

Looking northeast across Marsh Valley. Putnam Mountain is in the distance, north of Inman Pass. Two peaks can be distinguished, North and South Putnam Peaks. The 600,000 year old Basalt of Portneuf Valley fills the middle of Marsh Valley. Marsh Creek is on the west side, in the foreground, and the Portneuf River is on the east side. Interstate Highway 15 runs along the middle of the lava flow. Arcuate scars in the lava flow in the center of the photo are dry waterfalls carved during the Lake Bonneville Flood about 14,500 years ago, (July, 1990).

View looking west across Marsh Valley at Old Tom Mountain (left) and Scout Mountain (right). The Basalt of Portneuf Valley fills the low part of Marsh Valley, (July, 1990).

Eastbound Oregon Short Line freight train at McCammon, (1894). Bannock County Historical Society Collection.

Indian Reservation. He also became partner in a bank in Corinne, Utah, which moved to Ogden in 1878. For his ranching endeavors Harkness imported the best stock and bred horses, cattle, and mules. He grew rich fields of potatoes and grain.

Henry and Catherine Harkness had no children. A year after Catherine's death in 1898, Harkness married her niece, Sarah Scott, who had come to care for Catherine during her last illness. Sarah bore five children. When he married for the second time Henry O. Harkness was 65 years old.

James L. Onderdonk, Territorial Controller for the Territory of Idaho, wrote, in "Idaho, Facts and Statistics" in 1885:

"In his back yard he has fenced in one of the noblest water powers in the United States, where the Port Neuf River, a deep, rapid and unfailing mountain stream, takes a perpendicular leap of eighteen feet. The water power is worth an immense sum of money." (Cited by Gittins, 1976, p. 73-74.)

The building of the U & N Railway to Pocatello in 1878 saw the end of the freighting business and of steady use of Portneuf River toll bridge, but Harkness turned to other ways to make money. The Oregon Short Line

railway bridges over the Portneuf River at McCammon were constructed near Harkness' bridge and farm. He built the grand and spacious Harkness House hotel to take advantage of the increase in traffic brought by the railroad. The chief competition was the Pacific Hotel, operated by the railroad in Pocatello, 25 miles away. By 1891, he had built a flour mill powered by waterfalls on the Portneuf. "We lead, others may follow" was advertised on bags of his flour. By 1893, the Harkness hydroelectric generating plant was established. Harkness expanded into the booming sheep business in the 1900s. In February 1905, he marketed a trainload of sheep in Chicago. In 1907, Idaho ranked third in the nation in amount of wool produced and fourth in size of flocks.

Bad floods occurred on the Portneuf River after January rains in 1911. The floodwaters destroyed some of Harkness' buildings and the stress brought on by the flood no doubt hastened his death in April 1911, at the age of 77. In June 1913, fire, a recurring scourge on the early towns of southeast Idaho, destroyed the Harkness House hotel.

Harkness' children moved away from McCammon and only remnant structures of the grand farm and ranch spread remain today.

Camp Downey

Although World War II was the most popular war in American history, a few people, because of religious convictions, refused to participate in an enterprise that involved killing one's fellow human beings. A

Civilian Public Service Camp for conscientious objectors was established on 27 acres one-half mile east of Downey using what had been a Civilian Conservation Corps camp built in 1939 (Olinger, 1991). The camp consisted of 21 buildings and could hold 150 persons. It was operated by the Mennonite Central Committee, for the purpose of soil conservation and general farm work during manpower shortages caused by the war. The camp was closed in 1946, after the fall harvest.

Gravestone of H.O. Harkness, in the Gentile Cemetery, McCammon, Idaho. The memorial ironically makes no mention of the great farm, hotel, electric power generator and flour mill that Harkness constructed on the Portneuf River east of here, (June, 1989).

Oxford Mountain after a spring snowstorm, looking south from Downey, (May, 1991). The steep-sided summit is not a volcanic cone, but an up-faulted north-south trending ridge of Late Proterozoic Brigham Group.

Southern Bannock County

Residents of southern Bannock County generally have thought themselves separate from the dirty urban center of Pocatello. Before 1960 several towns had commercial centers, but the building of the Interstate Highway System of the 1960s and the decline of rail transportation produced the present system of people who live in the country, but go to Pocatello if they need to do some serious shopping.

References

Gittins, H. Leigh, 1976, Idaho's Gold Road: Moscow Idaho, The University Press of Idaho, 165 p.

Haines, A.L., ed., 1965, Osborne Russell's Journal of a Trapper: University of Nebraska Press, 191 p.

Olinger, J.C., 1991, A Place of Conscience: Camp Downey, Pocatello, Idaho, Idaho State University Press, 61p.

View looking southeast up Marsh Creek toward Arimo. Jensen Road is in the center of the view. The Utah & Northern right of way can be seen as a straight line with a few trees to the right (west) of the creek, south of Jensen Road. In the foreground the grade rounds a curve and is followed by a drainage ditch, full of water, (June, 1992).

Site of Oneida Station west of Arimo, view looks southwest, (June, 1990).

Leigh Gittins, discussing Henry O. Harkness, (September, 1989).

Portrait of Chief Arimo, around 1890. Idaho Museum of Natural History collection.

Narrow gauge right-of-way looking south beside Marsh Creek along Jensen Road west of McCammon. The trees on the right-of-way are river hawthorns (September, 1995).

Union Pacific Freight Train, with a now-vanished caboose on the end (September, 1989). Photo is taken from the site of the Port Neuf toll bridge, looking west at the UP main line which crosses over what was formerly the Idaho Gold Road.

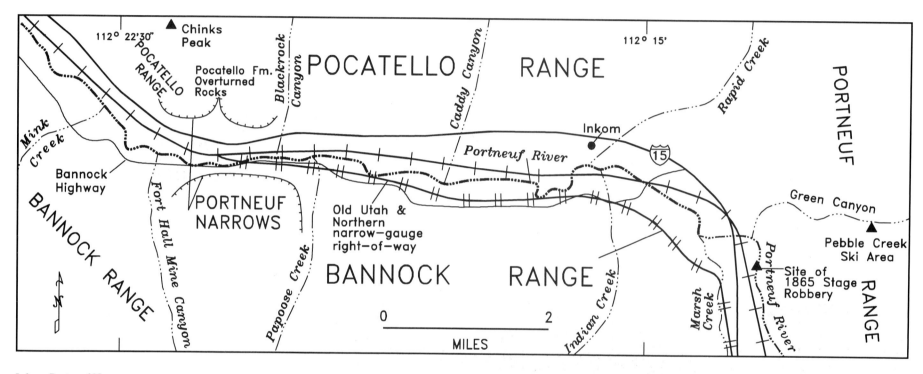

Inkom-Portneuf Narrows map.

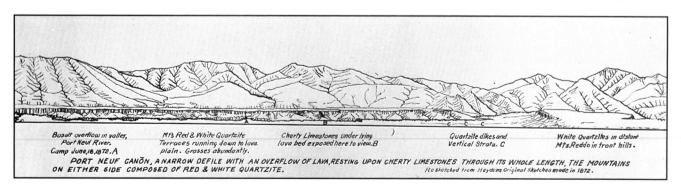

Sketch redrawn by Abe Lillibridge, from original by the Ferdinand V. Hayden expedition of the U.S. Geological Survey. View looks north and east across the Portneuf River from near Blackrock toward the Pocatello Range, the city of Inkom, Rapid Creek, and the Portneuf Range on the right. Note: in the caption to the illustration, "do" means "same as above." Hayden failed to recognize that the limestones on the east end of the canyon (Cambrian Elkhead Limestone) are younger than those near Blackrock on the west end (Late Proterozoic Blackrock Canyon Limestone). We now know the mountains to be made up mostly of the Late Proterozoic and Cambrian Brigham Group. The Basalt of Portneuf Valley in the foreground is about 600,000 years old.

The Gateway to the Northwest

The narrow canyon of the Portneuf River through the Bannock Range between Inkom and Portneuf Narrows is the geographic key to the development of southeast Idaho and the city of Pocatello. It was this water-level route that became the Idaho Gold Road followed by stages and freighters from 1864 to 1878, and then the route of the Utah & Northern and the Oregon Short Line railways. This was not, however, the route followed by the Oregon Trail.

The canyon was probably cut by the ancestral Bear River, on the order of a million years ago, in response to the subsidence of the area of the Snake River Plain near Pocatello after passage of the ancestral Yellowstone Hot Spot.

The canyon follows a line of weakness along the east-west Portneuf Narrows tear fault that probably formed in Cretaceous time during folding of rocks of the Putnam thrust plate. This tear fault passes north of the Portneuf River at Portneuf Narrows and separates rocks of the Late Proterozoic Pocatello Formation to the north and underlying Chink's Peak, that are structurally overturned, from correlative strata on the south side of the fault that are right-side-up.

The rocks exposed between the west side of Portneuf Narrows and Inkom span about 250 million years of earth history, that is from Late Proterozoic to Upper Cambrian time (750 to 500 million years ago). They thus were deposited during the development of complex invertebrate life forms which appeared on earth between about 610 and 540 million years ago. Several of the references cited at the end of this section discuss the complex geology of the Portneuf Narrows area.

Aerial view of Portneuf Narrows from the west. Into the narrow gap are crowded the meandering Portneuf River, following the broad path of the Lake Bonneville Flood, the main line of the Union Pacific Railroad, Interstate 15 and the Bannock Highway on the south side of the river. In this locality, the Lake Bonneville Flood was about 300 feet deep. This gap was its narrowest constriction. In the distance is the Portneuf Range, with the high point Mount Bonneville. On the left of the Narrows is the south ridge of Chinks Peak. The Portneuf Narrows tear fault runs through the straight gully immediately left of the scar of the roadcut on the Interstate highway, (June, 1989).

Column of basalt lava from the Basalt of Portneuf Valley near Inkom. Dark holes in the lava are vesicles or gas bubbles which exsolved out of the molten basalt. Basaltic lava tends to cool to six-sided columns as it shrinks during the change from liquid to solid, (June, 1989).

Drainage History

In the Miocene, about 8 million years ago, the Yellowstone Hot Spot was located near Pocatello. The Pocatello-Blackfoot area was a high volcanic plateau, and drainage in the Inkom area was probably to the south. After the Hot Spot migrated northeastward and the former high plateau subsided, the direction of drainage was reversed. This was when the Portneuf Narrows was cut, by the ancestral Bear River. The gap was cut when streams began to flow north to what became the west-flowing Snake River, draining west in the wake of the east-migrating Hot Spot.

The floor of the Narrows had been lowered by 600,000 years ago to near the level of the present valley floor. Basaltic volcanic activity in Gem Valley, near present-day Bancroft, produced the Basalt of Portneuf Valley, which flowed down this canyon for about 50 miles, through the Narrows and to what is now Ross Park in Pocatello. Two lava flows can be distinguished.

The Bear River was diverted by these or associated volcanic eruptions to flow south into southern Gem Valley, and eventually to cut a passage at Oneida Narrows into the Lake Bonneville basin. The Portneuf River is thus the remnant of the ancestral Bear River.

Portneuf Narrows from the southeast, looking west to Pocatello, (July, 1990). Gibson Mountain is on the horizon at the left, and Howard Mountain on the far horizon at the right. Late Proterozoic rocks of the Pocatello Formation are present north of the Gap, on the overturned limb of a large fold. Rocks of the same age on the south side of the gap are right-side up. The boundary is the Portneuf Narrows tear fault, which cuts through the small saddle about 1/3 of the way up the slope on the north side of the gap.

Between Salt Lake City, Ogden, Pocatello, Ashton—Yellowstone, Victor and Butte

WESTBOUND—Read Down / EASTBOUND—Read Up

Table No. 36 — The Overland Route
For other trains between Salt Lake and Ogden see Table No. 31. (Mountain Standard Time)

Park Special *35-47 Daily	Butte Special 35 Daily	MILES	Station	Elevation	Butte Special 36 Daily	Park Special *48-96 Daily
7.30	7.30	0	Lv Salt Lake City 1,2,3,4,20,40... Utah Ar	4251	8.00	8.00
8.20	8.20	36	Ar Ogden 1,2,3,4,38,40... "	4298	7.05	7.05
8.55	8.55	0	Lv Ogden (Ogden Canyon) " Ar	4298	6.35	6.35
E.	A.	9	" Hot Springs (Mineral Springs) "	4274	A.	H.
E.	A.	14	" Willard (Great Salt Lake to west) "	4265	A.	H.
9.25	9.25	21	" Brigham City 38 {Wasatch Mts. "	4306	6.05	6.05
E.	A.	30	" Honeyville { to east "	4266	A.	H.
E.	A.	36	" Dewey (Bear River) "	4324	A.	H.
E.	A.	40	" Collinston "	4416	A.	H.
E.	A.	45	" Wheelon (Bear River Canyon) "		A.	H.
10.10	10.10	49	" Cache Junction 37 "	4445	5.25	5.25
E.	A.	57	" Trenton "	4461	A.	H.
E.	A.	61	" Cornish "	4481	A.	H.
E.	A.	62	" Utida (Utah-Idaho boundary) "	4522	A.	H.
E.	A.	65	" Weston... Idaho	4605	A.	H.
f10.37	f10.37	71	" Dayton (Battle Creek Butte to east) "	4746	f4.59	f4.59
E.	A.	75	" Clifton "	4747	A.	H.
E.	A.	81	" Oxford "	4748	A.	H.
E.		84	" Swan Lake (Red Rock Pass) "	4779	A.	H.
11.04	11.04	90	" Downey (Oxford Peak to east) "	4854	4.34	4.34
E.		100	" Virginia "	4795	A.	H.
E.		105	" Arimo "	4605	A.	H.
11.25	11.25	111	Ar McCammon 20 (Columnar basalt) "	4751	4.15	4.15
11.25	11.25	111	Lv McCammon "	4751	4.15	4.15
	A.	121	" Inkom "	4525	A.	H.
11.55	11.55	134	Ar Pocatello 20 (Portneuf River) "	4463	3.45	3.45
12.55	12.25	134	Lv Pocatello "	4463	2.30	2.05
		140	" Tyhee { Ft. Hall Indian "	4459		
	f12.45	146	" Fort Hall {Reservations-Bannocks "	4447	f2.04	
		151	" Gibson { and Shoshones "	4466		
	1.00	158	" Blackfoot 56 "	4500	1.50	f1.00
	f1.13	169	" Firth (Snake River) "	1568	f1.36	
	f1.20	175	" Shelley (5 Buttes west, Caribou Pk. north) "	1627	1.29	
2.30	1.33	185	Ar Idaho Falls 39,40,57,58... " Lv	4708	1.13	f12.10
3.00		185	Lv Idaho Falls {West and South entr-... Ida. Ar	4708		11.45
5.45		51	Ar Ashton 39,40 {ances to Yellowstone- "	5255		10.20
7.30		107	Ar Victor {Grand Teton Nat'l "	6205		8.15
			See Table No. 40 {Parks.			
	1.43	185	Lv Idaho Falls (Falls in Snake River)..Idaho Ar	4708	1.03	
	f1.52	191	" Payne "	4745	f12.51	
	f1.58	197	" Bassett "	4770	f12.45	
	2.06	202	" Roberts "	4775	12.39	
	f2.17	217	" Hamer "	4802	f12.19	
	2.36	223	" Camas "	4816	f12.11	
	2.50	235	" Dubois "	5149	11.58	
	3.12	248	" Spencer (Beaver Canyon) "	5883	11.37	
	f3.29	258	" Humphrey "	6512	f11.19	
	3.41	265	" Monida (Idaho-Mont. boundary)....Mont. "	6798	11.09	
	f3.55	273	" Snowline "	6564	f10.54	
	4.05	280	Ar Lima "	6258	f10.45	
	4.10	280	Lv Lima "	6258	10.40	
	4.27	288	" Dell "	6014	10.29	
	4.34	294	" Kidd "	5819	f10.18	
	4.45	302	" Red Rock "	5495	f10.05	
	f5.10	320	" Barratts "	5258	f 9.40	
	5.27	328	" Dillon (State Normal College) "	5096	9.30	
	5.43	340	" Apex "	5427	f 9.06	
	f5.59	348	" Navy "	5000	f 8.53	
	6.13	359	" Melrose { Phosphate Beds "	5183	8.38	
	6.35	370	" Quinn { Fossil remains South "	5294	8.27	
	6.35	370	" Divide "	5397	f 8.17	
	6.53	381	" Feely "	5814	f 8.00	
	7.15	390	Ar Silver Bow "	5338	7.45	
	7.30	397	Ar Butte (Largest mining camp on earth).. Lv	5490	7.30	

Snack and Beverage Service now available on Trains 35 and 36 between Salt Lake City and Butte.

SEE TABLE O FOR SLEEPING CAR EQUIPMENT
Footnotes for Page 28

(f) Stops only on signal.   † Daily except Sunday.
A Stops to take on or to let off paying passengers.
E Stops to let off paying passengers; also to take for Idaho Falls or beyond.
H Stops to take paying passengers; also let off from Idaho Falls or beyond.
■ Nos. 35 and 36 between Salt Lake City and Pocatello, Nos. 47 and 48 between Pocatello and Victor, operate into and out of Victor via Ashton only during Yellowstone Park and Grand Teton Park summer season, from June 16 through August 21.
● Local freight with combination coach-baggage car.
♦ Connecting motor bus between Ashton and Old Faithful, for passengers holding Yellowstone Park tour transportation only. Breakfast stop at Stage Coach Inn.

Cache Junction — Logan — Preston

Mixed *303	Mls.	Table No. 37 (Mountain Time)	Mixed *304
† 5.30	85	Lv Cache Jct. Utah Ar	† 3.00
f 5.55	93	" Mendon... "	† 2.15
f 6.15	99	" Wellsville... "	f 1.55
f 6.30	103	" Hyrum... "	f 1.30
6.55	109	" Logan... "	1.10
f 7.22	117	" Smithfield.. "	f12.30
f 7.45	122	" Richmond... "	f12.01
8.25	129	" Franklin....Ida. "	f11.20
† 9.30	136	Ar Preston... " Lv	†11.00

Ogden – Brigham – Malad

Mixed *311	Mls.	Table No. 38 (Mountain Time)	Mixed *312
† 6.35	36	Lv Ogden 1, 2, Utah Ar	† 2.15
	42	" Randall... "	
f 6.56	45	" Hot Springs... "	f 1.50
f 7.04	50	" Willard... "	f 1.42
7.20	57	Ar Brigham City 36 Lv	1.30
7.30	57	Lv Brigham City 36 Ar	1.30
f 7.45	63	" Corinne... "	f12.57
f 8.02	71	" Cropley.... "	f12.40
8.15	75	" Tremonton... "	f12.30
8.30	77	" Garland.... "	12.20
f 8.46	82	" Fielding.... "	f12.05
f10.15	94	Ar Malad...Ida.Lv	†11.01

Salt Lake–Ashton–Yellowstone (Summer Season)

35-47 Daily	Mls.	Table No. 39 (Mountain Time)	48-36 Daily
■ 7.30	0	Lv Salt Lake City....Ut. Ar	8.00
8.55	36	" Ogden... "	6.35
11.55	170	" Pocatello....Ida. Lv	3.45
12.55	0	Lv Pocatello....Ida. Ar	2.05
3.00	101	Lv Idaho Falls 36...Ida. Ar	11.45
5.45	102	Ar Ashton 36, 40... " Lv	■10.20
♦ 6.00	0	Lv Ashton (Yellowstone Park Co., Transportation Div., Motor Bus.)	♦ 9.30
■11.55	86	Ar Old Faithful " Lv	6.30

Salt Lake–Idaho Falls–Ashton–Victor

35-Mixed *477	35-47 Daily	Mls.	Table No. 40 (Mountain Time)	48-36 Daily	Mixed *478 36
7.30	7.30	0	Lv Salt Lake City...Utah Ar	8.00	8.00
8.55	8.55	36	" Ogden... "	6.35	6.35
12.25	12.55	170	" Pocatello... "	2.05	2.30
1.33	2.30	221	" Idaho Falls 36...Ida. Lv	12.10	1.13
†6.00	3.00	221	Lv Idaho Falls...Ida. Ar	11.45	†4.40
6.23	f 3.18	229	" Ucon... "	f11.28	4.15
		233	" Garry... "		
6.42	3.34	235	" Rigby... "	11.18	4.00
f 6.50	f 3.44	239	" Lorenzo... "	11.12	f 3.45
6.57	f 3.51	242	" Thornton... "	f11.08	f 3.35
7.10	4.12	247	" Rexburg... "	11.01	3.20
7.20	f 4.23	251	" Sugar City... "	10.55	3.10
7.35	4.46	258	" St. Anthony... "	10.45	2.55
8.10	5.45	272	Ar Ashton... " L	10.20	2.20
8.30	5.55	272	Lv Ashton 36... " A	♦ 9.55	1.55
8.40		274	" Marysville... "		1.47
f 8.55		278	" Grainville... "		f 1.33
9.10	f 6.13	281	" Drummond... "	♦ 9.32	1.22
f 9.25		285	" France... "		1.08
f 9.35		288	" Lamont... "		f12.58
f10.08		291	" Felt... "		
10.23	f 6.59	302	" Tetonia... "	f 8.47	12.09
10.42	f 7.13	309	" Driggs... "	f 8.33	11.50
†11.05	f 7.30	318	Ar Victor...Ida. Lv	f 8.15	†11.20

Union Pacific timetable, January 27, 1964. Note the reference to "columnar basalt" at McCammon.

The Lake Bonneville Flood

About 14,500 radiocarbon years ago, Lake Bonneville, which occupied much of the presently settled part of Utah, overflowed through a dam of alluvial fan material at Red Rock Pass at the north end of Cache Valley and produced the catastrophic Lake Bonneville Flood which scoured and cleaned loose rocks from the canyon west of Inkom. It is estimated that at Portneuf Narrows the floodwaters were 300 feet deep, (O'Conner, 1990).

The flood removed the Basalt of Portneuf Valley from the Portneuf Narrows area and deposited basalt Boulders which are common in parts of downtown Pocatello. The topography left behind by the flood is called scabland topography, and is manifested in dry waterfalls, alcoves, scoured bedrock surfaces, and Boulder bar accumulations along the flood path. Such topography is easy to see both south and west of Inkom.

The Abandoned Utah & Northern Railway Grade

The Utah & Northern narrow-gauge rail line followed a grade along Marsh Creek and generally on the south side of the Portneuf River through the canyon west of Inkom. It crossed the Portneuf River on a bridge that still exists near Blackrock and ran parallel to the present Union Pacific right of way through Portneuf Narrows.

The streamlined City of Portland, late spring, about 1950. Picture was taken from lava flow just west of Inkom, looking southwest toward Portneuf Narrows. The diesel engines were manufactured by EMD (Electro-Motive Division of General Motors), and were geared for passenger operation to speeds of 105 m.p.h. Bannock County Historical Society Collection.

Fort Hall Mine

Copper was mined in the 1890s and early 1900s in the Fort Hall Mine west of Portneuf Narrows. A railroad siding was built and a bunkhouse existed at the mouth of the canyon. In 1905 it is reported that Eugene O. Leonard, the founder of Idaho State University pharmacy school, made a trip to visit the mine, operated at that time by Henry Palmer. Leonard observed a rich vein of chalcopyrite Copper ore in one of the mine's drainage pits. This vein was covered up during subsequent operations, and even though 4,000 feet of tunnel were dug in the mine, its location was never found again.

Aerial view taken August, 1989, looking southwest at Portneuf Narrows and the Fort Hall Mine Canyon, site of the Bannock County landfill. The rocks directly under the airplane are on the south ridge of Chinks Peak. They belong to the Pocatello Formation and are structurally overturned.

References

Anderson, A.L., 1928, Portland cement materials near Pocatello, Idaho: Idaho Bureau of Mines and Geology Pamphlet 28, 15 p.

Burgel, W.D., Rodgers, D.W., and Link, P.K., 1987, Mesozoic and Cenozoic structures of the Pocatello region, southeastern Idaho: *in* Miller, W.R., editor, The thrust belt revisited, Wyoming Geological Association, 38th Annual Field Conference Guidebook, p. 91-100.

Darling, R.S., 1985, Mineralization in the Fort Hall Mining District, Bannock County, Idaho: *in* Kerns, G.J. and Kerns, R. L., Jr., editors, Orogenic patterns and stratigraphy of north-central Utah and southeastern Idaho: Utah Geological Association Publication 14, p. 167-173.

Link, P.K., 1987, The Late Proterozoic Pocatello Formation: A record of continental rifting and glacial marine sedimentation, Portneuf Narrows, southeastern Idaho: *in* Beus, S.S., editor, Rocky Mountain Section of the Geological Society of America, Centennial Field Guide volume 2, p. 139-143.

Link, P.K., and Smith, L.H., 1992, Late Proterozoic and Early Cambrian stratigraphy, paleobiology, and tectonics: Northern Utah and southeastern Idaho: *in* Wilson, J.R., editor, Field Guide to Geologic Excursions in Utah and Adjacent Areas of Nevada, Idaho, and Wyoming: Utah Geological Survey Miscellaneous Publication 92-3, p. 461-481.

Link, P.K., Jansen, S.T., Halimdihardja, P., Lande. and Zahn, P., 1987, Stratigraphy of the Brigham Group (Late Proterozoic-Cambrian), Bannock, Portneuf, and Bear River Ranges, southeastern Idaho: *in* Miller, W.R., editor, The thrust belt revisited: Wyoming Geological Association, 38th annual field conference guidebook, p. 133-148.

O'Connor, J., 1990, Hydrology, hydraulic, and sediment transport of Pleistocene Lake Bonneville Flooding on the Snake River, Idaho: [Ph.D. Thesis]: Tucson, Arizona, University of Arizona, 192 p.

Trimble, D.E., 1976, Geology of the Michaud and Pocatello quadrangles, Bannock and Power Counties, Idaho: U.S. Geological Survey Bulletin 1400, 88 p.

Weeks., F.B., and Heikes, V.C., 1908, Notes on the Fort Hall mining district, Idaho: U.S. Geological Survey Bulletin 340, p. 175-183.

Utah & Northern grade along Marsh Creek, looking east between McCammon and Inkom near Indian Rocks Park. The right of way can be seen at the foot of the basalt flow, on the far side of the river. It was this part of the grade that was prone to flooding, (June, 1992).

Portneuf River at Blackrock, looking north, (June, 1992). The arched stone bridge over the river in the center was built over the original Utah & Northern bridge. Old Bannock Highway is in foreground; Old Highway 30 and double track Union Pacific tracks are in upper part of picture.

Aerial view looking east toward the city of Inkom. Old Union Pacific quarry is on the right, where Late Proterozoic quartzite was mined for railroad ballast. The faint trace of the Utah & Northern right of way can be seen in the central part of the view, crossing the Portneuf River on a frame bridge in left center of photo. This picture also shows the sharp meanders of the Portneuf River and the two lava flows (on the left), (June, 1992).

Portneuf Narrows and Portneuf School. View looks east, 1920s. Cook photo, Bannock County Historical Society Collection.

Original Inkom cement plant, looking east at Mount Bonneville, early summer, (1929). Cook photo, Bannock County Historical Society Collection.

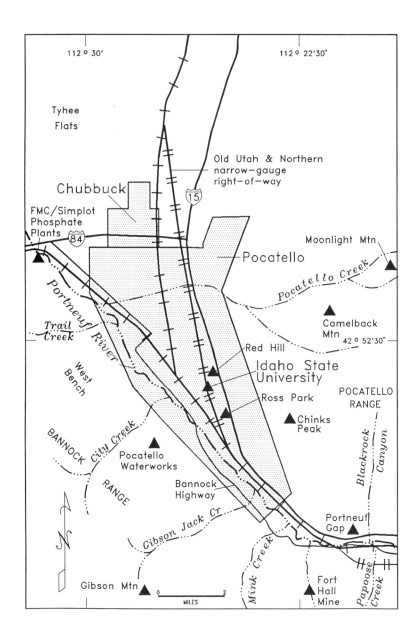

Map of Pocatello area.

Pocatello, initially a treeless sagebrush plain, carved from the Fort Hall Indian Reservation, settled by railroaders, owes its location directly to its geographic setting at the gateway to the Snake River Plain. Its layout was dictated by the railroad, around which the town was built. Its politics have reflected a never-affluent, pluralistic blue-collar town at the edge of Mormon country. These inherent internal conflicts have repeatedly stymied Pocatello's efforts to become prosperous. It has been a town without an upper class. In Idaho in the 20th century, things traditionally have come to Pocatello last. Now, in the 1990s, the prospect of growth and prosperity have returned.

Early Pocatello
The Townsite and the Indian Reservation

The early community of Pocatello, from 1882 until 1888, had to exist within the confines of the Oregon Short Line right of way because the Fort Hall Indian Reservation surrounded the area. Houses were erected along the west side of the railroad right of way, with prefabricated buildings moved in from railroad settlements at Omaha, Nebraska, and few from Battle Creek, Idaho, (north of Preston). Some were moved from Eagle Rock (Idaho Falls) to Pocatello in 1887. The townsite was too small and trespass on the Reservation was practiced by many. It was a tense situation.

There were not at first any churches in the community. A railroad official, who was a Mason, arranged for a school to be established in one of the railroad houses during the day; upstairs at night the first Masonic chapter in the area met and on Sundays a Congregational Church service was held.

Exquisite aerial photograph looking southeast at Pocatello and Portneuf Narrows, about 1940. The Gould Street Overpass crosses the Union Pacific mainline in the foreground. The city of Pocatello is laid out on a northeast-southwest grid, parallel with the railroad tracks. By convention the streets parallel with the tracks are said to run north-south and the cross streets east-west. The Yellowstone branch of the Oregon Short Line (the former Utah & Northern route) heads north-northwest to the left of the extensive railroad yards. The rural town of Alameda is laid out on a north-south grid northwest of Oak St. and east of Yellowstone Avenue. The northern addition to Pocatello is the rural land northwest of Gould Street and west of Yellowstone Avenue.

The University airstrip is visible on the east bench east of Red Hill and the University of Idaho, Southern Branch (i.e., the "Twig").

The subdivision of West Pocatello was recently laid out. Newly planted trees can be seen in the right foreground. Three Pocatello city water reservoirs are the only developments on the West Bench, between City Creek and Cusick Creek. On the West Bench, in the lower right are some of the miles of contour ditches dug in the 1930's by the Civilian Conservation Corps.

The meandering Portneuf River winds through downtown, unencumbered by a concrete channel. The photograph shows clearly the truncated East and West Benches, which were cleaned off by the Lake Bonneville Flood 14,500 years ago. They had existed at least by 600,000 years ago when the Basalt of Portneuf Valley flowed down the course of the ancestral Bear River.

In the distance is Portneuf Narrows cut in the Bannock Range, and beyond that Marsh Valley and the Portneuf Range, with peaks Mount Bonneville and Haystack Mountain. Photo from Abe Lillibridge collection, Idaho State University.

At left: Panoramic view of Pocatello from the West Bench in about 1889. The townsite had been restricted until the previous year by the Fort Hall Indian Reservation, upon which construction or occupation by non-Indians was illegal. In 1889 Pocatello was most certainly a company town. Pocatello Creek is the prominent canyon in the center background. Directly below it is Oregon Short Line shop facility and the old coal tipple (long dark building). The original route of the Utah & Northern Railway is the faint white line on the flat in the middle distance. The narrow gauge Utah & Northern tracks head north in the left center, along the present-day Yellowstone Branch. The Y-shaped area between the Oregon Short Line and the Utah & Northern became a logical place for the railroad shops. This necessitated expansion of the railroad's facilities which was accomplished by the treaty of 1888. On the extreme right is the Pacific Hotel, a combination passenger station, hotel, and dining room for railroad passengers. The Mansard Roof was added in about 1885. The Freight Depot is in the middle right north of the Pacific Hotel. The square houses on the left center of the photo are along North Harrison Street and comprise Company Row, made of houses moved into Pocatello from Eagle Rock, Battle Creek, and Omaha by the railroad to house employees. There are at least two reasons this picture looks alien. The mountains in the background have been retouched and thus can not be matched to the actual mountains. Secondly, there are no trees. All the trees in Pocatello have been planted, as indeed have all the trees except cottonwoods and junipers from here west to Boise. Photo from Abe Lillibridge collection, Idaho State University.

Panoramic photograph taken about 1922 by Todd Photographic. View looks straight northeast (so-called "East") along West Center Street. The old General Hospital is the white building west of the Portneuf River, at the corner of South Johnson and West Center. The Riverside hotel is south of West Center, west of the river. Note that houses line both banks of the still-natural Portneuf River. Red Hill can be seen on the right with the Academy of Idaho to the left of it. Note the coal smoke and cinders generated by the coal-fired steam engines of that time. The Union Pacific heating plant chimney is on the skyline to the left, with shop area immediately to the right.
The new Pocatello High School, rebuilt after the 1914 fire, can be seen to the right of the chimney. The large black structure on the horizon just to the right is the new coal tipple. The spire of St Joseph's Catholic church and walled compound can be seen to the left of the chimney. Abe Lillibridge collection, Idaho State University.

At left: Panoramic view of Pocatello in 1895 (population 4,000), from the west, along Highland Drive (leading to the West (Valleyview) Bench). Red Hill occupies the middle right distance. Chink's Peak is in the right skyline with Camelback Mountain behind and to its left. The Portneuf River meanders through marshy ground, which in 1899 was developed into a hydroelectric dam and race. In the early 20th century, houses and Raymond Park were built on the river flood plain. This unwise construction of homes led to repeated flood damage, first in 1911 and periodically until 1963. A concrete channel was built along the Portneuf by the U.S. Army Corps of Engineers and finished in 1965.
The fenced compound between the city and the river surrounds St. Joseph's Catholic Church, school, and convent. Pocatello High School, built in 1894, is the largest building on the west side of the tracks. Photo from Abe Lillibridge collection, Idaho State University.

Treaties and Enlargement of Pocatello

By the time the Treaty of May 27, 1887, was signed, which resulted in the Act of September 1, 1888, affirming the use of Indian lands by the Utah & Northern Railway Company and setting aside a townsite for Pocatello, Oregon Short Line Railway Company and Utah & Northern Railway Company together were occupying about 63 acres for right of way, shops and related facilities. An additional 150 acres were provided for by the Treaty. Included in the treaty and Act of Congress was recognition of the Utah & Northern right-of-way for which Oregon Short Line paid to the United States $7,621.04, at approximately $8.00 an acre. In addition, it paid $13,182.72 for the additional right-of-way and land acquired under the Treaty.

Also included in the 1888 Act of Congress were almost 50 acres for a reservoir and pipeline from City Creek to the railroad right of way. This right-of-way reverted to the U.S. Government in 1992, and a parkway, connecting downtown with the Portneuf Greenway system was constructed, starting in 1996.

Surrounding the railroad premises was the townsite of Pocatello, consisting of 1,840 acres, less the land occupied by the railroads. The townsite plat contained no parkland and did not acknowledge that the Portneuf River meandered through its flood plain in the middle of town. The river is not indicated on the plat. The individual lots contained in the townsite were surveyed and sold at public auction in 1891, though it was understood that persons already in possession were to have first choice. Under the 1888 Act, lots not sold at auction became part of the public domain, subject to purchase by the public. Accordingly, permanent buildings began to be erected throughout the townsite prior to the 1891 auction. Photographs of downtown Pocatello taken in 1889 show many large, permanent buildings. Even after the auction, there was an almost immediate need for the new town to expand, but it could not because the lands surrounding the townsite were reservation property.

Reduction of Area of the Fort Hall Indian Reservation

The original Fort Hall Reservation had approximately 1,500,000 acres; the first reduction was contained in a treaty entered into between the Indians and the government in 1880 but not ratified by Congress until February 23, 1889, restoring the southern one-third of the reservation to the public domain.

View looking east at the Pacific Hotel in the middle of the railroad tracks, taken from the corner of Arthur and West Center, about 1894. Note the covered wagon. The Cook Building is the stone structure with the turrets on the south side of West Center. Maag Drug occupies this building in 1996. The short peaked steeple on the north side of the road is the Congregational Church with its bell, the first church bell in Pocatello, installed in about 1890. Photo from Abe Lillibridge collection, Idaho State University.

View looking east from the 400 Block of West Center Street from near the Arthur Street intersection, downtown Pocatello, about 1916. This picture is taken about one block west of the one above; note the north end of the Pacific Hotel has been removed to allow construction of the Center Street viaduct. The original Bannock Hotel is on the right. The second, seven-story hotel that became a city landmark, was torn down in 1982. Simplot Square now occupies the spot. Note Center Street viaduct, built in 1911 and replaced with the present subway in 1934. The newly constructed Kane Building is the light-colored stone structure on the south side of the 300 Block of West Center. Photo from Abe Lillibridge collection, Idaho State University.

Land run in Pocatello, 12:30 p.m., June 17, 1902. Photo by G. Leonard. This line up is near Fredregill Rd. on the south side of Pocatello. This land run opened southern Bannock County to settlement by whites. Bannock County Historical Society Collection.

View of the north side of the 200 block of West Center Street, about 1914. The Hub Building on the corner is now (1993) occupied by The Paris women's clothing store. The building on the extreme right is the Bannock National Bank, now occupied by the First National Bar. Note the sign on the front of the Monarch Hotel building in the center of the block. Bannock County Historical Society Collection.

View looking west on West Center, about 1890. The Hub Building is on the right hand side. The next cross street is Main (then Cleveland Avenue). The Pioneer Building is southeast of the intersection of West Center and Main. Bannock County Historical Society Collection.

The Oregon Short Line right of way was sold in 1882. Pocatello townsite and the Utah & Northern right of way were removed in 1888. The next major reduction was by an 1898 treaty, which was ratified in 1900, removing the middle third of the Reservation upon proclamation by the president. This proclamation was issued by President Theodore Roosevelt in 1902, causing a land rush in the area surrounding Pocatello and south to McCammon.

Rapid Growth in the 1890s

Although the townsite had not yet been surveyed nor the lots sold, a government was provided for the future town by the commissioners of Bingham County on April 29, 1889. In 1889 the two railroads merged, becoming known as the Oregon Short Line and Utah & Northern Railway Company. Growth was rapid and by 1893, a new county, Bannock, was carved out of Bingham County by the State Legislature, with Pocatello as its county seat.

Southwest is West; Southeast is South

The railroad line ran through Pocatello townsite in a south-easterly to north-westerly direction and when the streets of Pocatello were laid out, they followed the railroad configuration, resulting in some confusion throughout the years. We follow custom in this book, referring to the northwest-southeast streets as running North-South, and the northeast-southwest streets as running East-West.

View of the 100 block of South Main Street looking north, August 1913. Both horse-drawn and internal combustion vehicles are on the street. The Nicolet (Whitman) Hotel occupies the tall light-colored building. The Palm Cafe (originally the Wrensted Building) to the right of the hotel was destroyed by a windstorm in June, 1992. The site was rebuilt in 1993 as the Continental Bistro. The Pioneer Building is on the southeast corner of Center and Main. In 1996 the downtown U.S. Post Office branch was relocated there. The Petersen Furniture building can be seen in the distance on the east side of Main. This street was, until 1906, called Cleveland Ave., but the name was changed because of retrospective political animosity toward the Democrat, the only man to be twice President. Bannock County Historical Society Collection.

The Legacy of No Urban Planning

In his reminiscences of life in territorial Idaho just before statehood, Oscar Sonnenkalb, a surveyor and civil engineer, commented on the layout of Pocatello with vitriolic language. The practice of building on either side of the railroad established, in effect, two competing villages, laid out without regard to drainage, natural barriers or the desirability of providing streets where buildings would have the "desirable equal chance for morning and afternoon sunlight."

> Pocatello Townsite, Sonnenkalb charged, was laid out with little foresight because the plans were not worked out by practical civil engineers but by clerks in the Land Office,
>
> ".... who, without doubt were not interested in the advantages of a sensible city place for the coming generations, but divided up the donated land mechanically into streets and blocks along the Rail road tracks without providing for a practical width of business street, park reservations along the river banks, or in any other part of the extensive selected city terrain, without paying attention to the drainage of the ground, or the rocky surface of the ground west of the river, etc." (Harstad, 1972, p. 11)

Visitors often comment on the narrow streets of Pocatello, but both Pocatello and Idaho Falls were laid out with them. That was the norm in city planning at that time. The lack of parkland along the river banks has remained a blight on the ambiance of downtown Pocatello.

Naming the Streets of Downtown

The matter of naming the streets tells us something of the political character of the early town. At the outset, streets paralleling the railroad were named for presidents, beginning with the current president, Harrison, next to the right-of-way, and moving westerly by earlier presidents in a reverse order, that is, Cleveland, Arthur, Garfield and so forth. The equivalent streets east of the railroad were given number designations, viz. 1st, 2nd, 3rd, etc. East-west cross streets on both sides of the tracks were given letter designations, A, B, C, etc.

By 1906, the growing municipality felt the need to require the numbering of buildings to facilitate "free" mail delivery and to give some streets more appropriate names. The east-west street designations were changed from letters to the names of early explorers, trappers, generals, railroad officials and the like, which

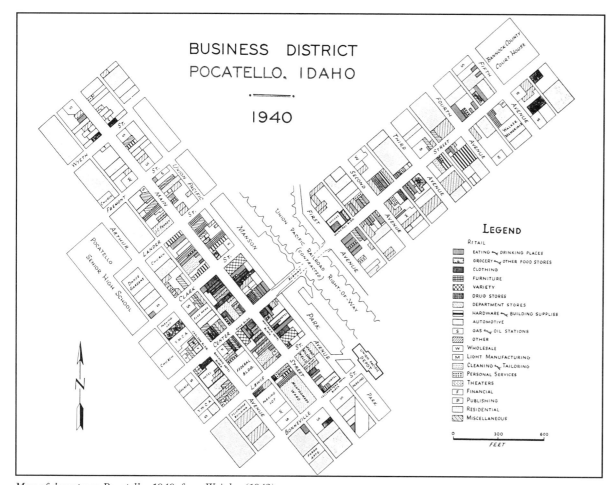

BUSINESS DISTRICT
POCATELLO, IDAHO

1940

LEGEND

RETAIL

	EATING and DRINKING PLACES
	GROCERY and OTHER FOOD STORES
	CLOTHING
	FURNITURE
	VARIETY
	DRUG STORES
	DEPARTMENT STORES
	HARDWARE and BUILDING SUPPLIES
	AUTOMOTIVE
S	GAS and OIL STATIONS
	OTHER
W	WHOLESALE
M	LIGHT MANUFACTURING
	CLEANING and TAILORING
	PERSONAL SERVICES
	THEATERS
F	FINANCIAL
P	PUBLISHING
	RESIDENTIAL
	MISCELLANEOUS

0   300   600
FEET

Map of downtown Pocatello, 1940, from Wrigley (1942).

Early 1920s postcard of Main Street, Pocatello, looking north near the intersection with Lewis. On the left is the Benson Hotel. On the right is the present Station Square, then the Fargo-Wilson-Wells Department Store, which housed the bus depot and the Western Union office. Bannock County Historical Society Collection.

View looking north from East Center Street at the Bannock County Courthouse in foreground and Bonneville School in background, about 1903. Note the lack of trees. The Courthouse was built in 1902, added onto in 1913 and razed in 1955. It occupied what is now the parking lot of the new courthouse, which was built in front of it. The school (on the present site of the U.S. Post Office) was built in 1895 and razed in the early 1960s. The Bear Lake County Courthouse (still standing in Paris) has the same architectural design as the old Bannock County Courthouse. Bannock County Historical Society Collection.

names they still bear. One American president was slighted in the naming of Pocatello's streets. As already noted, the street next to Harrison was Cleveland. In 1906, a Republican city council responded to a petition signed by every merchant along Cleveland Avenue by changing its name to Main Street. Not only that, but in later years a plat annexed to the north side of town bore the names of the presidents following Harrison, and although the next president in time was Cleveland, the new plat picked up the president names with McKinley, so that the man who was president twice does not have a street named after him in Pocatello.

Dusty Streets and a City Divided

The problems faced by the young town were those of all frontier communities. The fine loess soil produced clouds of dust when wagons rolled over dry streets. The streets were not paved so it was necessary to water the streets to keep the dust down. However the city water supply was privately controlled and little water was made available for this purpose. Sidewalks were slow in coming.

The only way to cross the tracks between the two sides of town was by using at-grade crossings. Because of the number of trains using this busy terminal, it was hazardous to cross the tracks, especially for school children. Coal smoke from steam engines was always in the air and cinders found their way into every nook and cranny.

Parade of Indians cross the railroad from the east on Lander Street, 1904. Indians in full regalia often participated in 4th of July Parades. They usually camped on the east side of the tracks near between Lander and Fremont Streets. Bannock County Historical Society Collection.

Looking south towards Center Street, in the 100 block of Front Street (North 1st Ave.), about 1892. This was the rough side of town in the early years, and the interface with the Indian Reservation. Notice that the businesses are generally saloons and restaurants. The Wood River Restaurant is a long way from the Wood River. The Chinese compound and the walled city were one block south of Center on the east side of First Ave. The Phoenix Building stands at the southeast corner of First Ave. and East Center at the far right of the photo, Bannock County Historical Society Collection.

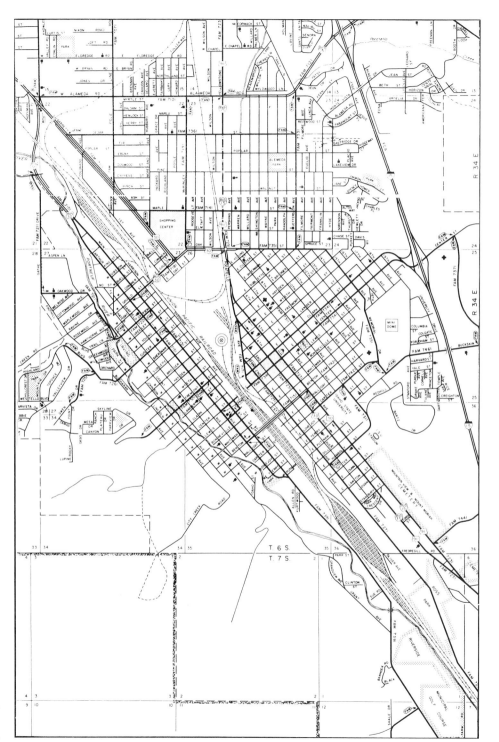

1992 map of the central Pocatello area, elevation 4,461. 1990 population of the metropolitan area (including Chubbuck) was 53,701. The area north of Oak Street was the original city of Alameda. Map from Idaho Transportation Department.

East end of Center Street Viaduct, spring 1914. Note the Mansard Roof of the Pacific Hotel, which had to be partly destroyed to make way for the viaduct. The old freight depot is north of the Pacific Hotel, with the peaked roof. The right angle bend was required by East Center Street merchants who feared they would be cut off from business if the east slope of the structure were continued to street level. Pocatello economic development has always been difficult, and sometimes stupid decisions had lasting impacts. This was one. Bannock County Historical Society Collection.

Pluralism

At the turn of the century "Downtown" was on the west side of the tracks, as were the best residences and several churches. On the east side there were more commercial establishments, many being of a kind not desired on the west side, such as the "walled city" red-light district, a number of saloons and houses of minorities. Being a railroad town, in the 1910s and 1920s Pocatello became a city of cultural diversity with communities of Blacks, Greeks, Italians, and Chinese. This mosaic flavor remains today, with the addition of University Professors.

The Center Street Viaduct

The Center Street Viaduct and the Halliday Street Subway were built in 1911 by the Union Pacific Railroad, on contract to the city of Pocatello, to allow traffic to cross the tracks without danger or interference with railroad operations. The viaduct opened Oct. 3, 1911, and the subway in August, 1911. The viaduct was replaced with the present subway in 1934.

Congregational Church

The Congregational Church was the first church in Pocatello. Its history is recorded by Minnie Howard (1927). Starting in 1887, the church met in one of the houses owned by the railroad in Company Row east of

View of West Center Street from Center Street Viaduct, August, 1915. The automobile had taken over personal transportation from the horse. The Kane Building, built in 1915, is the white brick structure on the south side of West Center. The hand written date on the photo is incorrect. Bannock County Historical Society Collection.

Parade with Santa Claus at the head on the west side of the Center Street Viaduct, December, 1913. Picture taken from the corner of Center and Main. The Hub Building is on the left, and the Pioneer Building is on the right. Bannock County Historical Society Collection.

West side of Center Street Viaduct over the Union Pacific tracks, summer 1912. This viaduct was the source of the term "going over town." Note the Indian riding a horse accompanied by his dog on the sidewalk. Three early motorcars are on the crest of the bridge. The Pacific Hotel (reduced in size) can be seen north of the viaduct. Bannock County Historical Society Collection.

View of east side of Center Street Viaduct, 1914. Eastbound traffic off the viaduct made a right turn and a full clockwise circle under the viaduct to get back onto East Center. Westbound traffic turned north on 1st Ave. and then back south on an on-ramp to get onto the viaduct. The Phoenix Building is to the right of East Center. The Pocatello House Hotel with the pointed cap is east of it. The building with the gabled top was the Pocatello Opera House, which burned in 1899 and was rebuilt as an auditorium. It now is occupied by Southeast Furniture Store. The gable is no longer there. The Commercial Hotel (later the Keystone Hotel) is the large building on the north side of East Center. Bannock County Historical Society Collection.

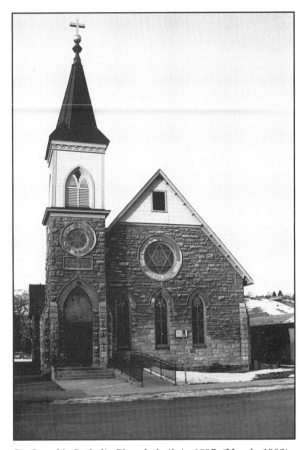

St. Joseph's Catholic Church, built in 1897, (March, 1993).

Trinity St. Andrew's Episcopal Church, built in 1898 in Gothic Style. First stone Episcopal Church in Idaho, (March, 1993).

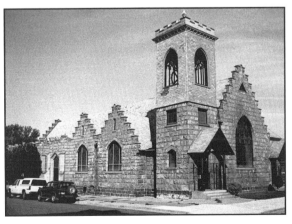

First Congregational Church, Pocatello, Idaho, built in 1894 with rear addition added in 1928, (March, 1993).

Harrison Avenue. The first sermon by a Congregational minister took place at 145 North Harrison on February 24, 1888. Formal organization of the Congregational Church took place on July 8, 1888, with 13 charter members.

On November 10, 1888, construction was commenced on a separate church building on West Center Street by the alley between Cleveland (now Main) and Arthur Avenues. This was a small structure, only 22 x 36 feet, but it had a steeple, built in 1890, to house the first church bell in Pocatello.

Need for a larger building was apparent and under the direction of Rev. C.W. Luck, lots were purchased where the present church stands, at the northwest corner of North Garfield and Lander, despite objections that this was "too far out" of town. The new church was occupied in 1894 and enlarged in 1928.

Aerial view of the Pocatello West Bench and location of Pocatello water department. At end of the straight gravel road is the reservoir built by James Murray, which provided Pocatello's water as a private company until 1916. The reservoir north of the road was built in 1892. The large white structure south of the circular tank was built in 1935, but leaked and was not used long. A new State women's prison was built in 1994 on the site south of the water buildings. City Creek, the source of the first Union Pacific water supply is on the right side of the view. A right-of-way for a water pipeline was provided for in the Act of 1888, (June, 1991).

St. Joseph's Catholic Church

Catholicism was the most successful European religion in the western United States during the early fur trapping period. In efforts to convert Native Americans to the white man's religion, Catholics were much more successful than Protestants, the trappings and mysticism being more attractive than the straight-laced Calvinist doctrine. Beginning with the missionary zeal of Father Pierre Jean De Smet in 1840, there was a strong Catholic presence among the Pioneers, the railroad workers and the early settlers in Idaho Territory.

An Idaho Vicariate was formed in Boise in the 1860s and this church served the religious needs of Idaho Catholics in the Pocatello area until 1889. At that time, a small church was erected in the 100 block of South Garfield. In 1891, the present properties where St. Joseph's Church and Convent are located were obtained, but the church on South Garfield continued to be used and a parochial school was conducted in the building beginning in 1892.

The small church could not accommodate the school and growing church attendance and in 1896 ground was broken on the present property for a permanent church which was completed and dedicated in 1897.

Growth was constant and in 1914, St. Anthony Church was built on the east side (the ethnic side) of town. In 1919, ground was broken for a school building and convent next to St. Joseph's church.

The Need for Water in a Semi-Desert City

Early Pocatello used the Portneuf River for all its water needs. Hemmed in by the reservation, and severely so until 1888, the railroad junction had other problems than a pure source of water. Since the site was a barren sagebrush flat and covered with fine loess soil, the perennial late summer winds made it a dusty and scruffy place.

Pocatello Portrait and the Water System

The book "Pocatello Portrait" by H. Leigh Gittins, chronicles the early history of the city and especially the water system. A group supported by banker James A. Murray of Butte, Montana developed the first water supply in Pocatello in 1892, from Gibson Jack and Mink Creeks. Parts of the flume can be still seen on the north side of Mink Creek. A reservoir was built on the West Bench, and trees were planted. After fifteen years, this had become a "beautiful park-like area." In 1893, the city attempted to buy the system from Murray, but the matter was defeated by the city council. As was predicted at the time, this was an expensive mistake for the growing city. Murray was never anxious to spend his money to upgrade the system and conflict continued for twenty years.

In 1898, an outbreak of typhoid fever caused alarm, as did the customary finding of dead gophers, toads, and rotting debris in the screens in the reservoir. In 1898 the City Council established water rates favorable to Mr. Murray, and for a time he and his water superintendent George Winter, took better care of his system. In 1899, the city council passed an ordinance to contract for sprinkling of parts of the downtown streets. Since no one had water meters, excessive use could not be controlled, and summertime water shortages were standard procedure. A fire during a time of low water pressure would have been disastrous. The Union Pacific Railroad provided water from Batiste Springs west of town during emergencies.

Droughts and Urban Conflict, 1900s Style

The droughts of 1900 and 1901 caused enmity. Water system owner Murray at times was stubborn and intransigent. The poor quality and uncertain quantity of water provided by Murray's water system was a recurring concern. To prevent problems like those of August, 1903, when two full bands of sheep were found bedded down on the intake dam on Mink Creek, the Pocatello Forest Reserve was established later that year around the headwaters of Gibson Jack, Mink, Cusick, and City Creeks. However periodic drought and lack of maintenance remained troublesome. The flood of January, 1911, was a catastrophe, especially after the dry year of 1910. A lynch mob or "posse" was sent to the water reservoir in August, 1911, after Superintendent Winter had fired shots at a deputy sheriff. Winter was arrested quietly, and eventually convicted of resisting an officer. A major building boom began in 1913, but concerns over inadequate water supplies continued.

Fire destroys Pocatello High School, December, 16, 1914, two years before the city obtained control of its water system. After this fire and a severe drought in 1915, fire underwriters refused to insure the city because of low water pressure. The new Pocatello High School was built on the same spot, and opened two years later, in 1916. A major addition, including the gymnasium, was built in 1939. Bannock County Historical Society Collection.

Pocatello Warehouse district, 1920s. The vehicles represent a sample of those used by Garrett's Transfer and Storage Co. Photograph by Cook Photography, Bannock County Historical Society Collection.

Dedication of Union Pacific baseball field, 1929. Ballpark was located at the southwest corner of Oak and Yellowstone. Photograph by Cook Photography, Bannock County Historical Society Collection.

Pocatello around 1926, looking northwest from Bannock Hotel toward Howard Mountain and Trail Creek Pass. First Ward L.D.S. church is across the street with its recreation hall under construction. Next to it is a service station operated here until the mid 1930s. The building with the "1916" is the Pocatello Tribune building, north of it is the Railroad YMCA. Pocatello High School is farther north. Across the street is the Congregational Church, and in the distance is the spire of St. Joseph's Catholic Church. Behind it is the rectangular white Idaho Power Company substation. The Brentwood (Wooley) Apartments, with their complex system of bay windows, are in the middle of the view on Hayes and Lander. The Carnegie Library and mirror-image Methodist Church are in the left foreground. In the extreme left, middle distance is the flat roof of the Bogert Chevrolet building, recently finished, on West Center between Hayes and Grant, Photograph by Cook Photography, Bannock County Historical Society Collection.

Downtown Pocatello, looking southeast from the Bannock Hotel in early 1934 or 1935. The Center Street Subway is in use; it was dedicated in January, 1934. The white building in the left middle, on the east side of Main Street, is the Hotel Nicollet, later renamed the Hotel Whitman, which still operates. On the extreme left is the rear of the Kane Building. The Ford Pool Hall is south of the Whitman Hotel. The Kress Building is relatively new. The Block Building (now the Brokerage) at the corner of West Lewis and South Main was not constructed. The Fargo-Wilson-Wells Department Store (F.W.W.) occupies what is now Station Square. Kiddy corner from this was the Capitol Theater. The Yellowstone Hotel stands at the corner of Main and Bonneville. Across Main Street from Fargo's is the Hotel Benson and south of it is the Montgomery Ward store. The chimney in the right foreground is on the Federal Building at the corner of South Arthur and West Lewis. Note weather station on right. A parking lot now occupies the site of the Orpheum Theater.

The Oregon Short Line Depot, built in 1915, stands as a monument to the importance of the railroad to the city. Across the tracks on the roof of a long railroad freight dock is the name Pocatello, a north arrow, and an indication of the direction to the airport, five miles away. Such "roof-art" was required in the 1930s to help early pilots find where they were, and show the direction to the airport.

Beyond the railway on the left side of the view are the Phoenix Building and the Porters and Waiters Hotel. Across Center Street is a "Bee Hive" sign, on a building later used for the Pocatello City Offices and Block's Department Store. The Keystone Hotel is east of it. The Auditorium Theater (with broad peaked roof) is south of Center and across from the Keystone. The sharp peaked roof beyond it is the Pocatello House Hotel at east Center and 2nd Avenue.

In the right distance are the University of Idaho, Southern Branch, Red Hill with small quarry, and on the skyline, Chinks Peak, named for Chinese miners after the turn of the century.

Photograph by Cook Photography, Bannock County Historical Society Collection.

At left: Same view as above, mid 1930s. A new gas station has been built at the corner of Garfield and Center. The Congregational Church addition has been built and the First Ward recreational hall is complete. The Downard Funeral Home has been built across Lander Street from the Congregational Church, but the Pocatello High School addition, completed in 1939, has not yet been started. The Trail Creek power line has been built, probably because of completion of the American Falls Dam, but there are no homes yet on the West Bench. Both photographs by Cook Photography, Bannock County Historical Society Collection.

Establishment of a Public Water System

The city took James Murray and company to court over rates and finally, in 1914, won ownership of the water company. A water bond was passed August 26, 1914. However, appeals of the decision to the Idaho Supreme Court and intransigence by Murray delayed city possession until 1916. Water meters were installed shortly thereafter.

Water Meters and Annexation of Alameda

Some progress comes slowly in Idaho. In 1996, much of what had been the town of Alameda still did not have water meters in private houses, pursuant to an agreement made when Alameda was consolidated with Pocatello in 1962. The mayor of Alameda at the time was George Hansen, later long-time congressman and convicted felon. The annexation made Pocatello, for a short time, Idaho's largest city. Boise immediately annexed ground on its perimeter and regained first place.

The Bannock Range

"Looking to the southward (from Ferry Butte), one sees the city of Pocatello nestled among the beautiful hills, and beyond the Bannock Mountains . . ." Susie Boice Trego, (*in* Brown, 1932, p. 429).

Although many in Idaho and even some in Pocatello, do not know this, the Portneuf River area contains a great diversity of natural settings where birds and wildlife may be seen through all twelve months. Glenn Ray Downing's 1991 book "Days Out Of Doors" contains a year's cycle of vignettes on nature close to Pocatello. Despite years of industrial abuse, the Portneuf Valley remains a gentle and beautiful place.

The Fort Hall Canal and Syringa Elementary School, looking south toward Kinport Peak and the Bannock Range, (June, 1992).

View looking northeast from dance pavillion above South Lincoln St., 1922 or 1923. The photo must have been taken on a Sunday morning, as the streets are empty. Even so the lack of cars is remarkable. Perhaps residents were requested to move them? Perhaps streets were built first and the cars came later? Most of Pocatello's downtown buildings had been constructed. The Bannock Hotel is prominent in the middle of the view. The Union Pacific smokestack and power plant are in full operation. The smokestack, visible from all over town, still stands, unused, as a symbol of early days in Pocatello and the Union Pacific Railroad. The Center Street viaduct is in the middle of the view. Emerson School is in the lower right, with the Portneuf River behind it. Note that buildings have been constructed as close to the river as possible, with no allowance for the flood plain. Indeed, surveyed lots of the original Pocatello townsite, carved from the Fort Hall Indian Reservation in 1891, are strictly rectangular, parallel to the railroad. The original plat does not include the Portneuf River and many lots go across the river. As pointed out by Oscar Sonnenkalb, such an urban design without any account for the natural terrain could only have been done by the Federal Government from afar. Since the land was removed from the Indian Reservation, the Federal Government, rather than local business, determined how the city would be laid out. Sadly for Pocatello, this mistake was a permanent one. The river is now hemmed in not only by private property, but by a concrete flood control channel built to protect that private property. Photograph by Cook Photography, Bannock County Historical Society Collection.

Mountain View Cemetery and the Bannock Range from Red Hill. At the foot of the hill, the Fort Hall Canal until the mid-1980s provided cool relief for joggers and their dogs. Progress dictated that the water be put underground.
In the distance, from south to north, are Scout Mountain, Indian Peak, and Portneuf Narrows, the Gateway to the Pacific Northwest, (July, 1992).

Public Water and Growth before World War I

With public ownership of the municipal water supply in 1916, growth was facilitated. The Pocatello water case was a benchmark in the early years of the Idaho Public Utilities Commission, but the lasting solution to Pocatello's water problems did not come until 1926, when the first city well was drilled at what is now Lower Ross Park. The Pocatello water system uses several wells to tap the Portneuf River Aquifer, which easily has sufficient capacity for today's use. Even during prolonged drought years the levels of the city wells historically have dropped only a few feet.

The Fort Hall Canal

In 1907, Idaho Senator Fred T. Dubois, who had risen to power by advocating and exploiting anti-Mormon laws of the 1880s, helped negotiate the building of the Fort Hall Canal, which would provide water by May, 1911, to 14,000 acres of Indian land and 12,000 acres of land ceded to whites. The canal ran along Hiline road, through the east side of Pocatello, along the alley between 5th and 6th Avenues, across the Idaho State University campus and behind Mountain View Cemetery. It is an interesting geographic fact that this water comes from the Blackfoot River rather than from Ross Fork or the Portneuf.

Frank Paradice

Frank C. Paradice, Jr. was Pocatello's foremost architect in the first half of the 20th century. Paradice designed or redesigned most of the buildings in downtown Pocatello between 1913 and 1952. These include the Valentine Building (former First Security Bank), Fargo Building (Station Square), Central Building (Harrison's Jewelers), the Old Federal Building (Dudley's), and Pocatello High School. Paradice was a master of the Art Deco and Neoclassical Revival styles.

The Standrod House

A majestic house on the west side of Pocatello is on the National Register of Historic Places. Built in classical revival style, the two-story, turreted castle cost around $12,000 to build in 1902, at a time when a dollar was a dollar. The 16 room structure is faced with stone which was quarried in the McCammon area. After a period of little use, the City of Pocatello acquired the house in 1974 and it was available to rent for special events until 1995. Because it was not handicapped-accessible it was sold in 1995, and is presently occupied by the Backroom furniture store.

The Standrod House was built by Judge D.W. Standrod. Standrod was born in Kentucky in 1858, and lived first in Idaho in Malad City where he was associated with banks. He was a member of the drafting committee for the Idaho Constitutional Convention in 1889. While he ran for several political positions, he was never elected (he was a Republican from a Democratic city). He was, however, a power in Republican politics in eastern Idaho. He served as a district judge in Pocatello.

The Standrod family was prominent in civic and cultural affairs. Mrs. Standrod was active in women's clubs. A daughter who was active in school activities and a

The Standrod House, north Garfield Ave., (June, 1992).

Carnegie Library, Garfield Ave. and Center St., (June, 1992).

leader of her class died at 16, to the great distress of the family. A son, Drew Standrod, Jr., lived in Pocatello for many years and died in 1937. A veteran of World War I, he was a well-known attorney, was musical and a leader in community cultural activities.

The judge died in 1942. The castle passed to his wife, who died in 1946, and the house passed to Drew Jr.'s wife who lived in it for a few years, then moved to the east, boarding up the house. It was sold in 1957 to Mrs. Madelyne Roper who lived in it until she sold it to the city.

The Carnegie Library

In the early 1900s, steel industrialist Andrew Carnegie began a program to encourage education by financing community libraries across the United States. Carnegie was an immigrant from Scotland who had little education but who realized the importance of education, especially for the stream of immigrants who lacked sufficient education to compete in the American job market. His public program furnished libraries for thousands of communities across the country.

Many towns in Idaho have such libraries. The one in Pocatello, at the corner of West Center and South Garfield, was completed in 1907 at a cost of $12,000. The two story structure was larger inside than it appears but the library service outgrew the building prior to World War II. It was not until the 1950s that the city could construct a larger building on East Clark Street to replace the cramped Carnegie facility. In 1994 a new, larger Marshall Public Library was built on the original site, attached to the original Carnegie Library. The Bannock County Historical Museum occupied the old library building until its grand new home in Ross Park was completed in 1990.

The initial Carnegie Library was a city service, administered by an appointed library board and full-salaried librarian. The first board chairman was Judge F.S. Dietrich. Dr. Minnie Howard, prominent Pocatello physician, historian and women's rights advocate, who lived just next door to the structure, where the new library now stands, also was a member of the first board.

In the 1910s a matching structure was erected across from the library on the east side of South Garfield as a Methodist Church. It, too, was outgrown and was replaced in the late 1950s by the present church at the corner of North 15th and East Clark. The original structure no longer exists.

Hydroelectric Power

In 1892 Daniel Swinehart built a 60 kw power plant and mill at 1000 N. Grant, near Irving Junior High School.

The power house in the picture below was built in 1899, and owned by the Pocatello Power and Irrigation Company. It was located at the corner of West Wyeth and North Johnson, and had a capacity of 100 kw. The dam backed up a reservoir in the area of the present Memorial Building which was a park, and used for skating in the winter. The Rainey Park area was also flooded and the ice harvested for refrigeration. In 1902 the power plant was sold to the American Falls Power, Light and Water Company. In 1915 all power companies were acquired by what was to become Idaho Power Company, and operations were moved to the

Pocatello Power and Irrigation Company dam, looking south after 1899. The mill building still stands on the corner of North Johnson and West Wyeth Street where a footbridge crosses the river. Bannock County Historical Society Collection.

Snake River at American Falls. In 1926 the American Falls Dam was built.

Floods in the Portneuf Valley

The Portneuf River, occupying the channel of the Bonneville Flood, and following the path first carved by Bear River, in summer is quiet, muddy, and easily waded. However, it has repeatedly flooded the downtown Pocatello area. The floods have been caused either by heavy winter rains in January and February on snow-covered and frozen ground, or by high runoff of the melted snowpack in May. After two successive February floods, in 1962 and 1963, Pocatello City and Bannock County requested the help of the U.S. Army Corps of Engineers. The Corps designed and built (in 1965) the concrete flood control channel which now winds through the west side of downtown Pocatello.

This channel, functional though it may be, is a scar on the tree-lined neighborhoods of the west side and an albatross around the image of Pocatello as a beautiful city nestled against the southeast Idaho mountains. The open sewer or river channel remains, stark, fenced, and sterile, but it cannot be easily removed, since it belongs to the U.S. Government, was built to highest

Flood on the east side of the 100 block of South First Ave., January 1911, caused by a rapid thaw and rainstorm. The floodwaters came west from the hills at the head of Center Street. The Phoenix Building is on the corner of South First and Center Street. The Rooming House south of it became the Porters and Waiters Club, which was owned by a black man and one of the only places that transient blacks could stay in Pocatello at that time. Bannock County Historical Society Collection.

engineering standards, and does an excellent job of controlling floods.

Pocatello: Idaho's Industrial City

Pocatello located at the mouth of Portneuf Narrows for reasons of transportation, and has always been a transportation and industrial center. It remains, in 1996, the only truly industrial community in Idaho. Processing plants using phosphate rock from the mountains to the east employ hundreds. Many light industries are found in Pocatello, serving all of eastern Idaho. There is still a sizable blue collar work force.

Pocatello is also unique in that it has ethnic communities who have lived there for many decades. These groups came with the railroad, and stayed through labor disputes and layoffs, and now serve to make Pocatello ethnically and racially diverse, another anomaly in Idaho.

Reflecting this blue collar and ethnic population base, Pocatello generally has elected Democrats to the State Legislature although the area outside Pocatello and indeed most of the state is traditionally strongly Republican. This political fact has contributed, in recurrent manner, to the general fact that in Idaho, Pocatello and Idaho State University get State programs last.

Aerial view looking east, of the phosphate plants west of Pocatello. The FMC elemental phosphorous plant is in the foreground with the J.R. Simplot Company phosphate fertilizer plant (with the white domes) in the background. Waste products or "slag" from these plants were used until the 1990s to surface the streets of Pocatello. This practice was stopped because of concerns over health hazards related to the higher than normal background content of radioactive minerals in the slag, (July, 1990).

The Anhauser-Busch Clydesdale Horses and Wagon on display on South First Avenue, looking northwest, in the summer of 1934. Clothing styles are typical of the Depression Era. The fellow pushing a big stomach, wearing a hat, is obviously the Boss. The occasion probably was a 4th of July Parade.

Note the "N.R.A." blue eagle signs on both the beer wagon and the north window of the Idaho Wholesale Company. The National Recovery Act was one of President Franklin Delano Roosevelt's New Deal programs for economic recovery. It was adopted in 1933 and declared unconstitutional in 1935. This type of ruling by the Supreme Court caused Roosevelt to propose a "court-packing" constitutional amendment to enlarge the Court. This was not approved by Congress. But it accomplished its purpose of liberalizing the Court. Photograph by Cook Photography, Bannock County Historical Society Collection.

FMC elemental phosphorous plant, Pocatello, (August, 1990).

Phosphate ore delivery system at FMC plant west of Pocatello. After the black shale ore is piled up, this wheel delivers it to conveyor belts at the appropriate rate needed by plant facilities, (August, 1990).

Bonneville School, 7th Ave. and East Clark St., just before it was torn down to build U.S. Post Office, Spring, early 1960's. Christy and Ricky Cuoio in foreground. Note ball in the Air! Photograph by Fred Cuoio.

Union Pacific yard and shop facilities from Sherman to Lander Streets (left to right). The white building east of Harrison Ave. is Edd Bailey Hall, a retired railroad workers' gathering place named for a former President of the railroad. The site of the Ramsey Transfer was directly south of Edd Bailey Hall. The parking lots west of the railroad define the original right of way. "Company Row" was located east of North Harrison Ave., South of Edd Bailey Hall. The original steam engine turntable remains in the middle of the railroad facilities, but the roundhouse, the steam engines and the coal smoke are gone. A connector to the Union Pacific Montana mainline runs north in front of the white grain elevator.

Downtown Pocatello, from Fremont to Lewis Streets. Main Street (by rights "Cleveland Ave.") is in the lower part of the photo. The large white-roofed building west of Main Street between Clark and Lander is the Chief Theater, destroyed by fire on March 20, 1993. The Center Street underpass is in the lower right center of the photo. The corner of Center and Main is generally thought of as the "center" of town.

The Pacific Hotel was located on Center Street, between the railroad tracks, from 1883 to 1915. For the first 30 years of their city, Pocatellans crossed the railroad at grade in front of the Pacific Hotel, at risk of life and limb. In 1911 a viaduct was built over the tracks and the south half of the Pacific Hotel was demolished. The viaduct was replaced by the present underpass in 1934.

On the east side of the tracks is "Newtown," traditionally the "rough" side of town. The Center 151 Building on Third Ave. between Center and Clark Streets and the new Federal Building and U.S. Court House on Fourth Ave. between Bonneville and Whitman, were built in the mid-20th century, part of a process of "gentrification." They supplanted the ethnic neighborhoods that had existed on the east side of the tracks.

Simplot Square, built on the site of the Bannock Hotel, and dedicated in 1989, (March, 1992).

Sequence of Aerial Views of Downtown Pocatello

Center to Benton Streets, in the center, the Union Pacific Railway Station is at the end of West Bonneville. The original railroad right-of-way extended west to Harrison Avenue, directly in front of the station. The offices of the railroad, in 1996, share this grand building, built in 1915, with facilities of Amtrak, which has operated the national rail passenger network since 1971. The Pacific Greyhound Building, built on the original right-of-way by the Union Pacific during World War II, is in front of and south of the train station. It replaced a bus station in what is now Station Square (the Fargo building) at the corner of West Lewis and South Main. The Yellowstone Hotel stands on the northeast corner of West Bonneville and South Main.

The Idaho Division dispatchers' office for the railroad was located in the park area immediately north of the train station. In 1989, the entire Union Pacific and Missouri Pacific dispatching system was centralized at Omaha, Nebraska. Dispatchers are but one of several categories of railroad jobs that Pocatello has lost to centralization.

Note the triangular building left (north) of the off ramp to the Benton Street bridge. This building (the Elk's Club) conforms to the right-of-way for a water pipeline granted to Oregon Short Line in the Act of 1888. Part of the network of parks of the Portneuf Greenway will be built on this right-of-way.

East of the tracks, between Lewis and Bonneville Streets and First and Second Avenues, was the location of the walled city (red light district). This was also the ethnic side of town, the only places where Black, Chinese, and European immigrant railroad workers could rent a room in the early 20th century. The north end of the Warehouse district occupies the area immediately east of the tracks from Bonneville Street to the south. Note several buildings built with a triangular shape because of railroad sidings, now long gone. A small rectangular building with a black roof north of Lewis Street is the Shaw Building, originally built to house the telephone office. The former Pocatello City Police Station (hidden by trees) is across Lewis Street from the Shaw Building.

Pocatello Warehouse district from Benton to Dillon Streets. South Fifth Avenue and Idaho State University are at the upper edge of the view. Benton Street Overpass is on the left. The Halliday Street Subway was one block south of the overpass, and was closed when the overpass was opened in 1966.

Fire destroys Chief Theater in downtown Pocatello, predawn March 20, 1993. The Chief was built in 1937.

North to South (Left to Right), May, 1992.

Southern Branch of the University of Idaho, 1926. Many of these buildings are now gone. View looks north from Red Hill. On the right is Colonial Hall, under construction. The gabled building is Swanson Hall, before its third floor was added. West of it is the newly completed Frazier Hall, with a flat dark roof and concert hall with rounded east end. Science Hall was not yet built, nor was the L.D.S. Institute, nor the Dispensary. South of Frazier is Turner Hall, a women's dormitory, and east of it is the original Reed Gymnasium.
In the distance to the right is the town of Fairview (Alameda). The dark line at an angle across the right distance is the connector to the Union Pacific Montana Main Line. The dark area past the smoke in right distance is the tie treating plant, which bordered Old Highway 30 near the old Kraft Cheese Plant. Note the newly planted trees in a new subdivision on the northwest end of town. In downtown the Brentwood (Wooley) Apartments and the Bannock Hotel are prominent, as is the Petersen Furniture building on North Main, which still stands. The Center Street Viaduct crosses the railroad in the center of the view. Photograph by Cook Photography, Bannock County Historical Society Collection.

Idaho State University

As Pocatello began to change from the railroad town of the early 1890s to an industrial city, a need was felt in the community for an institution of higher learning. The State University in Moscow was a long way from southeastern Idaho and seemed to have little interest in extending service to such a remote area. There were few public high schools as well. Most students received no education beyond grade school.

Public spirited citizens in Pocatello campaigned for an institution which could fill the needs of the community and after the establishment of Bannock County in 1893, with Pocatello as the county seat, the campaign intensified. Senator Theodore F. Turner from Pocatello drafted a bill entitled "An Act to establish and maintain a school to be called the Academy of Idaho at Pocatello."

The Act provided for a board of trustees, for the sale of bonds for erecting and equipping buildings and made an initial appropriation. The bill was passed unanimously by the Idaho Legislature on February 25, 1901. One of the most noteable trustees was Theo Swanson, for whom Swanson Hall was named.

The Act established the purpose as being the teaching of all the subjects commonly taught in high schools, "including also the various studies pertaining to a good common school education" and it contained a unique provision that its enactment was contingent upon the citizens of Pocatello donating to the board of trustees prior to May 1, 1901, two blocks of land adjacent to each other within the Pocatello townsite. There was considerable maneuvering and posturing over this provision but ultimately four blocks on the far southeast side of

town were donated at the very last minute and the academy was assured. At first the academy served as a high school for students from southeast Idaho, and generally not from Pocatello, since it had its own high school.

A building program was commenced and by the opening bell on September 22, 1902, the Main Building, later called Swanson Hall, was completed. It was modern in every respect. A boy's dormitory, named Faris Hall, was completed in 1903. Room and board cost $16.00 a month. There was no tuition although out-of-state students were charged $5.00 a term.

There were forty students and four teachers at the opening bell but a total of seventy students were enrolled during the term. By the third year of operation, student enrollment was 122 and the faculty had increased to six. By 1906, a girl's dormitory was finished and student enrollment was up to 186, with construction of a mechanical arts building nearly completed. A library was planned and an infirmary constructed by 1907.

Originally, admission was restricted to students who had completed the eighth grade and could pass examinations in arithmetic, grammar, geography, history, reading, spelling and penmanship, or could show latent ability to do the work. In 1905 the Academy inaugurated a preparatory program to encourage the enrollment of students who had not had an eight grade education but were deserving of the opportunity to progress. In 1907, when President John W. Faris was succeeded by President Miles F. Reed, emphasis was placed on technical and teacher training, and preparatory classes.

In 1915, the academy was renamed the Idaho Technical Institute and given a two-fold purpose, as a vocational trade school and a junior college, with emphasis on occupational courses necessary in the industrial town of Pocatello. During the "Tech" period, Reed Gymnasium, Residence and Colonial Halls, Frazier Hall and

Postcard view of the Academy of Idaho from Red Hill before 1910. Swanson Hall, built in 1903, is in the foreground. It was torn down because of foundation failure in 1973. In the background are Howard Mountain, the Union Pacific back shop building, and power plant chimney. Idaho State University Library Collection.

The view of Idaho State University from Red Hill, (June, 1992).

View from Red Hill to the upper ISU campus and the Snake River Plain. The ISU Holt Arena is the prominent building in the right foreground. East Butte is behind the Holt Arena, with Middle Butte farther west and the Lost River Range behind, (October, 1985).

Aerial view to the north in the fall of 1944 toward the newly quarried Red Hill, a football game in progress in the "Spud Bowl," and the original Idaho Technical College airstrip on the site now occupied by the upper University residential neighborhood and Holt Arena. On the campus, Swanson Hall is prominent as is the heating system chimney on the present site of the Liberal Arts Building. The new pharmacy building is on the west side of the campus. Graveley Hall, women's dorms, and the Student Union, now the Administration Building, are northwest of Red Hill, note the CCC ditches on the south side of Red Hill. Abe Lillibridge collection, Idaho State University.

Southern Branch of the University of Idaho Campus, around 1928. On the extreme right is the newly finished Colonial Hall. Closer is Residence Hall, just north of Terry St. The white house-like building in between is the famed hang-out, the College Inn. On the west side of 8th Ave., from right to left are Faris Hall (replaced in 1963 by the Physical Sciences Building), the "beanery" or college dining hall, the Engineering Building (set back from the road), and behind it the new science hall (Baldwin Hall, razed in 1992). At the southwest corner of 8th and Terry is the dispensary (where the Administration building now stands), and across Terry Street is the original L.D.S. Institute. The long dark roof is the Mechanical Engineering Building, the haunts of Abe Lillibridge; Across the field is the first Reed Gymnasium, and west of it is Hutchinson Field. Continuing in a clockwise manner are the Heating Plant, Turner Hall, Frazier Hall (renovated in 1993), and Swanson Hall, with its third story added and gabled roof removed. Baldwin Hall is south of Swanson, by the snow-covered field. Only the arch of Swanson Hall stands in 1993. Note that there is no development on South Fifth Avenue. Emerson School is in the far left corner. Note the smoky sky and the dark cloud emanating from the Union Pacific power plant. A northbound steam-powered train is in the middle distance, above the ISU heating plant smokestack. Photograph by Cook Photography, Bannock County Historical Society Collection.

a larger engineering building were added to the campus. A pharmacy school also was added. As the institution continued to move from technical and vocational emphasis to traditional academic courses, it was associated with the State University and the name was changed to the Southern Branch of the University of Idaho, commonly referred to as "The Branch," or often as "The Twig." Pharmacy became a four-year, degree granting curriculum.

Agitation began to establish the school as a four-year degree-granting college, and for years attempts to pass such a bill in the legislature were defeated, the University at Moscow arguing that its role in providing higher education for the state would be damaged even though it was not providing such education for southern Idaho. A survey of education in Idaho in 1946, performed by the Peabody Educational Survey Commission, stated that the education needs in

southern Idaho were not adequately served. The commission recommended establishment of the Pocatello school as a degree-granting institution and such a bill passed the legislature unanimously in 1947. It was named Idaho State College.

In the early 1960s, pressure mounted to establish the school as a university and in 1963, the legislature created Idaho State University. Enrollment that year was about 6,000. In the 1995-96 school year enrollment was over 12,400. Both academic and vocational degrees are offered, with over 100 programs of study leading to bachelor's degrees, 46 masters degree programs, and 11 doctoral degrees, as well as 22 certificate programs in vocational education. The 800-acre campus includes more than 50 buildings and the first enclosed stadium in Idaho, formerly the Minidome and now the Dubby Holt Arena.

Most of the early buildings at Idaho State University have been torn down over the years, in notable contrast to many European and eastern U.S. Universities. Some of the early buildings had problems with unstable foundations, especially exacerbated by shaking due to earthquakes. Others were simply too small for modern uses. Baldwin Hall, the former science building, was the latest casualty, torn down in 1992 because of foundation damage.

The soils on the east side of town contain collapsible loess and clays deposited in marshes and lakes at the head of the ancestral American Falls Lake. Soils on the west side of town are on sands and Boulder gravel of the Lake Bonneville Flood and have proven more competent to supporting late 19th century buildings.

The Future: Pocachub, Pocabuck, Chubpo or Chubatello

The boundaries of Pocatello have been enlarged gradually over the years, although they have reached a rather acrimonious limit at the border of what is now Chubbuck, an initially rural community that now blocks Pocatello's growth to the north and threatens Pocatello's place as Idaho's second city. Chubbuck politicians, in the best tradition of Idaho obstructionism, have refused to even discuss the possibility of the merger. The merger might occur when the present generation of politicians passes, sometime in the 21st century. Federal standards impose "rural" status on communities of less than 50,000. Without Chubbuck's population, Pocatello was, until 1996, classified as "rural," resulting in reduced Federal funding of various programs, to the detriment of Chubbuck as well as Pocatello.

Archway of Swanson Hall on the ISU campus, (January, 1993). Note crows in the elm trees along the Ralph Wilson Memorial Tree Walk, most of these trees are now gone and the Physical Science Building addition, completed in 1996, stands to the right of the arch.

Baldwin Hall immediately prior to demolition, (October, 1992).

McHan-Henderson Funeral Home, 1950s. The home stood west of South Arthur near West Lewis. The mortuary was torn down but the pillars can now be found on Red Hill, a gift of the Jack Henderson family. Some say the pillars are to mark the "Athens of the Intermountain West." Bannock County Historical Society Collection.

Pillars of learning on Red Hill, with Big Southern Butte in the background, view looks northwest, (June, 1992).

Early morning on a frigid January day, 1995. View is from Fremont Heights to the east toward downtown Pocatello. The fog is due to an atmospheric inversion.

Union Pacific domeliner on special executive train, Pocatello depot, (July, 1992).

McCarty's Warehouse, late 1930s. This building was destroyed, allegedly by a ten year old arsonist in June, 1992. Bannock County Historical Society Collection.

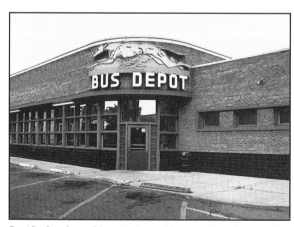

Pacific Greyhound bus station, with neon sign of a sprinting "northbound dog," West Bonneville Street, Pocatello structure was built by Union Pacific Railroad in the early 1940s, (June, 1992).

The first hump yard on the Union Pacific System, south of Pocatello, opened 1947. Hump yards use gravity to send freight cars downhill and to sort them onto several possible tracks on which trains are made up. Scout Mountain is in the background. Bannock Highway and the channelized Portneuf River can be seen to the right (west) of the tracks, (May, 1990).

Memorial Building, on the west bank of the Portneuf River at Fremont Street. The Memorial Building was built in recognition of World War I veterans and dedicated on May 30, 1926. Alex Mathers, Pocatello contractor, was the largest individual contributor to the building cost. Note the piled up rip-rap on the west bank of the river, consisting of boulders of basalt, carried by the Lake Bonneville Flood. The Memorial Building is one of the few Pocatello public meeting halls where alcohol can be served. The open-air porch on the second floor has been closed in and the concrete Portneuf River flood control channel has replaced the wall of boulders.
The long-term plan for the Portneuf Greenway includes a riverside plaza around the Memorial Building.
One block downstream, at the north end of what is now Memorial Park, is the site of the power plant and dam of the Pocatello Power and Irrigation Company, which provided electric power to Pocatello until 1902. Boaden Photo, Bannock County Historical Society Collection.

Portneuf Greenway

The Portneuf Greenway Foundation, founded in 1993, has taken upon itself the task of spearheading the reclamation of the Portneuf River for the people of Pocatello, through a string of parks and paths. Whether the concrete channel can be molded into something approaching the greenways of Boise, Idaho Falls, Blackfoot and other cities is a difficult issue. In any event, the building of the Greenway will enhance real estate values, recreational opportunities, and quality of life in Pocatello.

A major positive step for the Portneuf greenway was announced in June 1996 when the J.R. Simplot Co. purchased the Swanson Ranch on the north end of Pocatello. The Simplot Co. plans to leave the river in its natural state and construct trails along it.

Portneuf River flood channel looking west at (L to R) Clark to Wyeth Streets. Memorial Building is in center of view. Idaho Power dam site was at the intersection of Wyeth and the river, (March, 1991).

Portneuf River flood control channel and storm drain, after a summer thundershower, looking south from the Memorial Building, (July, 1991).

References

Bannock County Commissioners, 1993, The History of Bannock County: Pocatello, Idaho, 3 volumes.

Brown, Jennie Broughton, 1932, Fort Hall on the Oregon Trail: (with Ferry Butte by Susie Boice Trego). Caldwell, Idaho, The Caxton Printers, Ltd., 466 p.

Dion, N.P., 1969, Hydrologic reconnaissance of the Bear River Basin in southeastern Idaho: Idaho Department of Reclamation, Water Information Bulletin 13, 66 p.

Downing, Glenn Ray, 1991, Days out of Doors: A Portneuf Valley Chronicle: Pocatello, Idaho, Glenn Ray Downing, 960 Wayne Ave., Pocatello, Id. 83201, 295 p.

Etulain, R.W., and Marley, Bert W., editors, 1974 (3rd printing 1983), The Idaho Heritage: A collection of historical essays: Pocatello, Idaho, The Idaho State University Press.

Gittins, H. Leigh, 1983, Pocatello Portrait: The Early Years, 1878 to 1928: Moscow Idaho, The University Press of Idaho, 224 p.

Hansen, Sam, and others, 1984, Hard times in Idaho between the great wars: Pocatello, Idaho, The Idaho State University Press (reprinted from Rendezvous, Idaho State University Journal of Arts and Letters, volume XX, no. 1), 90 p.

Harstad, P.T., editor, 1972, Reminiscences of Oscar Sonnenkalb, Idaho Surveyor and Pioneer: Pocatello, Idaho, The Idaho State University Press, 66 p.

Howard, Minnie F., 1928, Early life and times of the First Congregational Church of Pocatello: Pocatello, Idaho, The Tribune Co. 65 p.

Idaho State Historical Society, 1976, Idaho: An Illustrated History: Boise, Idaho, Idaho State Historical Society, 250 p.

Kissane, Leedice, 1983, Pocatello Memories, Pocatello, Idaho: The Idaho State University Press, 129 p.

Maughan, Ralph W., 1992, Anatomy of the Snake River Plain: An Amateur's View: Pocatello, Idaho, The Idaho State University Press, 69 p.

Norvich, R.F., and Larson, A.L., 1970, A reconnaissance of the water resources in the Portneuf River Basin, Idaho: Idaho Department of Reclamation, Water Information Bulletin 16, 58 p.

Palmer, Tim, 1991, The Snake River: Window to the West: Washington D.C., Island Press, 320 p.

Stegner, Wallace, 1964 (reprinted 1971), The gathering of Zion: The story of the Mormon Trail: New York, McGraw Hill Book Company, 331 p.

Swetnam, Susan Hendricks, 1991, Lives of the Saints in southeast Idaho: An Introduction to Mormon Pioneer Life Story Writing: Moscow, Idaho, The University of Idaho Press, 188 p.

Wrigley, R.L., Jr., 1942, The Occupational Structure of Pocatello, Idaho [Ph.D. dissertation]: Chicago, Illinois, University of Chicago Libraries, 211 p.

Wrigley, R.L., Jr., 1943, The Early History of Pocatello, Idaho: Pacific Northwest Quarterly, v. 34, p. 353-365.

Brady Memorial in Mountain View Cemetery, Pocatello (April, 1996). The chapel was built in memory of James H. Brady, Idaho Governor from 1908 to 1911 and U.S. Senator from 1913 to 1918. The chapel was dedicated on Memorial Day, 1922, the same date as the dedication of the Lincoln Memorial in Washington D.C.

Funeral of Mrs. Dominic Salvucci, Mountainview Cemetary, Pocatello; October, 1940s. "From the dust ye are created. To the dust ye shall return." Photograph by Fred Cuoio.

Snake River Plain

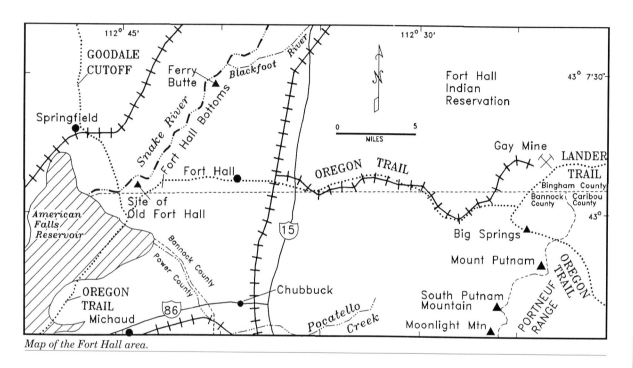

Map of the Fort Hall area.

Founding of Fort Hall

Osborne Russell's journal states

"On the 11th (July, 1834) we left Bear River and crossed low ridges of broken country for about 15 miles in a N East direction and fell on to a stream which runs into Snake River called Black Foot. Here we met with Capt. B.L. Bonneville with a party of 10 or 12 men. He was on his way to the Columbia and was employed killing and drying Buffalo meat for the journey. The next day we travelled in a west direction over a rough mountainous country about 25 miles and the day following after travelling about 20 miles in the same direction we emerged from the mountain into the great valley of Snake River on the 16th. We crossed the valley and reached the river in about 25 miles travel West. Here Mr. Wyeth concluded to stop, build a fort and deposit the remainder of his merchandise, leaving a few men to protect them and trade with the Snake and Bannack Indians. On the 18th we commenced the Fort which was a stockade 80 feet square built of Cotton wood trees set on end sunk 2 1/2 feet in the ground and standing about 15 feet above with two bastions 8 ft square at the opposite angles. On the 4th of August the Fort was completed. And on the 5th the "Stars and Stripes" were unfurled to the breeze at Sunrise in the center of a savage and uncivilized country over an American Trading Post," (*in* Haines, 1965).

Unfurling an American flag actually was a violation of the Treaty of Ghent ending the War of 1812, which provided that the northwest should be jointly occupied by the U.S. and Great Britain. Fort Hall was actively used first as a fur trading outpost by Andrew Wyeth and associates, and after 1837, by the Hudson's Bay Company. It was closed in 1856.

Site of Old Fort Hall on the south bank of the Snake River. The Fort was located about at the small white monument between the slough and the sharp curve in the dirt road. A remnant of the Oregon Trail branch to the Fort can be seen cutting obliquely across the field in the middle of the photograph, (June, 1992).

Oregon Trail ruts along Lone Pine (Gay Mine) Road on the Fort Hall Indian Reservation, aerial view looking south, September, 1988. The Gay Mine railway crosses the road in the middle right part of view. Several paths of ruts can be distinguished on the north side of the road, east of the rail crossing. Ross Fork is in the distance meandering through cliffs of basalt.

Route of the Oregon Trail in the Fort Hall area

Apparently the Oregon Trail followed several routes through the Fort Hall Bottoms. The unpublished recollections of W.A. Scadden who worked in the area of the old fort, make the somewhat heretical conclusions that the Trail did not, as generally thought, pass directly by the site of Fort Hall. Accounts are not very clear, but the ruts which are at the Fort do not seem to reflect travel by over 50,000 Pioneers and their wagons and stock.

Originally, the Trail generally followed present-day Sheepskin Road west from the present town of Fort Hall and after dropping down to the Bottoms, approached the old fort from the north. A trace of this route can be seen upstream from the Fort. It crosses the slough east of the site of the fort to the open area next to the walls where until 1843, Pioneers were convinced by Fort personnel to leave their wagons and instead to proceed further by foot or horseback. The Hudson's Bay Company wished Pioneers to believe that the route to the west was too rough for wagons, thus discouraging exploration and settlement. According to Scadden, as time went by, the main route of the Trail shifted away from the Fort and after coming down onto the Bottoms more than a mile south of Sheepskin Road, it forded Clear Creek and ran parallel to Spring Creek to the Portneuf River, with a branch crossing Spring Creek to the Fort, about four miles away. This main trail eliminated several creek crossings and after the Clear Creek ford, which is only inches deep on a good base, there remained only the ford of the Portneuf River as the Pioneers moved to the west.

Persons wishing to go to the old Fort could cross Spring Creek at a major ford and reach the Fort, four miles distant, after fording Big Jim Creek. This route actually is shorter than the north route. Hudson's Bay Company abandoned Fort Hall in 1856, after reducing its use for several years, so there was no longer any reason to visit Fort Hall.

View of the slough at Old Fort Hall from near the site of the old fort. The Oregon Trail branch probably crossed this slough here, (September, 1988).

Photo at right taken at Old Fort Hall, August 29, 1916. Ezra Meeker (old man on the left of the front row) was a pioneer who travelled the Oregon Trail in the 1850s and settled in Washington State. In 1916 he returned along the trail with a covered wagon and a team of oxen. Joe Rainey, an Indian and former U.S. Army Scout (left background) pointed out the site of the original fort, which had been lost in the marshes and meanders of the Fort Hall Bottoms. Dr. Minnie Howard and her husband Dr. W. Howard (behind and to her left) were champions of preservation of Oregon Trail and Pocatello history. They were both medical doctors and had four sons who became doctors. Howard Mountain, the volcanic hill northwest of the city, is named for the family. As this picture suggests, Dr. Minnie was not known for frivolity. Minnie Howard Collection, Idaho State University Library.

141

Blackfoot

In 1880, Blackfoot was the largest city in Oneida County and residents thought that after the 1880 reapportionment of the Legislature their city was destined to become the new capital of Idaho territory. Eastern Idaho had more people than western Idaho. Oneida County had 2,000 more settlers than Ada County. But in a scenario which has been repeated time and time again in Idaho history, eastern Idaho came out on the short end. The apportionment committee was pressured by a group from Boise. Eastern Idaho received one vote less than the western counties, leaving Boise as the territorial capitol. Now Blackfoot is county seat of Bingham County and the Potato Capital of the World.

World Potato Exposition at the restored Oregon Short Line Depot and world's largest potato, downtown Blackfoot, (March, 1993).

The Nuart theatre, downtown Blackfoot, (March, 1993).

View of Ferry Butte and irrigated farmland south of Fort Hall, looking northwest from Interstate 15. Behind Ferry Butte on the left is Middle Butte, in the middle is the south end of the Lemhi Range, and on the right is East Butte, (June, 1992).

Ferry Butte

"Anyone wishing to view some of the striking beauties of Idaho scenery has a delightful treat in store if he journeys to the summit of Pogowa, better known as Ferry Butte. Located in Bingham County on the south side of a curve in the Snake River, it affords a wonderful opportunity to feast one's eyes upon the expanse of mountain, lake, river, and fertile field, whose beauty is most inspiring. From this vantage point can easily be visualized in the mind's eye, the stirring scenes that occurred in Pioneer Days as the immigrants wound their way around Mount Putnam, down Ross Fork Creek, across the bottoms to Old Fort Hall."
(Jennie Broughton Brown, introducing text on Ferry Butte written by Susie Boice Trego (*in* Brown, 1932, p. 421)).

Gay Mine

The rocks north of Big Spring, east of Fort Hall, include the Permian Phosphoria Formation, which was mined at the Gay Mine (named for J.R. Simplot's daughter) from 1946 to 1993. Simplot, born in Dubuque Iowa, and raised in Declo, south of Burley, was an eighth grade dropout, and millionaire at the age of 30. In the 1990s he is one of the last American industrial barons. After beginning in the potato growing and shipping business, he developed a potato and onion dehydration plant near Caldwell, Idaho, in 1941, and sold his product mainly to the U.S. Government to feed soldiers in World War II. A scarcity of fertilizers prompted Simplot to enter the phosphate fertilizer business with the construction (using low-cost government war loans) of Idaho's first phosphate fertilizer plant west of Pocatello in 1944.

J.R. Simplot, in the 1970s, J.R. Simplot Company Collection.

Aerial photograph of one of the southern pits of the Gay Mine, (September, 1989).

In 1946, Simplot negotiated a deal with the Bureau of Indian Affairs to open a mine on the Reservation east of Fort Hall, and in 1948, a rail line leading to the mine was built by Morrison-Knudsen Company under contract with Union Pacific Railroad.

The Gay Mine was closed down in 1993. Its ore reserves have nearly been exhausted. In the late 1980s, the Simplot Company opened a new phosphate mine at Smoky Canyon west of Afton, Wyoming, and FMC opened in the early 1990s, a similar new mine in Dry Valley, northeast of Soda Springs.

Coiled teeth of Helicoprion, a Permian shark whose teeth are stored inside its head. Helicoprion teeth are common fossils in the Permian Phosphoria Formation. J.R. Simplot Company Collection.

In 1977 Simplot and two of his companies pleaded no contest to charges of tax evasion and were fined $40,000 for failing to report $1.3 million in income. J.R. always pushed things to the limit. In a 1980 interview with an Associated Press reporter Simplot said "I'm an old man, but a tough old man. I've been lucky. I've had good people with me. I've had some breaks. But I made a lot of my breaks, son. I've been overextended all my life. It keeps me hustling."

References

Brown, Jennie Broughton, 1932, Fort Hall on the Oregon Trail, (with Ferry Butte by Susie Boice Trego): Caldwell, Idaho, The Caxton Printers, Ltd., 466 p.

Haines, A.L., editor, 1965, Osborne Russell's Journal of a Trapper: University of Nebraska Press, 191 p.

Hladky, F.R., Kellogg, K.S., Oriel, S.S., Link, P.K., Nielson, J.W., and Amerman, R.E., 1992, Geologic map of the eastern part of the Fort Hall Indian Reservation, Bannock, Bingham, and Caribou Counties, Idaho: U.S. Geological Survey Miscellaneous Investigations Series Map I-2006, scale 1:50,000.

Link, P.K., Nielson, J.W., McDonald, C., and Smith, J.L., 1990, History and geology of the J.R. Simplot Company Gay Mine, Bingham County, Idaho: in Robinson, Lee, editor, 1990 Symposium on Engineering Geology and Geotechnical Engineering, Pocatello, Idaho, p. 24-1 to 24-12.

Lohse, E.S., and Holmer, R.N., editors, 1990 (2nd printing 1992), Fort Hall and the Shoshone-Bannock: Pocatello, Idaho, The Idaho State University Press, 60 p.

Captains of Industry at the dedication of Gay Mine railhead, September 22, 1948. L to R, Jack R. Simplot, Harry Morrison of Morrison-Knudsen (builders of the railroad), Jack Avery (Vice President of the Union Pacific) holding Gay Simplot, Sprague Haney; J.R. Simplot Company Collection.

Sign at entrance to Fort Hall Indian Reservation, (July, 1984).

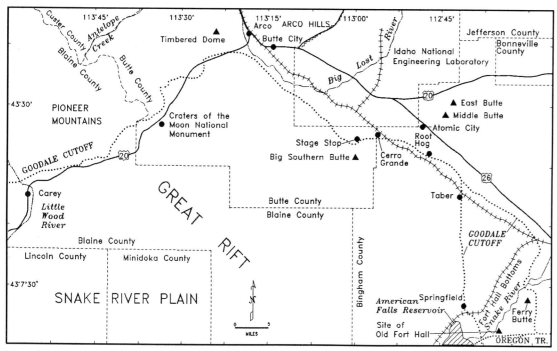

Map of the east-central Snake River Plain.

Geology of the Snake River Plain

The Snake River Plain contains Pleistocene basalt and interbedded sediment in the upper few hundred feet. The Snake River Plain Aquifer, the key to southern Idaho's agricultural economy, mainly consists of basalts and interbedded sediments, deposited in Pleistocene time (the last 2 million years). The underlying rhyolite does not seem to be a major aquifer because many of the pore spaces are filled with chemical precipitates. Within basalts, permeable zones are mainly the tops and bottoms of lava flows, with columnar jointing providing vertical transmission of water.

Big Southern Butte

The Big Butte, elevation 7,560 feet, is a prominent landmark visible from the entire Pocatello-Fort Hall-Blackfoot-Burley-Arco area. The Butte is a composite rhyolite dome that was intruded about 300,000 years ago and poked through a capping of basalt lava. This uplifted lava is now present on the north and east side of the Butte. For more discussion of the Butte and the surrounding geology see Bonnichsen and Breckenridge (1982), Pierce and Morgan (1992), and Hackett and Smith (1992).

Morning commuter buses approaching CFA (Central Facilities Area) at the Idaho National Engineering Laboratory, 7 a.m., September 15, 1992. East and Middle Buttes rise out of the sagebrush desert in the background. View looks east.

144

Shaded relief map of the Snake River Plain.

East Butte, a 600,000 year old rhyolite dome, looking east from Highway 26, (July, 1991).

View in June, 1993, looking southwest at Big Southern Butte and an island in the Big Lost River near the crossing of Highway 26 on the Idaho National Engineering Laboratory. The river flowed for 6 weeks in 1993, and for much of the summers in 1995 and 1996. Before that the river had been completely dry since 1986.

Goodale or Jeffrey's Cutoff

The Goodale or Jeffrey's Cutoff of the Oregon Trail headed north from Fort Hall toward the Big Butte, crossed the Snake River Plain and wound along its northern margin through Camas Prairie to the main Oregon Trail west of Mountain Home. Its use increased after 1864 as use of the southern route fell off.

Toponce Stage Line and Root Hog

In 1878, a stage line was established by Alexander Toponce, who had previously begun a cattle business in the Northern Portneuf Range. The stage ran from Blackfoot to the copper mines near Houston (Mackay), and north to Challis.

A stage station northeast of the Big Butte tapped a spring on the side of the Butte that was the only reliable water source between the Snake River and the Big Lost River. In the 1880s, the proprietors reportedly let pigs run loose at the stage stop to keep down the rattlesnakes.

Half way from the Snake River to the Big Butte stage stop was another station known as "Root Hog or Die," later shortened to Root Hog. Water was hauled to Root Hog from the Big Butte by the stage company.

On June 25, 1887, the Idaho News of Blackfoot reported that

"travelers on the Challis Stage Road find the Big Butte Station a pleasant place to stop" and also that "Root Hog is as lively as ever." (Dykes, p. 10).

NRF (Naval Reactor Facility), Idaho National Engineering Laboratory. View looks south. Note sewage lagoons in foreground. Water from these and other ponds has leaked downward to the Snake River Plain Aquifer, (June, 1988).

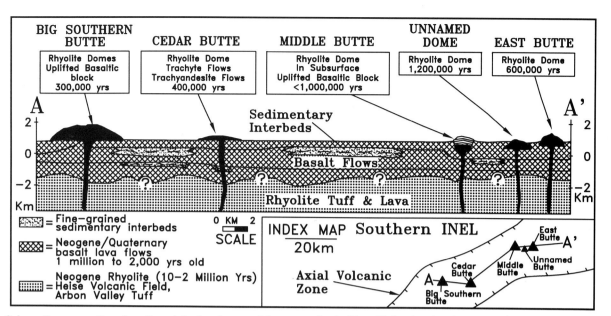

Schematic cross section along the axial volcanic zone of the eastern Snake River Plain, showing the ages, rock types, and known or inferred relationships of Pleistocene silicic volcanic domes. Neogene = 35 to 2 million years old, Pleistocene = less than 2 million years old. Ka = thousand years old. Rhyolite, trachyte, trachyandesite rocks, and basalt are volcanic rock types, redrawn from Hackett and Smith (1992).

Oregon Short Line freight train at Arco depot, 1912. The branch through Arco was completed in 1901. Its primary customer was the Empire copper mine southwest of Mackay. Eli Oboler Library, Idaho State University.

Atomic City

There was a great influx of settlers to the Furrey (Midway) area between 1910 and 1920. Every tillable acre was taken. A wet period ended about 1919, and wheat prices plummeted. Most of the homestead land was abandoned. After the "National Reactor Testing Station" (NRTS) was begun in the desert to the north, a flurry of excitement caused local boosters to extol the virtues and growth possibilities of the town and to rename it Atomic City, but its remote location and lack of amenities caused the boom to bust.

Idaho National Engineering Laboratory

The Idaho National Engineering Laboratory (INEL) was established as the Nuclear Reactor Testing Station in 1949. The INEL site is 890 square miles of sagebrush desert, and contains large areas of young basalt lava flows as well as East and Middle (or Twin) Buttes, which are small rhyolite domes. It is the site of secret activities related to nuclear research. It is also a land of acronyms (CFA, RWMC, TAN, SPERT, NRF, and etc.) The "Site" first generated electricity with nuclear reactors in 1951. In 1955 Arco became the first town in the United States lighted by nuclear power. In 1992, the INEL employed about 10,000 people, providing almost 5% of the jobs in Idaho; it is the mainstay of the economy of Idaho Falls area. The INEL budget, in 1987, was $800 million, two-thirds as large as the budget for the state of Idaho ($1.2 billion).

It is ironic that this politically conservative and philosophically independent region, most of whose legislators are perennially distrustful of Federal Government programs and always opposed to any increase in taxes, is largely subsidized by Federal tax dollars raised mainly in other states.

Idaho and Federal Dollars

"On a per-capita basis, Idaho ranked eighth among the forty-eight states in expenditures of the anti-Depression agencies of the New Deal, ranking first in Rural Electrification Administration expenditures (and) second in Civilian Conservation Corps expenditures . . . .

"Accepting the political folklore of the 1930s, one gets the impression that Franklin Roosevelt staged a giant barbecue which supported millions of people and forced the nation irretrievably into debt . . . . Compared with expenditures of recent years, however, New Deal expenditures were quite modest . . . the total expenditures in Idaho of all New Deal agencies during the seven years 1933 to 1939 was only $470 per capita, or an average of $67 per person per year." In 1969, that was "less than half the estimated annual per capita expenditures of the National Reactor Testing Station of the U.S. Atomic Energy Commission at Arco." (Arrington, 1969, reprinted in Etulain and Marley, 1974, p. 132)

The New Deal per capita expenditure was an order of magnitude (ten times) smaller than the expenditure in 1990 of Department of Energy money for the Idaho National Engineering Laboratory ($800 million dollars for 1 million people, or $800 per capita).

A gathering summer thunderstorm over the southern end of the Lost River Range. Photo taken from near Craters of the Moon, (July, 1987).

Route of Goodale Cutoff skirting the lava to the north, taken from U.S. Highway 26, west of Craters of the Moon National Monument. The route clung to the north edge of the Snake River Plain, avoiding the lava flows, (June, 1992).

Snake River Plain Aquifer

The Snake River and its aquifer in many ways control the economy of Idaho. Three million acres of farmland on the Snake River Plain are irrigated, with about 1/3 of this from wells and the rest from canals. Idaho has the highest per capita water consumption in the U.S.

At the INEL, the water table is 200 to 1000 feet below the ground surface. The groundwater flow rate is 5 to 20 feet per day. An injection well, at the Idaho Chemical Processing Plant, was used to dispose of waste water used for cooling nuclear reactors from 1953 to 1984, and there has been surface disposal for thirty years. Leakage from evaporation ponds at the Test Reactor Area (TRA) has produced perched bodies of ground water containing radioactive isotopes above the main aquifer. Disposal of radioactive wastes at the INEL has not yet harmed the quality of the Snake River aquifer in a major way, but radionuclides have been detected in the aquifer west of the INEL, having migrated up to 7.5 miles in 20 years.

A more important, but less politically sensitive, threat to the purity of the Snake River Plain aquifer is agricultural runoff including potato processing waste, fertilizer and animal waste. In fact, these agricultural activities have near-sacred cow status among Idaho politicians.

Big Lost River Playas

The area at the mouth of the Little Lost River is a playa or dry lake bed, that fills with water from the Big Lost River during wet years. During wetter times in the Pleistocene, the two Lost Rivers and Birch Creek flowed into pluvial Lake Terreton, centered near modern Mud Lake.

Aerial view looking southwest at Craters of the Moon National Monument. Lobate lava flow at the right flowed northward out of a fissure south of the highway, (July, 1987).

Queen's Crown, a landmark north of Carey, and Silver Creek flowing south from Picabo. View looks southeast. The crown is made of tilted Miocene rhyolite tuff of the Idavada Volcanics, (June, 1995).

Folded Paleozoic limestones at the south end of the Lost River Range directly east of Arco. View looks northeast. Arco is in the tree-covered area in the center right distance, (June, 1992).

Arco

The Big and Little Lost River valleys have seen many visitors who left no traces of their presence. Each of these valleys was a route for fur trapping parties between 1813 and the 1840s. For a number of years after the trappers left, little took place in the area, but after European visitors came again, this time to search for precious metals, some stayed and small farming communities began to form.

> Elaine Petersen Mann wrote in her diary about the view from her home in Arco, and is quoted by Swetnam (1991, p. 39).
>
> I remember how beautiful the Big Butte looked in the early morning sun when it was covered with snow.... Then the pink shades of morning with the blue shadows in the valleys with a wide expanse of desert—and off to the Southwest were those other mountains-not so big and definite but with all the beautiful snow, white then turned into orange and pinks and then to blue blue shadows.

A stage line, started by Alexander Toponce, connected the Salmon River mines and Challis with the railroad at Blackfoot. A stage station was established on the Big Lost River to serve this line. It was known as Kennedy Crossing and was about 5 miles south of the present town of Arco. Because the Challis route and another leading to the Wood River joined here, application was made for a post office, to be named Junction. There were too many places named Junction and the postal service did not want another one. The U.S. Post Office suggested the name of Arco, to honor a visiting count,

who had never been to Idaho. The citizens needed postal service and accepted the name.

Some have suggested that the name, instead, came from a rancher named Arco Smith, but perhaps he was named for the town instead of the other way around. In 1880, the stage station moved to another site south of the present town and remained there until the Mackay Branch of the Oregon Short Line Railroad Company was built through the area in 1901, at which time the town moved again, to its present location.

Lost River Range and the Big Lost River Valley

The Lost River Range contains one of the best continuous exposures of Paleozoic sedimentary rocks in Idaho. The rocks of the range are tilted eastward, and the range is bounded on the west by the segmented Lost River normal fault, which was last active in October, 1983, at Borah Peak. The interior of the range is rugged and forbidding. There are few roads and fewer perennial streams, since the porous limestone generally soaks up the snowmelt and any summer rain.

The Big Lost River valley remains grand and empty, populated by a few hardy ranchers, miners, and government workers. Mackay, the only town of any size north of Arco, started as a copper mining service town, and attracted a diverse gathering of ethnic Pioneers (Green, 1992). Here the "Idaho Cowboy" remains a mythology and even a viable life-style. Very little of the "Californication" that has so drastically changed the Wood River Valley has yet reached the waters of the Big Lost.

Craters of the Moon

The Craters of the Moon National Monument, established in 1924, contains the products of basaltic volcanic activity between 15,000 and 2,100 years ago. The monument contains superb examples of pahoehoe and aa type basalt lava flows, cinder cones, lava tubes, spatter cones, and tree molds. The area is well studied geologically, and is a showpiece for basaltic volcanic features. References on the geology of the area include Kuntz and others (1987; 1988).

Spires of rafted lava and spatter in the North Crater basalt lava flow (Kuntz and others, 1989). Looking north toward Pioneer Mountains, Craters of the Moon National Monument, (May, 1991).

The crumbling remains of the mill of the Empire Mine in the White Knob Mountains southwest of Mackay (Oct. 1995). The mine operated continuously from 1902 to 1930 and sporadically after that to the 1960s. It produced over $9,000,000 of metals, mainly copper. It was the base of the early economy of Mackay.

References on History and Geology of the INEL Area

Arrington, Leonard J., 1969, Idaho and the Great Depression: Idaho Yesterdays, v. 13, Summer, 1969, p. 2-8, reprinted in Etulain, R.W., and Marley, B.W., editors, 1974 (3rd printing, 1984), The Idaho Heritage: A collection of historical essays: Pocatello, Idaho, The Idaho State University Press, p. 129-133.

Bonnichsen, Bill, and Breckenridge, Roy M., editors, 1982, Cenozoic Geology of Idaho: Idaho Bureau of Mines and Geology Bulletin 26, 725 p.

Champion, D.E., Kuntz, M.A., and Lefebvre, R.H., 1989, Geologic map of the North Laidlaw Butte quadrangle, Blaine and Butte Counties, Idaho: U.S. Geological Survey Geologic Quadrangle Map GQ-1634, scale 1:24,000.

Crowder, David L., 1981, Tales of Eastern Idaho: KID Broadcasting Corporation, Idaho Falls, Idaho, 220 p.

Dykes, Fred W., 1985, A view of Idaho history as seen from Big Butte: unpublished, Fred. W. Dykes, Box 4414, Pocatello Id 83205-4414, 17 p.

Dykes, Fred W., 1989, Jeffrey's Cutoff; Idaho's forgotten Oregon Trail route: Fred. W. Dykes, Box 4414, Pocatello Idaho 83205-4414.

Green, Roberta H., 1992, They Passed This Way: Summerhouse Press, P.O. Box 770, Challis, Idaho 83226, 56 p.

Hackett, William R., and Smith, Richard P., 1992, Quaternary volcanism, tectonics, and sedimentation in the Idaho National Engineering Laboratory area: in Wilson, J.R., editor, Field guide to geologic excursions in Utah and adjacent areas of Nevada, Idaho, and Wyoming: Utah Geological Survey Miscellaneous Publication 92-3, p. 1-18.

Hackett, Bill, Pelton, Jack, and Brockway, Chuck, 1986, Geohydrologic story of the eastern Snake River Plain and the Idaho National Engineering Laboratory: United States Department of Energy, Idaho Operations Office, Idaho National Engineering Laboratory, Idaho Falls, Idaho, 32 p.

Kuntz, M.A., Champion, D.E., Lefebvre, R.H., and Covington, H.R., 1988, Geologic map of the Craters of the Moon, Kings Bowl, and Wapi lava fields and the Great Rift volcanic rift zone, south-central Idaho: U.S. Geological Survey Miscellaneous Investigations Series Map I-1632, scale 1:24,000.

Kuntz, M.A., Champion, D.E., and Lefebvre, R.H., 1987, Geology of the Craters of the Moon lava field, Idaho: in Beus, S.S., editor, Rocky Mountain Section of the Geological Society of America: Boulder, Colorado, Geological Society of America Centennial Field Guide, Volume 2, p. 123-126.

Kuntz, M.A., Champion, D.E., and Lefebvre, R.H., 1990, Geologic map of the Fissure Butte quadrangle, Blaine and Butte Counties, Idaho: U.S. Geological Survey Geologic Quadrangle Map GQ-1635, scale 1:24,000.

Kuntz, M.A., and twelve others, 1992, Geologic map of the Idaho National Engineering Laboratory and adjoining areas, eastern Idaho: U.S. Geological Survey Miscellaneous Investigations Series Map I-2320, scale 1:100,000.

Kuntz, M.A., Lefebvre, R.H., and Champion, D.E., 1989, Geologic map of the Inferno Cone quadrangle, Butte County, Idaho: U.S. Geological Survey Geologic Quadrangle Map GQ-1632, scale 1:24,000

Kuntz, M.A., Lefebvre, R.H., and Champion, D.E., 1989, Geologic map of the Watchman quadrangle, Butte County, Idaho: U.S. Geological Survey Geologic Quadrangle Map GQ-1633, scale 1:24,000.

McCurry, M., Estes, M., Fromm, J., Welhan, J., and Barrash, Warren, 1994, Three-dimensional chemical structure of the INEL aquifer system near the Idaho Chemical Processing Plant: in Link, P.K., ed., Hydrogeology, Waste Disposal, Science and Politics, Proceedings 30th Symposium, Engineering Geology and Geotechnical Engineering, College of Engineering, Idaho State University, p. 207-219.

Pierce, K.L., and Morgan, L.A., 1992, The track of the Yellowstone Hot Spot: Volcanism, faulting, and uplift, in Link, P.K., Kuntz, M.A., and Platt, L.B., editors, Regional Geology of Eastern Idaho and Western Wyoming: Geological Society of America Memoir 179, p. 1-53.

Scott, W.E., 1982, Surficial geologic map of the eastern Snake River Plain and adjacent areas, 111° to 115° W., Idaho and Wyoming: U.S. Geological Survey Miscellaneous Investigations Series Map I-1372, scale 1:250,000.

Swetnam, Susan Hendricks, 1991, Lives of the Saints in Southeast Idaho: Moscow, Idaho, The University of Idaho Press, 188 p.

Whitehead, R.L., 1986, Geohydrologic Framework of the Snake River Plain, Idaho and Eastern Oregon, U.S. Geological Survey Hydrologic Investigations Map HA-681, scale 1:1,000,000

Whitehead, R.L., 1992, Geohydrologic Framework of the Snake River Plain Regional Aquifer System, Idaho and Eastern Oregon, U.S. Geological Survey Professional Paper 1408-B, 32 p.

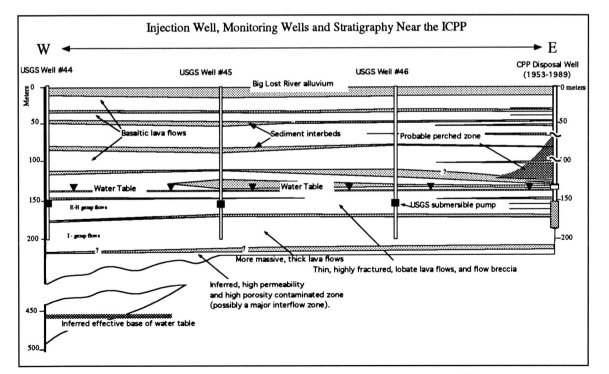

Injection Well, Monitoring Wells and Stratigraphy Near the ICPP

Simplified subsurface stratigraphy west of the Idaho Chemical Processing Plant (ICPP) at the INEL. This reconstruction is based on interpretation of drill-hole data. The subsurface consists of basalt lava flows and thin sediment interbeds, (from McCurry and others, 1994.)

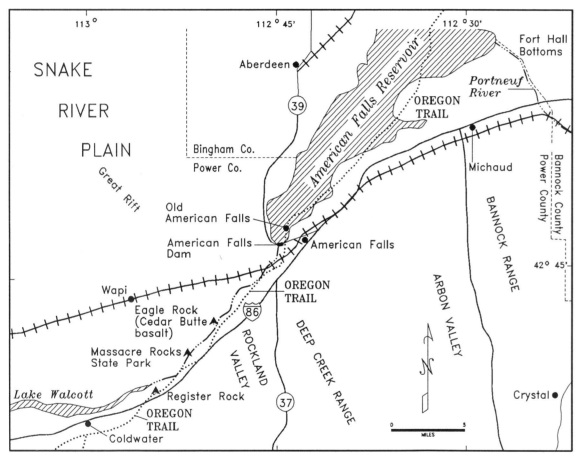

Map of American Falls area.

American Falls Lake

The ancestral American Falls Lake formed north of a basalt dam that formed at Duck Point, east of Massacre Rocks, about 72,000 years ago. The ancestral lake covered a larger area than the present one, and may have reached into what is now downtown Pocatello. The American Falls "lake beds" contain a lower fluvial member and an upper light-colored clay member deposited under water of a perennial lake. The flood plain and lake margin sediments contain a unique assemblage of Pleistocene mammal fossils, including *Bison latifrons*, camels, short-faced bears, ground sloths, horses and mammoths. They overlie an older sequence of lake beds known as the Raft Formation. Early reports concluded that the American Falls Lake existed at the time of the Lake Bonneville Flood and was drained catastrophically by it (Malde, 1968). Recent geological studies favor the view that a flood plain and fluvial complex had developed on the American Falls Lake beds by the time of the Lake Bonneville Flood (Hearst, 1990).

Bannock Peak at the north end of the Deep Creek Mountains, looking west from Rattlesnake Creek. The distinctive peak can be seen for miles, even though it is less than 9,000 feet high. It is composed of thrust-faulted Paleozoic rocks, (May, 1996).

Michaud Flats and Lake Channel

The Lake Bonneville Flood about 14,500 radiocarbon years ago deposited a flat-topped delta of boulders, gravel, and sand in the area of Michaud Flats, up to an elevation of about 4,400 feet near the Pocatello airport. The flood waters cut "Lake Channel," a now-dry channel north of the Snake River and west of present American Falls Dam, which provided a means for the floodwater to escape the flat American Falls area.

Aerial view, looking northwest at American Falls Dam and the bridge of the Union Pacific Railroad. Note that the reservoir water is at about 1/3 of its full level, (August, 1989).

Aerial view looking north across the Snake River at Duck Point and the island Eagle Rock, southwest of American Falls. Duck Point was the site of the lava flow dam to the ancestral American Falls Lake. The white beds on the north side of the river in the middle distance are American Falls Lake Beds. The area was scoured by the Lake Bonneville Flood. Lake Channel is a few miles to the west of the photo. The irrigated farmland in the background is west of Aberdeen, (August, 1989).

Several other smaller channels exist near Lake Channel, but they carried less water and were abandoned when the main Snake River cut the basalt dam at Duck Point, allowing the floodwaters to follow the present Snake River. The water from Lake Channel emptied back into the Snake River just west of and across the river from Massacre Rocks State Park.

Oregon Trail near Massacre Rocks

The Oregon Trail followed the south side of the Snake River from the Fort Hall area across Idaho to Three Island Ferry. At Massacre Rocks, west of American Falls, and at other areas west of there ruts of the trail are still visible.

Oscar Sonnenkalb wrote

"American Falls was for many surrounding miles the only oasis for the thirsty cowboy, sheep men and the farmers from scattered ranches, turning in from the wild outdoor life to enjoy a day of two of social life spiced with poker playing, improvised horse races and endless drinking bouts. Whenever I had a call from American Falls for some surveying work to be done, some drastic occurrence had just been played off; a free-for-all fight in the saloons, a dueling or wounding with knife or pistol, some wild rides through the streets and painting and shooting up the village. A good many of these feats seemed to be considered, by the natives at least, as quite harmless, and in fact were mostly mere pranks of whiskey loaded rowdies, but for the outsider and the eastern traveller these wild tournaments were considered to be quite serous affairs." (Harstad, 1972, p. 21.)

American Falls

The town of American Falls grew up during construction of the Oregon Short Line Railway and became a major center for the wheat and stockgrowers of the area south and west of Pocatello.

Part of the old town of American Falls was moved in 1926 to higher ground during construction of the reservoir. Only the top of the grain elevator now pokes above the waters of the lake. In late summer when the water of the reservoir is low, foundations, sidewalks, and tree stumps of the old town are accessible.

American Falls itself, before the construction of the dam, was 800 feet wide with a drop of 50 feet over 200 feet. Oregon Trail pioneer Bryan McKinstry wrote in July 1850 that the water as it descends over the falls,

"works itself into a perfect fury, throws the spray into the air like rain which strikes you in the face, and when the sun shines forms a beautiful rainbow."

Aberdeen

Farmland near Aberdeen was initially settled, starting in 1906, by Mennonites from Newton, Kansas. Salesmen from the Twin Falls area had gone to the midwest and spoken to church groups about the new opportunities for irrigated farming on the Snake River Plain. The Mennonites are a sect of Anabaptist Christians, originally from Germany, who, because of their pacifist refusal to serve in war, were forced to flee from Holland and Germany to Poland and Russia, and later to immigrate to America. Building of irrigation canals allowed settlement of the Aberdeen area, and the town was incorporated in 1908, named for Aberdeen, Scotland.

The railroad branch line from Blackfoot, started by the Salmon River Railroad Co., but completed by Union Pacific, was completed in 1911. Also in 1911, The University of Idaho established the Aberdeen Agricultural Experiment Station. The next ten years were boom years.

The drought and agricultural depression of the 1920s and 1930s followed. The flooding of the American Falls Reservoir, in 1926, cut off the direct road across the Snake River to Pocatello. The town today remains quiet and agricultural, though Mennonites are no longer in the majority.

Mennonite Church, Aberdeen (April 1996). Left side of the church is the original structure, built in 1910.

Aerial view of Lake Channel, looking north. The Lake Bonneville Flood cascaded into this canal in the alcoves of now dry waterfalls in the right distance and flowed south toward the camera toward the Snake River, (August, 1989).

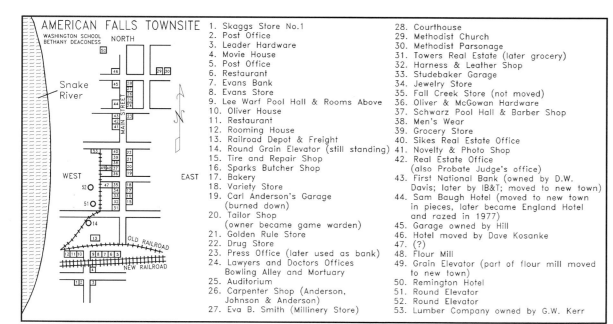

AMERICAN FALLS TOWNSITE		
WASHINGTON SCHOOL BETHANY DEACONESS NORTH		
Snake River		
WEST	EAST	
OLD RAILROAD		
NEW RAILROAD		

1. Skaggs Store No.1
2. Post Office
3. Leader Hardware
4. Movie House
5. Post Office
6. Restaurant
7. Evans Bank
8. Evans Store
9. Lee Warf Pool Hall & Rooms Above
10. Oliver House
11. Restaurant
12. Rooming House
13. Railroad Depot & Freight
14. Round Grain Elevator (still standing)
15. Tire and Repair Shop
16. Sparks Butcher Shop
17. Bakery
18. Variety Store
19. Carl Anderson's Garage (burned down)
20. Tailor Shop (owner became game warden)
21. Golden Rule Store
22. Drug Store
23. Press Office (later used as bank)
24. Lawyers and Doctors Offices Bowling Alley and Mortuary
25. Auditorium
26. Carpenter Shop (Anderson, Johnson & Anderson)
27. Eva B. Smith (Millinery Store)

28. Courthouse
29. Methodist Church
30. Methodist Parsonage
31. Towers Real Estate (later grocery)
32. Harness & Leather Shop
33. Studebaker Garage
34. Jewelry Store
35. Fall Creek Store (not moved)
36. Oliver & McGowan Hardware
37. Schwarz Pool Hall & Barber Shop
38. Men's Wear
39. Grocery Store
40. Sikes Real Estate Office
41. Novelty & Photo Shop
42. Real Estate Office (also Probate Judge's office)
43. First National Bank (owned by D.W. Davis; later by IB&T; moved to new town)
44. Sam Baugh Hotel (moved to new town in pieces, later became England Hotel and razed in 1977)
45. Garage owned by Hill
46. Hotel moved by Dave Kosanke
47. (?)
48. Flour Mill
49. Grain Elevator (part of flour mill moved to new town)
50. Remington Hotel
51. Round Elevator
52. Round Elevator
53. Lumber Company owned by G.W. Kerr

Map of part of the Old American Falls townsite, after Idaho State Journal, September 20, 1992. Original is in American Falls Library. Number 1 on the map identifies the location of store number 1 operated by the Skaggs Brothers whose grocery business expanded rapidly, ultimately becoming the Safeway chain.

American Falls Lake beds, deposited between about 80,000 years and about 30,000 years ago in the ancestral American Falls Lake, (September, 1988).

Stumps of mature trees on street of Old American Falls, now covered much of the year by waters of the American Falls Reservoir. The town was moved in 1926 when the dam was built and the reservoir flooded part of the townsite. In drier years, the old town is accessible late in the irrigation year when the reservoir is almost empty, (November, 1990).

Arbon Valley

In her historical review of Arbon Valley, Laurie Ward wrote

"As the homesteaders poured all their energy into the taming of the land, the long hours of hard work and sweat seemed to turn into pride when the finished product, a field clear of sagebrush, was put into grain and the land that was once untamed, was now producing crops."

No matter that most dryland homesteads were not practical. This was part of the American dream.

During the boom in dry farming in World War I, it is said that American Falls shipped more grain than any other station on the Union Pacific System. Homesteads had been settled in Arbon and Rockland Valleys and a prolonged wet period gave the farmers the taste of prosperity. This turned to the taste of failure with the crash in grain prices after World War I and several dry summers.

Rockland Valley

The sparsely populated Rockland Valley barely manages to support Rockland, a tattered town with a store, gas station, and Mormon church. This is mainly dry farming country, largely depopulated during the 1930s.

Here are some recollections of Virgil Allen, born in Rockland Valley in 1914.

"I was born and raised in Rockland, Idaho, and attended school there in grades one through nine. In 1928 we had just harvested the biggest and best dry farm grain crop of our lives. Everything looked rosy . . . We moved to Pocatello so my two older sisters could attend the University of Idaho Southern Branch. We planned to return to Rockland the next summer to resume farming. Grain prices were low in the fall so Dad decided to hold his crop until the price rose in the spring. But the price didn't go up. Instead it plummeted. The price of grain went so low that across America people were burning if for fuel because it was cheaper than coal . . . By 1928 Dad had acquired three homesteads to increase our holdings to more than a section of land... But when the Depression came, one foreclosure followed another until there was nothing in Rockland for us to move back to." (*in* Hanson, editor, 1984, p. 70.)

U.S. Highway 30 before it was paved (about 1930 or 1931), passing west through Massacre Rocks. The roadway was widened in the late 1930s and again in the late 1980s. Most of the rocks to the left of the road are gone. The Oregon Trail is just off the picture to the right. The 1862 massacre is generally thought to have been near here. Photograph by Cook Photography, Bannock County Historical Society Collection.

Aerial view of Old American Falls townsite, looking southeast, (September, 1988). Note the grain elevator, the layout of the old streets, and the old foundations. The former railroad right of way slants to the south, east of the elevator. The town was moved in 1926 during construction of the present dam. At the time of this photo the reservoir water had been drained by irrigation to near its lowest permissible level.

View looking northeast at American Falls Reservoir at about maximum level, (May, 1989). Note the grain elevator of the old town of American Falls poking through the waters of the lake.

Longitudinal dunes on the Snake River Plain northwest of American Falls. The dunes are shaped by the prevailing southwest wind along the axis of the Snake River Plain, (September, 1988).

Construction of the American Falls Dam
by Cook Photography, Bannock County Historical Society Collection.

The first three photos were taken looking east from nearly the same spot, on the northwest side of the Snake River, during construction of the new American Falls Dam and relocation of the original town.

Photo taken probably in March or April, 1925, during the first stages of construction of the American Falls Dam. The Snake River is impounded by a temporary dam, with its spillway in the right center. The new dam will be constructed on the rectangular impoundment (cofferdam) directly in front of the camera. The concrete-mixing batching plant will be located immediately southeast of the impoundment. The old town of American Falls, the old Oregon Short Line mainline and depot, and the grain elevator are still functioning. But, also note houses and buildings south of the railroad on high ground that was the original American Falls townsite. The area that was to be flooded ("Old American Falls") was called the "Riverside and Union Additions" in a 1924 town plat. In the center distance is the new school building; the new Power County courthouse has not yet been constructed. High spring runoff has raised the level of the river and flooded the trees in the foreground. The railroad bridge in the far right is the early one, not yet raised or enlarged, but the new mainline with new light-colored fill can be seen to the east of the bridge.

Building the American Falls Dam, probably early spring, 1926. In the left distance are new grain elevators and buildings, some moved from their previous location in the old town. Note the railroad yard and concrete batching plant in the center middle distance. The railroad is still using its original depot; the new one is not yet ready for use. The railroad bridge has not yet been elevated, but light-colored fill has been installed on the new mainline east of the river. Just on the west side of the river in the left foreground are construction vehicles (railroad cars towed by dinkey (small steam) engines). The rail line in the foreground was constructed for purposes of building the dam only.

View after completion of the American Falls Dam, probably spring of 1928. Spring runoff has filled the reservoir and flooded the former townsite; the grain elevator stands above the water and the drowned trees have sent out leaves for the last time. It is interesting that these trees were not cut down before the area was flooded. The new school is in the middle distance, with the courthouse in the right distance. Note that mature trees are present, in the original townsite. The railroad fill has been completed and the mainline bridge elevated. The bridge was enlarged and raised again in the 1970s. The railroad yard and batching plant that had been directly across the river are gone. The bare area in the middle distance, across the tracks and beyond the curve of the railroad mainline is now the American Falls golf course. The road over the dam is not yet finished.

Railroad bridge at American Falls, finished in 1927. Picture was probably taken in early 1926; looking northeast. In the middle distance under the bridge is the batching plant where concrete was mixed for the American Falls Dam, which is nearing completion. The growing reservoir is in the left distance. The mill race for the new power plant is off the picture to the right. The stone building in the right foreground is the first power plant, built at American Falls in 1902. The train on the new bridge is composed of Southern Pacific and Union Pacific refrigerator cars. These cars, operated by PFE (Pacific Fruit Express), were cooled by blocks of ice put in bunkers at the ends of the cars. A large icing plant was at the northwest end of the Pocatello railroad complex.

Massacre Rocks

Massacre Rocks is a late Miocene (5-6 million years) basaltic eruptive center along the Snake River. Rising basaltic magma encountered groundwater from the Snake River Plain aquifer, causing explosive "phreatomagmatic" eruptions. Among the rock types present at Massacre Rocks are tuff breccias, which originated as wet mudflows on the flanks of the volcanic crater, lava flows, ash and cinder beds, lava ponded in a lava lake, and basaltic dikes of the core of the volcano. The Massacre Volcanics overlie older rhyolite that extends under the Snake River Plain.

Massacre Rocks got its name because of an Indian attack on the Adams wagon train on the Oregon Trail on August 9 and 10, 1862. It was one of a series of Indian attacks on emigrants that summer along both the California Trail and this part of the Oregon Trail. These attacks were perpetrated mainly by the band of Northwestern Shoshoni led by Chief Pocatello. At Massacre Rocks, ten immigrants were killed either in the original attack or in skirmishes following it.

Culvert under the Oregon Short Line Railroad, Old American Falls townsite, (October, 1987).

References

Hearst, J.M., 1990, Paleontology and depositional setting of the Duck Point local fauna (Late Pleistocene: Rancholabrean) Power County, southeastern Idaho [M.S. thesis]: Pocatello, Idaho State University, 275 p.

Bright, R.C., 1982, Paleontology of the lacustrine member of the American Falls Lake Beds, southeastern Idaho, *in* Bonnichsen, Bill and Breckenridge, R.M., editors, Cenozoic Geology of Idaho: Idaho Bureau of Mines and Geology Bulletin 26, p. 597-614.

Hansen, Sam, and others, 1984, Hard times in Idaho between the great wars: Pocatello, Idaho, Idaho State University Press (reprinted from Rendezvous, Idaho State University Journal of Arts and Letters, volume XX, no. 1), 90 p.

Harder, E. B. and Harder, H. K. (compilers), 1982, Seventy-five years at Aberdeen: A History of the First Mennonite Church, Aberdeen, Idaho: First Mennonite Church, P. O. Box 246, Aberdeen, Idaho, 83210, 383 p.

Malde, H.E., 1968, The catastrophic late Pleistocene Bonneville flood in the Snake River Plain: U.S. Geological Survey Professional Paper 596, 52 p.

Malde, H.E., 1991, Quaternary geology and structural history of the Snake River Plain, Idaho and Oregon: *in* Morrison, R.B., editor, Boulder, Colorado, The Geological Society of America: Quaternary nonglacial geology: Conterminous U.S., The Geology of North America, volume K-2, p. 251-281.

Scott, W.E., Pierce, K.L., Bradbury, J.P., and Forester, R.M., 1982, Revised Quaternary stratigraphy and chronology in the American Falls area, southeastern Idaho: *in* Bonnichsen, Bill and Breckenridge, R.M., editors, Cenozoic Geology of Idaho: Idaho Bureau of Mines and Geology Bulletin 26, p. 581-595.

Ward, Laurie, 1982, Bannock Valley: Keith W. Watkins and Sons, Inc., Providence UT 84332, 322 p.

Wagon ruts of the Oregon Trail just east of Massacre Rocks State Park, south of Interstate 84. Some accounts place the 1862 massacre just east of here (October, 1987).

Beds of fragmental volcanic debris blown out of the Massacre Volcanic center about 5 million years ago. Photo taken southeast of Interstate 86 at the Massacre Rocks exit (April, 1995)

Magic Valley and City of Rocks

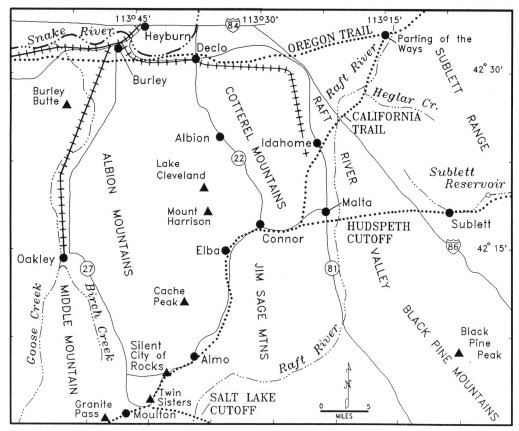

Map of City of Rocks — Burley area.

Aerial view of the City of Rocks, looking northwest at the junction of the Oakley Road and the road south to Twin Sisters. Register Rock is immediately below the intersection. Other named rocks include Bath Rock, south of the Oakley Road near the summit. The creek draining the Silent City of Rocks is Circle Creek, (September, 1988).

Writing by pioneers at Register Rock along the Oregon Trail in the City of Rocks, (September, 1987).

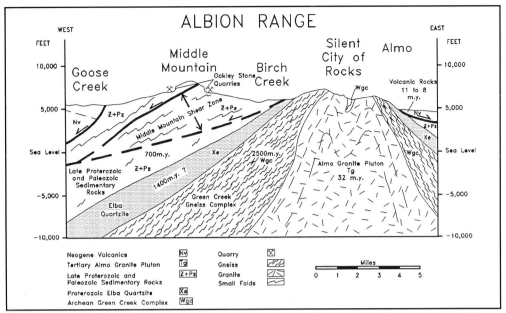

ALBION RANGE

WEST — EAST

Goose Creek · Middle Mountain · Oakley Stone Quarries · Birch Creek · Silent City of Rocks · Almo

Middle Mountain Shear Zone

Volcanic Rocks 11 to 8 m.y.

700 m.y. · 2500 m.y. Wgc · 1400 m.y. ?

Late Proterozoic and Paleozoic Sedimentary Rocks

Elba Quartzite

Green Creek Gneiss Complex

Almo Granite Pluton Tg 32 m.y.

Neogene Volcanics — Nv
Tertiary Almo Granite Pluton — Tg
Late Proterozoic and Paleozoic Sedimentary Rocks — Z+Pz
Proterozoic Elba Quartzite — Xe
Archean Green Creek Complex — Wgc

Quarry · Gneiss · Granite · Small Folds

Miles 0 1 2 3 4 5

Geologic cross section, west to east across the Albion Range—City of Rocks area. Geologic units are as follows: Nv = Neogene volcanic rocks; Tg = Tertiary granite (Oligocene City of Rocks pluton); Z-Pz = Late Proterozoic and Paleozoic sedimentary rocks; Xe = Middle Proterozoic Elba Quartzite; Wgc = Archean Green Creek Complex (gneiss and schist). For more information see Miller and others (1983), Saltzer and Hodges (1988) and Bandy (1992).

The California Trail

The California Trail left the Oregon Trail and the Snake River west of the mouth of Raft River and headed south and west toward the Nevada desert. It was joined by the Hudspeth Cutoff near the town of Malta, on the west side of the Raft River Valley, and the two wound up Connor Creek and south to the Silent City of Rocks. There, a cutoff from Salt Lake City joined them, and a single trail led westward over Granite Pass at the south end of Middle Mountain toward the Humboldt river drainage.

The Almo Massacre: Folklore, not Fact

A recurring story in the City of Rocks area is of the Almo Massacre, in which 300 Pioneers on the California Trail were said to have been massacred by Indians in 1861. All their stock and belongings were allegedly taken and nothing was left. The bodies are said to have been buried in dry wells, and have never been found. This fable has no basis in fact, was never reported in a newspaper account, nor does it appear in any Pioneer diary (Madsen, 1990). It is in the category of folklore, since it is a story that keeps surfacing. As such it must be culturally useful to those who hear and repeat it.

The Albion Range and the Silent City of Rocks

The Albion Range, including Mt. Harrison, Cache Peak, and the Silent City of Rocks exposes a "Cordilleran metamorphic core complex," one of several that extend from the Tucson, Arizona area north to northeastern Washington. The Silent City of Rocks is an Idaho treasure. The mysterious fins and monoliths eroded from the 30 million years old Almo Granite are perfect for rock climbing. A walk along the South Fork of Circle Creek when the aspens are golden is an unforgettable tour.

The upper part of the Albion Mountains is underlain by Paleozoic and Late Proterozoic metamorphic and sedimentary rocks, in places spectacularly folded, as along the road to the summit of Mount Harrison. The quartzites on the summit are structurally overturned. Below these is the green, micaceous Early Proterozoic Elba Quartzite, which can be seen in outcrops along the road below the Pomerelle ski area. South of Oakley thin-bedded micaceous quartzites including the Elba are quarried for decorative "Oakley stone," which is shipped throughout the United States and overseas. Under the Elba Quartzite is Archean gneiss and granite

Twin Sisters and the California Trail, looking west. The arcuate western contact of the Oligocene granite of the Silent City of Rocks pluton follows the edge of the granite monolith. West Twin Sister is the only rock made of Archean gneiss. The California Trail route can be seen in the foreground, slanting across the view. It passed behind the large light colored rock at the base of the view, (August, 1986).

The Twin Sisters, looking north from the California Trail as it leaves the Silent City of Rocks, (October, 1992).

159

Aerial view looking east at the Silent City of Rocks, (October, 1990). The fins of the Almo Granite pluton (intruded about 30 million years ago) trend north-northwest. In the distance is the old stage station west of Almo at the entrance to the City of Rocks.

View of rhyolite lava on the summit of the Cotterel Mountains, east of Albion, looking east across the Raft River Valley to the snow-covered northern Sublett Range (March, 1995).

Foliated quartzite of Oakley stone, Albion Range. Rock is Late Proterozoic schistose Clark's Basin Quartzite, (September, 1979).

of the Green Creek Complex, exposed where the Mount Harrison road turns off Highway 22.

The contact between the sedimentary rocks and the gneissic basement is a ductile fault or mylonite zone, the Middle Mountain Shear zone, produced during rapid uplift and stretching of the earth's crust from about 40 to 10 million years ago.

The bedrock in the Silent City of Rocks is an Oligocene granite pluton which cooled about 30 million years ago. The granite intrudes gneiss of the Green Creek Complex. The City of Rocks pluton is the youngest granitic body in Idaho. The rock is coarse-grained and unfoliated. It weathers into characteristic rounded monoliths and elongate fins controlled by systems of joints produced by unloading during uplift.

On the south edge of the City of Rocks, at the Twin Sisters, called the Sentinels or the Citadels by immigrants, just north of the California Trail, the contact between the 2400 million year Archean Green Creek Complex (South Sister) and the 30 million year Oligocene City of Rocks Granite (North Sister) can be seen.

A unique type of Oakley stone is the green micaceous quartzite seen on the front of many 20th century buildings in southern Idaho and northern Utah. The green color of this "Elba Quartzite" is given by a Chromium-bearing mica, fuchsite.

Sublett Range

The Sublett Range west of Rockland Valley is composed of upper Paleozoic sedimentary rocks, mainly limestone, from which many fossil corals and other invertebrates can be collected. Because the bedrock is limestone, surface water is sparse, since water sinks into underground channels.

Cotterel and Jim Sage mountains

The Jim Sage mountains west of Raft River Valley contain several tilted Miocene rhyolite lava flows and ash-flow tuffs. They are best known for rattlesnakes and obsidian.

Settlement of the Cassia County Area

The first settlers to Cassia County area were Mormon emigrants from northwestern Utah, who came in the early 1870s. Beecherville (now Elba, named after the Mediterranean island where Napoleon had been in exile) was founded on upper Cassia Creek, eighteen miles east of Oakley, in 1873. Almo was founded in 1878 and named Alamo, after the great cottonwoods that grew there. The name became shortened to Almo.

Mary Jane Gorringe Tolman, quoted in Arrington (1979, p. 38-39) speaks of Mormon cooperative farming in the Oakley area in the 1880s.

"In the spring we were very desirous of planting some crop, but could see no way out only to put our trust in the One who rules over us. At morning and evening in our prayers, we petitioned our Father in Heaven to help us . . . While my husband was in Oakley, a Brother William Whittle came to him and said, "Brother Tolman, do you need a little money to help you put your crop in? If so, I have $10 I can loan you till fall." A brother C.H. Carlson came to him and said, "I understand you have no team. You can take my team to put your crop in." My husband came home rejoicing. We felt that God had been good to us."

Albion

Albion, at the foot of the range that bears its name, was called Marsh Valley and used by cattlemen in the 1860s. It was settled in 1869 and was county seat of Cassia County from 1879 to 1919.

In the 1890s, J.E. Miller, one of Albion's Pioneers, gave 5 acres of land for a Normal School. In 1893, Idaho's second legislature established 2 normal schools, one of which was at Albion. The college was closed in a cost-cutting move in 1952. Its fine buildings stand today, in a state of purgatory between destruction and restoration.

Mount Harrison and Lake Cleveland

In 1888, a controversy arose over naming of the mountain south of Albion. Mormons from Elba wanted to commemorate Democratic President Grover Cleveland. Republicans from Albion wanted to honor the new President Benjamin Harrison. Harrison won the Presidential election and the mountain was named after him. The glacially carved lake below the summit was named after Cleveland.

Settling of Oakley

The largest group of LDS migrants into south-central Idaho was the one that founded Oakley and other towns in the Goose Creek valley. This migration began in 1879 and consisted of residents mainly from Tooele and Grantsville, Utah. Oakley quickly became the headquarters for the Mormon community in southern Idaho. Horton David Haight, a veteran of the Mormon settlement at Nauvoo, became the first bishop of Cassia Ward. His father was the first settler of Farmington, Davis County, Utah. Haight served as first president of the Cassia stake from 1887 to 1890. The children from the union of Horton and Louise Haight became prominent citizens of early day Oakley and built most of the large brick houses which still stand. Victorian style architecture was still in vogue there, in the 1890s, even if it had lost its popularity in the rest of the U.S.

By the time other Magic Valley communities developed, twenty years later, bungalows and cottages were the architectural standard.

Main administration and classroom building at Albion College in June 1991. Although the lilacs are in flower and the grounds maintained, the college has been abandoned since 1952.

In 1905, Oakley had 2,000 people. Rails came in 1910. The town, in the 1990s sits at the western gate to the Silent City of Rocks and has potential as a tourist center, even though such catering to the whims of long-haired out-of-state rock-climbing tourists is antithetic to the ideological foundations of the city.

Victorian brick home, built in the 1890s in Oakley, Idaho, (July, 1992).

	SECOND CLASS				Time Table No. 77			SECOND CLASS
Length of Sidings in feet, elevation of scales, Fuel and Turning Stations	Hours Operators on Duty	**123** Mixed	Distance from Burley		December 13, 1914.	Distance from Oakley	**124** Mixed	
		Leave Daily Ex. Sunday			STATIONS		Arrive Daily Ex. Sunday	
19,198 WY	8AM to 8PM	11.00AM	0.0	D-R	**BURLEY** Bu 3.2	21.8	3.30PM	
823		11.10	3.2		BEETVILLE (Spur) 2.0	18.6	3.21	
1,617		11.17	5.2		PELLA 3.9 (Spur)	16.6	3.16	
791		11.26	9.1		KENYON (Spur) 7.4	12.7	3.10	
678		11.46	16.5		TROUT (Spur) 1.3	5.3	2.50	
1,750		11.51AM	17.8		MARION 4.0	4.0	2.45	
5,742 Y	8AM to 8PM	12.01PM	21.8	D-R	**OAKLEY** Oa	0.0	2.35PM	
		Arrive Daily Ex. Sunday			(21.8)		Leave Daily Ex. Sunday	
		(1.01) 21.4			....Time over District.... ....Average speed per hour....		(0.55) 23.8	

December 1914 rail schedule, Oakley Branch.

Raft River Valley

In the early 1800s, Raft River was a deep stream that inconvenienced trappers and travelers. Today it is depleted by upstream irrigation and is a muddy ghost of its former self.

A major effort at exploration for geothermal energy was made in the 1980s in the Raft River Valley south of Malta. A pilot plant for production of electricity by geothermal means was constructed by the Department of Energy, but the effort has not proven economically feasible.

Burley

Burley was settled in about 1910, as the headquarters for the Minidoka and Southern Railroad, and named for the first rail agent. Union Pacific completed building of the Twin Falls Branch line after taking over the Minidoka and Southern. The flat and productive fields between Oakley and Burley are irrigated with water from Goose Creek Reservoir, to the south of Oakley.

References

Arrington, L.J., 1979, The Mormon Settlement of Cassia County, Idaho 1873-1921: Idaho Yesterdays, v. 23, no. 2, p. 36-46.

Bandy, Philip J., 1992, Structural and kinematic analysis of the City of Rocks lobe of the Almo Pluton, Cassia Co., Idaho: An application of granite tectonics [M.S. thesis]: Pocatello and Boise, Idaho: Idaho State University and Boise State University, 105 p.

Madsen, B. D., 1993, The "Almo Massacre" revisited: Idaho Yesterdays, v. 37, no. 3, p. 54-64.

Maley, Terry, 1987, Exploring Idaho Geology: Mineral Land Publications, P.O. Box 1186, Boise, Idaho, 83701, 232 p.

Maughan, Ralph W., 1992, Anatomy of the Snake River Plain: An Amateur's View, Pocatello, Idaho: The Idaho State University Press, 69 p.

Miller, David M., Armstrong, R.L., Compton, R.R., and Todd, V.R., 1983, Geology of the Albion-Raft River-Grouse Creek Mountains area, northwestern Utah and southern Idaho: *in* Gurgel, K.D., editor, Geologic excursions in the overthrust belt and metamorphic core complexes of the Intermountain region: Utah Geological and Mineral Survey Special Studies 59, p. 1-63.

Mytton, James, W., Williams, Paul L., and Morgan, William A., 1990, Geologic map of the Stricker 4 Quadrangle, Cassia County, Idaho: U.S. Geological Survey Miscellaneous Investigations Series, Map I-2052, scale 1:48,000.

Saltzer, S.D., and Hodges, K.V., 1988, The Middle Mountain Shear zone, southern Idaho: Kinematic analysis of an early Tertiary high-temperature detachment: Geological Society of American Bulletin, v. 100, p. 96-103.

Wright, Bessie, M., Oakley, Idaho, Cassia County, Pioneer Town: 1987, Horizon Publishers, Bountiful, Utah, 211 p.

Williams, P.L., Covington, H.R., and Pierce, K.L., 1982, Cenozoic stratigraphy and tectonic evolution of the Raft River Basin, Idaho: *in* Bonnichsen, B., and Breckenridge, R.M., eds., Cenozoic geology of Idaho: Idaho Bureau of Mines and Geology Bulletin 26, p. 491-504.

Williams, P.L., Mytton, J.W., and Covington, H.R., 1990, Geologic map of the Stricker 1 quadrangle, Cassia, Twin Falls, and Jerome Counties, Idaho: U.S. Geological Survey Miscellaneous Investigations Series Map I-2078, scale 1:24,000.

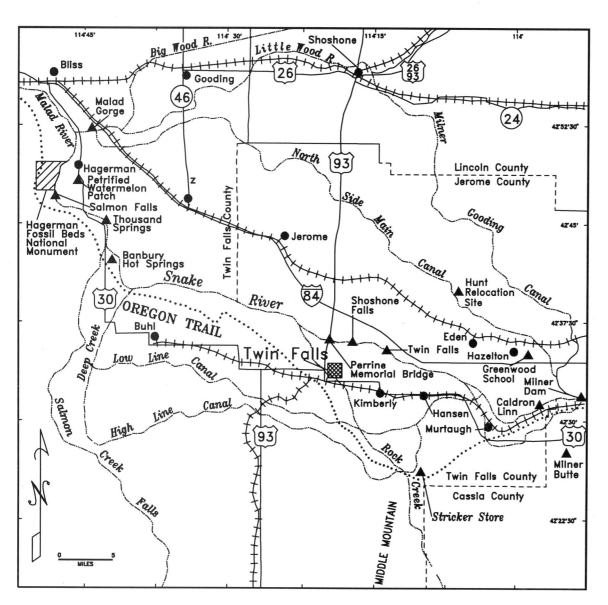

Map of Twin Falls area.

Twin Falls Area

Twin Falls is located on the south side of the Snake River Canyon in an area of Pleistocene lake beds. The soil is deep and rich except in areas scoured by the Lake Bonneville Flood on the north side of the canyon where the volcanic bedrock or fields of boulders or "petrified watermelons" remain.

The canyon of the Snake River exposes Miocene rhyolite underneath the cover of basalt lava. At Shoshone Falls and Twin Falls the Snake River cascades over this rhyolite in waterfalls carved during the catastrophic Lake Bonneville Flood about 14,500 years ago. Shoshone Falls are 212 feet high, higher than Niagara.

The dry waterfalls or alcoves (Blue Lakes alcove) north of the Snake River were also carved during the Bonneville flood.

Old Hansen suspension bridge over the Snake River, opened in 1919. It was originally two lanes, but as cars became wider the bridge was reduced to one lane. The old bridge was replaced with the present concrete bridge in 1966. Abe Lillibridge collection, Idaho State University.

Snake River Canyon at Murtaugh Bridge, looking west, downstream. The town of Murtaugh is immediately to the left of the view. Note the scoured Bonneville Flood path, on which there is not enough soil to grow even irrigated crops. Caldron Linn is just upstream (to the right) from here, (July, 1989).

Shoshone Falls, moderate water flow, (March, 1993).

Shoshone Falls in one of the rare times of high water flow, (May, 1983). The falls are cut in rhyolite lava beneath the basalt cap of the Snake River Plain. Photo was taken near the site of a hotel built for railroad visitors from Shoshone in 1886. This was replaced by a larger hotel in 1890 which, in later years, was served from Twin Falls by an electric interurban line.

Twin Falls, 125 feet high, before 1910. A power plant now blocks the right (south) channel. Abe Lillibridge collection, Idaho State University Library.

Caldron Linn, a narrow waterfall along the Snake River west of Milner Dam. The name was chosen by the Hunt Party of Astorians, who in 1811 abandoned their attempt at navigating the Snake at this place. The word "Linn" is an old Scottish word for waterfall. The boiling waters were likened to a caldron (cauldron). During low water a person can almost jump over the river at the narrowest point, (March, 1993).

Aerial view looking west, (June, 1991), of the Lake Bonneville Flood path near Murtaugh east of Twin Falls. The south branch of the flood followed the Snake River Canyon here while the farmland to the north of the river was not eroded by the flood waters. The north branch of the flood passed through the scoured basalt in the far right distance. The Hiline Canal can be seen to the south of the river.

"We Sagebrush Folks"

Farm life in the Magic Valley near Hazelton, as evocatively described by Annie Greenwood in "We Sagebrush Folks," was cruel. Even with the new irrigation schemes, there was never enough water. After several wet years, 1919 saw a severe drought. The Twin Falls Canal Company supplied only 30% of its normal amount.

Annie Pike Greenwood was the first school teacher in the Hazelton area. She was an educated woman who grew up in Provo, Utah, and wrote poignantly about early farm life in the Magic Valley. Her husband had dreamed of being a farmer, though he came from an upper class German family. They homesteaded in Hazelton in 1906, and soon after, the North Side (Milner-Jerome) canal was constructed. She said in retrospect "The last thing in the world I wanted to do was to go on a farm." It was never easy, and at times brutal, raising a family of four in beautiful, gentle yet harsh, rural Idaho. They lost the farm in 1924. "We lost the farm, thank God!" She became a teacher and a writer after leaving her husband, who sold insurance and then worked for the Soil Conservation Service. The Greenwood home and the Greenwood Community School can be seen just north of Interstate 84, east of Twin Falls. The Albion Mountains (her Minidokas) rise to the south.

Mount Harrison of the Albion Range (the Minidokas of Annie Pike Greenwood) viewed from Interstate 84 near Hazelton, (August, 1992).

Greenwood School, north of Interstate 84, east of Hazelton. Annie Pike Greenwood was the first teacher at this school in the 1910s. This is a sad picture of abandoned hopes. The school was formerly surrounded by huge cottonwood trees, (April, 1993).

Annie Pike Greenwood on farming near Hazelton (1934):

"Never were nights so sweet as those in Idaho. The air seemed to caress you; millions and millions of stars glowed in such a depth of the heavens as I have never seen elsewhere. Every sense was awakened, and soothed. Such was my first Idaho night . . . . Such was the last night I ever spent there. Such were nearly all the nights I saw and heard and breathed there." (p. 23).

"All my senses resounded to that sagebrush farm. Never a day passed that I was not thrilled with the changing beauty of the vast cloud-filled skies, the purple and gold sunsets, the blue and white mountains, our gray and green valley, our own lovely, undulating farm, with its ivory wheat-fields, its green beet-fields, its purple-blooming alfalfa. I loved to go to sleep to the chorus of the crickets in the grass just outside my window, with its thorough-bass of the frogs down along the canal. The cool, delightful summer nights; the limitless stretches of clean, white winter snow." (p. 170-171)

"The sweet November rain in Idaho, fragrant, musical, soaking the ground in preparation for winter, running in streams from eaves-- intoxicating delight of calm, delicately gray November days." (p. 136-137).

"I could see the road below, and the sight I saw will never again be duplicated-- a river of rabbits, running from west to east, the closely packed little animals moving like rippling water, on their way somewhere. And near at hand, because we were the invaders of the wilderness and not they, the sharp, staccato barks of the desert dogs, coyotes, and their long, maniacal wails. The sight, the sound, they struck a chill to my heart." (p. 94)

"As I sat forcing myself to study after school, when I was already tired beyond my strength, I often lifted my eyes from my books, and there through the window, across the dazzling, alabaster snow, the cold, white Minidokas stood, monumental, veined with blue, a faint pinkish light illuminating them from the setting sun. I forgot the page I had been studying, and a chill struck to my heart." (p. 94).

Aerial view of Twin Falls and alcoves where the Lake Bonneville Flood emptied back into the Snake River. Note the lack of soil on the north side of the river where it was all eroded by the flood, (June, 1990).

December, 1914 Timetable for the Northside Branch of the Oregon Short Line.

Rock Creek Store and Stricker Ranch

The Oregon Trail, and, in the 1860s, the Kelton, Utah to Boise, Idaho freight road, crossed Rock Creek about 6 miles south of what is now Hansen. This crossing avoided the deep canyon of Rock Creek to the north. The Rock Creek Store was built on this site in 1865, and purchased by Herman Stricker in 1876. After the closure of Fort Hall in 1856, this was the only place on the Snake River Plain where provisions could be pur-

Blue Lakes Alcove and spring-fed lake, looking north. Alcove was cut during the Lake Bonneville Flood, 14,500 years ago, (March, 1993).

chased east of Fort Boise. The Stricker family lived here for almost 100 years and served travelers, miners, dam construction personnel, and ranchers. The site and original buildings have been preserved by the Friends of Stricker Ranch, Inc., P.O. Box 2218, Twin Falls.

The Carey Act and Milner Dam

Ira Burton Perrine spearheaded the construction of Milner Dam and the Twin Falls project which was completed in 1905. At the time this was the largest privately financed irrigation project in the world. The Magic Valley lived up to its name and boom towns sprang up. This boom was directly caused by the availability of irrigation water. Investors (Wendell and Jerome Hill, Buhl, Hansen, Milner) in Perrine's scheme got towns named for them. Other towns founded after construction of the Twin Falls project included Kimberly, Filer, Hazelton and Eden.

In 1905, the rail line was finished to Twin Falls and on to the end of the branch at Buhl. By the end of the year, Twin Falls had a bank, doctor, attorney, dentist, barber, school, newspaper, restaurant and rooming house.

Sheep and Cattle Grazing

Cattle boomed in central Idaho in the late 1870s. Sheep came later, and the Idaho woolgrowers organized in 1893. Future governor Frank R. Gooding was president and the sheep industry held great political power in the early 20th century. As with other western rangelands, bitter conflict between sheepherders and cowboys ensued.

Road sign near King Hill, west of Twin Falls, (October, 1990). The petrified watermelons are boulders of basalt moved by the Lake Bonneville Flood about 14,500 years ago.

Malad River (Big Wood River) in Malad Gorge State Park. View looks downstream (southwest). The narrow canyon is geologically very young, cut in the last 2 million years, (March, 1993).

Hagerman Valley

The sheltered Hagerman Valley, with nearby towns appropriately named (Bliss), has a long growing season and abundant water supply, in stark contrast to the mountain and desert country just a few miles north or south of the Snake River Canyon. The Snake River here and to the west near King Hill, contains several "fields, or patches" of "Petrified watermelons," piles of basalt boulders left by the Lake Bonneville Flood.

The Hagerman Fossil Beds National Monument contains bones of Miocene horses, camels and other large animals that roamed the shores of Lake Idaho (a lake that occupied much of the Snake River Plain) between 7 and 3 million years ago.

View looking north at the Snake River Canyon below Murtaugh, west of Milner Dam. On the north side of the Snake River the road heads due north to beautiful downtown Hazelton. Greenwood is south of Hazelton and north of the Interstate Highway. The South Side Main Canal (Twin Falls Canal) parallels the river. The country in the distance that is not farmed is the scabland east of Eden. The farmland in the distance is near the Hunt relocation site, a World War II Japanese-American concentration camp, along the North Side Main Canal, (July, 1989).

References

Greenwood, Annie Pike, 1934, reprinted 1988, We Sagebrush Folks: Moscow, Idaho, The University Press of Idaho, 489p.

Malde, H.E., 1987, Shoshone Falls, Idaho; A Pleistocene relic of the catastrophic Bonneville Flood: *in* Beus, S.S., editor, Rocky Mountain Section of the Geological Society of America: Boulder, Colorado, Geological Society of America Centennial Field Guide, Volume 2, p. 135-138.

Malde, H.E., and Powers, H.A., 1972, Geologic map of the Glenns Ferry—Hagerman area, west-central Snake River Plain, Idaho: U.S. Geological Survey Miscellaneous Geologic Investigations Map I-696, scale 1:48,000.

Stearns, H.T., Crandall, L., and Steward, W.G., 1938, Geology and ground-water resources of the Snake River Plain in southeastern Idaho: U.S. Geological Survey Water-Supply Paper 774, 268 p.

Whitehead, R.L., 1986, Geohydrologic framework of the Snake River Plain, Idaho and eastern Oregon: U.S. Geological Survey Hydrologic Investigations Atlas HA-681, scale 1:1,000,000.

Whitehead, R.L., and Covington, H.R., 1987, Thousand Springs area near Hagerman, Idaho, *in* Beus, S.S., editor, Rocky Mountain Section of the Geological Society of America: Boulder, Colorado, Geological Society of America Centennial Field Guide, Volume 2, p.131-134.

Waterfalls coming from part of the Thousand Springs on the north bank of the Snake River where the Snake River Plain Aquifer empties into the Snake River and feeds America's largest trout farming businesses, (May, 1986).

Waterfall below Interstate 84, Malad Gorge, (March, 1993).

Wood River Valley

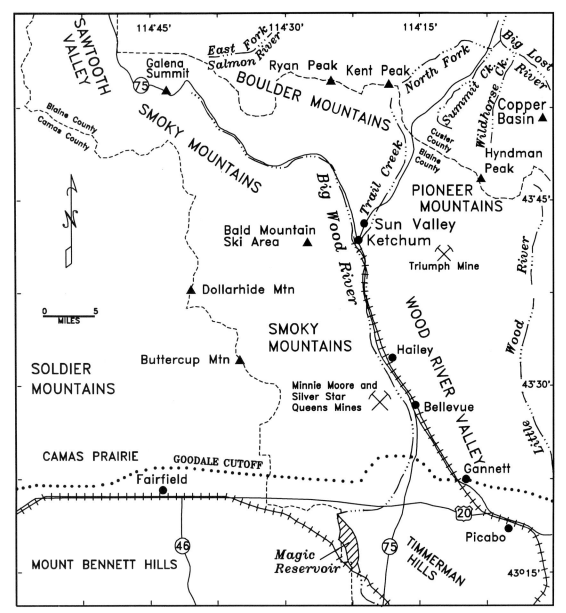

Abandoned mill, built in 1880s, in Boulder Basin, north of Ketchum, (July, 1987). This mill served the Golden Glow and Boulder Consolidated mines and produced silver-lead-zinc ore with smaller amounts of gold and copper.

View from the top of Mt. Baldy at the Sun Valley ski area, looking south (Jan. 1995). The Seattle Ridge Lodge (built 1994) is in the middle distance, with the southern Wood River Valley beyond. The streets of Hailey are easily visible.

Map of Wood River Valley and Camas Prairie.

Geology of the Wood River Area

The flat, alluvium-filled Wood River Valley is the gateway to the Pioneer and Sawtooth Mountains of central Idaho. The steep hills near the river are underlain by Paleozoic dark-colored shale and limestone. To the west is the great Atlanta lobe of the Cretaceous Idaho batholith. Most of the rich mineral deposits of the region are hosted by black shales of the Devonian Milligen formation and formed during Cretaceous magmatic activity and deformation. To the east is the geologically complex Pioneer Mountains core complex, which contains, in the high peaks, complexly deformed Early Proterozoic metamorphic rock intruded by Eocene plutons. Eocene volcanic rocks of the Challis Volcanic Group cover large parts of the area west of Hailey and Ketchum.

The Goodale Cutoff

Originally used by Oregon Trail emigrants, the Goodale Cutoff followed an Indian trail along the present route of U.S. Highway 20 from Carey over the summit north of the Queen's Crown and across the Camas Prairie. In the spring, near Fairfield and Hill City, the marshy areas are purple with the blooms of camas plants. Indians harvested the bulbs of this member of the lily family as a much valued food source.

Shield volcano north of Shoshone, (June, 1992).

The Camas War of 1878

The invasion of Europeans into western Indian lands was overwhelming to the native populations. Old ways of life could be followed no longer; tribal customs were subverted by the white society; old hunting and gathering lands were being turned into towns and farms. The reaction of many tribes was resignation. The technological and monetary power of American society was all too obvious and pervasive.

In 1878, the Fort Hall Bannock Indians, under Chief Buffalo Horn, found that settlers in the Camas Prairie east of Fairfield had cut up the marshes into fields. Cattle and horses were pastured on land where the Indians had gathered camas roots for generations. Pigs were allowed to dig up the roots that had been one of the Indians' major food sources. This provocation, on top of a general atmosphere of tension, led to a series of attacks in the summer of 1878.

Chief Buffalo Horn and his followers moved southwest from Fort Hall, toward their ancestral lands in Nevada, raiding as they went. They destroyed property and killed settlers and freighters at King Hill, in the vicinity of Glenns Ferry, and in the Bruneau Valley. Several skirmishes with irregular white forces resulted in the death of Buffalo Horn and some of his followers.

New recruits were picked up along the way from malcontent and restless tribes. Some battles took place in the vicinity of the Owyhee River and the band, now numbering several hundred, headed for the John Day country. Regular army forces under General Howard, aided by friendly Umatilla Indians, caught up with the marauders and the leaders were slain, bringing an end to the outbreak. The warriors broke into small groups and gradually returned to their reservations. The Camas War was the final blow to Indian rebellion. It was followed generally by an attitude of sullen and sated subjugation that has lasted for nearly a hundred years.

Fairfield

Fairfield is the county seat of Camas County, which in 1990 was the least populous county in Idaho, with 727 persons. Clark County was next with 762 persons. Fairfield is a long way economically and culturally from its upscale neighbors in the Wood River Valley.

Buttercup Mountain looking north up Willow Creek from Camas Prairie, northeast of Fairfield, (August, 1987). The mountain is underlain by Cretaceous rocks of the Idaho batholith and capped by Eocene Challis Volcanic Group.

Historical Marker south of Magic Dam on the Big Wood River south of Bellevue, (June, 1991). The dry years of 1987-1992 caused this reservoir to run out of water early and to deprive downstream farmers of irrigation water. The magic had ended. In 1990 and 1991 the water ran out in early July; in 1992 the water ran out in late May. After a wet year in 1993, when water was plentiful, 1994 was very dry and the canals were again empty. 1995 and 1996 were wet years.

Mining in the Wood River Valley

Early discoveries of mineralized quartz veins west of Hailey occurred in the 1860s, but Indian opposition culminating in the Bannock War of 1878 slowed development. Idaho miners concentrated their efforts farther west near Idaho City. By 1880, however, new technology for refining lead-silver ore had been developed, and the rush to the Wood River mines came with thousands of fortune hunters. The Oregon Short Line, financed by Jay Gould, followed the miners in 1882-1883, and the area boomed. Lead-silver mines became the staple of Idaho's mining economy and in the 1890s, Idaho politicians were solidly behind the doomed silver standard for the U.S. currency.

The first discoveries in the Wood River area were in May 1879, when David Ketchum found a few small lead-silver prospects near Galena Summit. The Queen of the Hills west of Bellevue was discovered in July of that year. Ketchum, Bellevue, and Hailey were settled in 1880. Smelters were built in Hailey and Ketchum in 1881, and Idaho's first electric light system and one of Idaho's first telephone systems were installed in Hailey in 1882. Investor capital poured into the area from St. Louis and Philadelphia. A branch of the Oregon Short Line reached Hailey in 1883 and Ketchum in 1884. Production from the Wood River mines was over $2 million a year from 1885 to 1887.

But the price of silver was falling and labor troubles developed. The output decreased sharply in 1888 and nearly stopped in 1892, with the collapse of the price of silver. Ketchum was nearly abandoned.

Mining was by no means finished as the Triumph mine southeast of Ketchum produced about $28 million between 1936 and 1957. Now in 1993, it is an Environmental protection agency "Super Fund Site." Ore was brought down from the mine to the Ketchum branch of the Union Pacific on an overhead tramway to Zinc Spur siding near present-day Ketchum. The Minnie Moore Mine was in active use until 1970. The entire production of the Wood River mines is over $62 million.

Midsummer view up Trail Creek to the Pioneer Mountains, north of Sun Valley, (July, 1987). The Trail Creek road snakes up the southeast side of the canyon.

West face of the Boulder Mountains, looking northwest from Idaho Highway 75, (February, 1987). Glacial moraines cover the low hills in the foreground. Eocene granite forms the low cliffs on the mountains, with Eocene dacite porphyry and Paleozoic sedimentary rocks above. The mountains are uplifted along a normal fault that bounds the east side of the Wood River Valley.

Photograph at left was taken at Ketchum, Idaho in the 1880s during the Wood River Valley mining boom. The Oregon Short Line had just reached the Wood River Valley and prosperity abounded. The bearded man holding his hat is Jay Gould, financier of the OSL. The older woman holding her hands together to the left of Gould is his wife. The woman in the polka dot dress in unidentified. Minnie Howard Collection, Idaho State University.

Passenger train just into the Shoshone Shops after a snowstorm on the Hill City (Fairfield) Branch about 1930. Arthur Peterson collection, Bannock County Historical Museum.

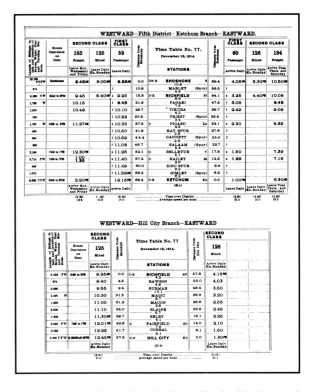

December, 1914, Union Pacific Timetables for Ketchum and Hill City Branches.

The north (Warm Springs) side of Bald Mountain, looking across the Big Wood River from north of Ketchum, February, 1987. Sun Peak in the foreground is underlain by Eocene dacite lava flows of the Challis Volcanic Group. Bald Mountain is underlain by Upper Paleozoic Sun Valley Group sedimentary rocks.

Sheep Grazing

Sheep and cattle raising became the main industries in the Wood River Valley in the 1890s. During this time more sheep were shipped on the Union Pacific from Ketchum than from any other point in the United States.

Sun Valley Resort

W. Averill Harriman, Chairman of the Board of the Union Pacific Railroad, arranged that Count Felix Schaffgotsch (an Austrian) should tour in 1935 the areas in the Rocky Mountains served by the railroad to locate a site for a resort to serve the newly growing sport of alpine skiing. Although the southern Wood River Valley is open, bare, and hardly alpine, the valley narrows to the north at Ketchum and the hills boast spectacular vistas of the Boulder, Pioneer, and Smoky Mountains.

Harriman bought the 3,888 acre Brass Ranch where the Sun Valley resort is located for $10.04 an acre in spring 1936. He proceeded to build a luxury resort where, in his words, "There isn't a single thing I could wish for that hasn't been provided." The Lodge cost $1,500,000 and was completed in December of that year. It was to become a resort for the rich and famous. In the last ten years, the area has grown faster than any nearby part of Idaho. Many say it resembles a piece of California transported to the Wood River. The transformation from slow and shabby Idaho ranch town to modern resort replete with million dollar homes occurs in distinct steps

Ketchum Fast Freight Line, about 1890. View looks west across the Wood River and up Warm Spring Creek near site of the Oregon Short Line passenger station. Photo number P-1100, Palmer Lewis Collection, Community Library, Ketchum, Idaho; used by permission.

as one drives north from Carey to Picabo to Gannet to Bellevue to Hailey to Ketchum to Sun Valley. The first time along the road is a strange trip for an Idahoan.

Naturally flocked trees, Sun Valley ski area (Jan. 1995).

Shoshone

As settlers began spreading throughout southern Idaho, some gathered at a spot along the Little Wood River. They called the community Bottoms. A few years later plans were announced by Oregon Short Line Railway Company to build a railroad through southern Idaho and this road would pass through the community. By late 1882, when the railway reached the town, it applied for a post office, to be named Naples.

Construction of the railway to the west halted while the Oregon Short Line built its first branch, extending into the mountains to the north to serve the mines at Hailey, which it reached in 1883. Later, the branch was extended to Ketchum where shipments of livestock were handled. The junction town was named Shoshone.

Heavyweight Pullman sleeping cars at Ketchum Train Station, late 1930s, view looks west toward the Wood River and Warm Spring Creek. The car in the center is a Ford from the late 1930s. Jeanne Lane Collection, Community Library, Ketchum, Idaho; used by permission.

Sun Valley resort and home to the rich and famous, Wood River Valley, looking southeast toward the Pioneer Mountains, (July, 1987).

Sun Valley
by Harald Wyndham

It's so refreshing, after the seemingly
endless parade of beautiful, gaunt aristocrats
in chic, expensive jogging suits and suntans,
to see, in Giaccobi Square, one genuine housewife,
a bit plump, wearing yellow bermudas with her hair
tied up in a bandana, pushing a grocery cart
between the BMWs and Porsches in the parking lot,
to load two bags of ordinary bread, milk, and vegetables
into the trunk of a battered-up blue 1967 Pontiac.

in Wyndman, editor, Famous Potatoes, 1986

Things to Do in Bellevue
Rick Ardinger

Ride your bike down Broadford Road
  and wet a line in the Wood.
Buy every calendar, box of cookies, Lion's Club
  broom, Jehovah's Witness pamphlet,
  and Boy Scout raffle ticket
from anyone who knocks at your door.
Write friends in Chicago, Portland and
  Pittsburgh
that the weather's great and will stay that way.
Trade garden advice and vegetables with
  neighbors.
Bump into friends in the skinny aisles of
  Glenn's Grocery.
Let your dog walk free as a man gone mad with
  laughter.
Stagger home from the Silver Dollar
  and howl at the waxing moon.
Buy a house with a leaky roof and a broken-
  down fence,
raise some kids, and stack the wood high for
  winter.
Keep four junk cars and a snarling dog between
  you and the IRS.
Make love while the church bells ring on
  Sunday, then walk to Guffy's for milk, eggs
  and a paper.
Walk heel to toe along a rail where trains don't
  ride anymore.
Shovel your roof after a storm and wave to
  others doing the same.
Stand on your porch late at night
  and watch the snow come down again.
Dress up crazy for the Labor Day parade.
Smile your widest smile when people from
  Ketchum
make jokes about Bellevue and keep what's
  secret.
Praise Jesus, praise Buddha, praise the
  mountains
crawling around you whenever you read about
  smog in L.A., Denver and Boise.

from Wyndham, editor, Things to do in Idaho,
  1989, p. 10.

Shoshone and the Railroad

After the Wood River Branch was completed, the main line continued to the west, and Shoshone became a substantial railroad community. A roundhouse was constructed, along with shops. A few years later, as the Oregon Short Line expanded its operations, a major division point and repair facility was established at Pocatello. Both Shoshone and Eagle Rock (Idaho Falls) were consolidated into the Pocatello operation, and the roundhouse at each locality was discontinued.

Shoshone remained the principal entry point for railroad services to the Wood River mines and communities, being the branch line terminal for both the Ketchum and Hill City lines. The town was the point of origin during the 1880s and 1890s for tours to Shoshone Falls, but with the development of farming lands in the Twin Falls area shortly after 1900, this business ceased. After Sun Valley was built in the 1930s, passengers bound for Sun Valley for skiing were transported from Shoshone by bus.

Sheep and cattle raising have become the major industries of Lincoln County, of which Shoshone is the county seat. Railroad operations have gradually nearly disappeared. Shoshone remains a stop for Amtrak trains (in the middle of the night, as usual) affording passenger service to the Wood River and Magic Valleys.

Special Union Pacific passenger train at Bellevue, 1972. Train is composed of both single and double deck cars, and powered by cab-style General Motors, Electromotive Division Diesel engines. Dick Beardsley Collection, Community Library, Ketchum, Idaho, Photo number 1025; used by permission.

Abandoned Oregon Short Line railroad bridge over the Wood River, south of Ketchum. The bridge is now used by a bike trail system, (March, 1993).

Collapsed lava tube north of Shoshone, (June, 1992).

References

Link, P.K., and Hackett, W.R., editors, 1988, Guidebook to the geology of central and southern Idaho: Idaho Geological Survey Bulletin 27, 318 p.

Link, P.K., Kuntz, M.A., and Platt, L.B., editors, 1992, Regional Geology of Eastern Idaho and Western Wyoming: Geological Society of America Memoir 179, 310 p.

Taylor, Dorice, 1980, Sun Valley: Sun Valley, Idaho, Ex Libris, Sun Valley, Idaho 83353, 264 p.

Wells, Merle W., 1983, Gold Camps and Silver Cities; Nineteenth century mining in central and southern Idaho (2nd edition): Idaho Bureau of Mines and Geology Bulletin 22, 165 p.

Worl, R.G., Kiilsgaard, T.H., Bennett, E.H., Link, P.K., Lewis, R.S., Mitchell, V.E., Johnson, K.M., and Snyder, L.D., 1991, Geologic map of the Hailey 1° x 2° quadrangle, Idaho: U.S. Geological Survey Open-File report 91-340, scale 1:250,000.

Wyndham, Harald, editor, 1989, Things to do in Idaho: Pocatello, Idaho, Blue Scarab Press, 243 S. 8th Avenue, Pocatello, Idaho 83201, 40 p.

Wyndham, Harald, editor, 1986, Famous Potatoes, Southeast Idaho Poetry: Pocatello, Idaho, Blue Scarab Press, 243 S. 8th Avenue, Pocatello, Idaho 83201, 64 p.

Mackay, Lower Cedar Creek canyon and Mount McCaleb, looking northeast from the Empire Copper Mine in the White Knob Mountains, 1930s; Bannock County Historical Society collection.

Brush fire northeast of Pocatello Creek Road, (September, 1992). Airplane is returning to Pocatello airport after dropping fire retardant. Such fires are common in Southeastern Idaho in the summer and fall.

About the Authors

E. Chilton Phoenix

Phoenix claims to be a native son of Idaho, having been conceived in Pocatello, although born in Portland, Oregon, in 1921. When he was 11, his family moved to Jerome ("The Mother City") and he has lived in Idaho ever since except for military service in World War II and attendance at law school. He was in private practice in Pocatello until he joined the law department of Union Pacific Railroad Company from which he retired after 35 years of service. He has a B.A. from the University of Idaho and a J.D. from Stanford University. He has been active in historical pursuits, being one of the founders of the Bannock County Historical Society, a long-time member of the Oregon-California Trails Association and the first state president of OCTA. He has written and lectured extensively on Idaho history, has taught history at Idaho State University and is a lecturer on historical subjects in Elderhostel programs offered at ISU. He is an adjunct professor in the ISU Sociology Department.

Rocks, Rails and Trails field trip, September 1987, right to left, Chilton Phoenix, Paul Link and Leigh Gittins. In the background is the Portneuf Range and the Utah and Northern narrow-gauge roadbed south of Inkom. Photo by Dianna Troyer.

Paul Link (with hat) and Chilton Phoenix enjoying life and each other, Rocks, Rails and Trails field trip, City of Rocks, September 1987. Photo by Dianna Troyer.

Paul Karl Link

Born in Madison, Wisconsin in 1953. Link was named after his father, Karl Paul Link, a biochemist at the University of Wisconsin, who developed the anticoagulent compound Coumadin, from which the drug Dicoumarol and the rat poison Warfarin are synthesized. Paul came to Idaho first in 1976 to start his Ph.D. thesis on the Pocatello Formation. He was lucky to be hired by the Idaho State University Geology Department in 1980. He has a B.S. from Yale University, a B.Sc. Hons. from the University of Adelaide, South Australia and a Ph.D. from the University of California, Santa Barbara. He is presently Professor of Geology and was Department Chair from 1986-1993. He is on the Board of Directors of the Portneuf Greenway Foundation. He and his wife Katie, with canine companions Blue (1980-1996), Rosie and Major Mitchell, live on the Pocatello West Bench, near where the photos on p. 114 and upper left p. 136. were taken.

Lieut. Commander John Philip Sousa and Committee
-Feb. 2 1926 Pocatello, Idaho-
-Shop Band and Employes.   Union Pacific Station-

References Cited

Alt, D., and Hyndman, D.W., 1995, Northwest Exposures—A geologic story of the Northwest: Missoula, Mt., Mountain Press Publishing Co., 443 p.

Anderson, A.L., 1928, Portland cement materials near Pocatello, Idaho: Idaho Bureau of Mines and Geology Pamphlet 28, 15 p.

Anonymous, 1976, Gold Mines of Cariboo Mountain, Idaho Yesterdays, v. 19 no. 4, p. 10-15.

Armstrong, F.C., and Oriel, S.S., 1965, Tectonic development of Idaho-Wyoming thrust belt: American Association of Petroleum Geologists Bulletin, v. 49, p. 1847-1866.

Arrington, Leonard J., 1969, Idaho and The Great Depression: Idaho Yesterdays, v. 13, Summer, 1969, p. 2-8, reprinted in Etulain, R.W., and Marley, B.W., editors, 1974 (3rd printing, 1984), The Idaho Heritage: A collection of historical essays: Pocatello, Idaho, The Idaho State University Press, p. 129-133.

Arrington, L.J., 1974, Charles C. Rich: Mormon General and Western Frontiersman: Provo, Utah, Brigham Young University Press, 386 p.

Arrington, Leonard J., 1979, The Mormon Settlement of Cassia County, Idaho 1873-1921: Idaho Yesterdays, v. 23, no. 2, p. 36-46.

Arrington, Leonard J., 1986, Irrigation in the Snake River Valley: Idaho Yesterdays, v. 30, nos. 1-2, p. 3-11.

Arrington, Leonard J., 1994, History of Idaho, 2 vols.: Moscow, Idaho, University of Idaho Press.

Arrington, L.J., and Jensen, Richard, 1973, Lorenzo Hill Hatch: Pioneer Bishop of Franklin: Idaho Yesterdays, v. 17, no. 2, p. 2-8.

Bandy, Philip J., 1992, Structural and kinematic analysis of the City of Rocks lobe of the Almo Pluton, Cassia Co., Idaho: An application of granite tectonics [M.S. thesis]: Pocatello and Boise, Idaho: Idaho State University and Boise State University, 105 p.

Beal, Merrill D., 1957, The Story of the Utah Northern Railroad: Idaho Yesterdays, v. 1 no. 2, p. 16-23.

Beal, Merrill D., 1980, The Utah & Northern Railroad: Pocatello, Idaho, The Idaho State University Press, 81 p.

Beck, W.A., and Haase, Y.D., 1989, Historical Atlas of the American West: Norman, Oklahoma, University of Oklahoma Press, 78 maps.

Beus, S.S., 1968, Paleozoic stratigraphy of Samaria Mountain, Idaho and Utah: American Association of Petroleum Geologists Bulletin, v. 52, p.782-808.

Bitton, Dennis, 1979, Peopling the upper Snake: The Second Wave of Mormon Settlement in Idaho: Idaho Yesterdays, v. 23, no. 2, p. 47-52.

Bjorklund, L.J., and McGreevy, L.J., 1971, Ground-water resources of Cache Valley, Utah and Idaho: Utah Department of Natural Resources, Technical Publication 36, 72 p.

Boag, P.G., compiler, 1992, Trails, Trappers, Trains, and Travelers: The Economic Development of Southern Bannock County as influenced by transportation: South Bannock County Historical Center, Lava Hot Springs, Idaho 83246, 17 p.

Boag, P. G., 1993, "The Indians of this place are Snakes in the Grass"—The Overlander perspective on Native Americans in southern Idaho, 1836-1860: Idaho Yesterdays, v.37, no. 3, p. p. 16-26.

Bonnichsen, Bill, and Breckenridge, Roy M., editors, 1982, Cenozoic Geology of Idaho: Idaho Bureau of Mines and Geology Bulletin 26, 725 p.

Bright, R.C., 1982, Paleontology of the lacustrine member of the American Falls Lake Beds, southeastern Idaho, in Bonnichsen, Bill and Breckenridge, R.M., editors, Cenozoic Geology of Idaho: Idaho Bureau of Mines and Geology Bulletin 26, p. 597-614.

Brown, Jennie Broughton, 1932, Fort Hall on the Oregon Trail, (with Ferry Butte by Susie Boice Trego): Caldwell, Idaho, The Caxton Printers, Ltd., 466 p.

Burgel, W.D., Rodgers, D.W., and Link, P.K., 1987, Mesozoic and Cenozoic structures of the Pocatello region, southeastern Idaho: in Miller, W.R., editor, The thrust belt revisited, Wyoming Geological Association, 38th Annual Field Conference Guidebook, p. 91-100.

Burnett, Betty, 1985, Goodale's Cutoff: Overland Journal, Winter 1985, p. 30-34.

Carney, Ellen, 1990, Ellis Kackley, Best Damn Doctor in the West: Bend, Oregon, Maverick Publications, 283 p.

Carney, Ellen, 1992, The Oregon Trail: Ruts, Rogues and Reminiscences: Wayan, Idaho, Traildust Publishing Co., 332 p.

Cerling, T.E., Poreda, R.J., and Rathburn, S.L., 1994, Cosmogenic ^{3}He and ^{21}Ne age of the Big Lost River flood, Snake River Plain, Idaho: Geology, v. 22, p. 227-230

Champion, D.E., Kuntz, M.A., and Lefebvre, R.H., 1989, Geologic map of the North Laidlaw Butte quadrangle, Blaine and Butte Counties, Idaho: U.S. Geological Survey Geologic Quadrangle Map GQ-1634, scale 1:24,000.

Coates, L.G., Boag., P.G., Hatzenbuehler, R.L., and Swanson, M.R., 1994, The Mormon Settlement of Southeastern Idaho, 1845-1900:

Codman, John, reprinted 1976, A Trip to Cariboo Mountain: Idaho Yesterdays, v. 19, no. 4, p. 18-24.

Colorado Railroad Museum, 1981, Colorado Rail Annual No. 15, Idaho-Montana Issue, Colorado Railroad Historical Foundation, P.O. Box 10, Golden, Colorado, 80401, 215 p.

Crowder, David L., 1981, Tales of Eastern Idaho: KID Broadcasting Corporation, Idaho Falls, Idaho, 220 p.

Currey, D.R., Atwood, Genevieve, and Mabey, D.R., 1984, Major Levels of Great Salt Lake and Lake Bonneville: Utah Geological and Mineral Survey Map 73, scale 1;750,000.

Darling, R.S., 1985, Mineralization in the Fort Hall Mining District, Bannock County, Idaho: in Kerns, G.J. and Kerns, R. L., Jr., editors, Orogenic patterns and stratigraphy of north-central Utah and southeastern Idaho: Utah Geological Association Publication 14, p. 167-173.

Derig, Betty, 1972, Celestials in the Diggings: Idaho Yesterdays, v. 16, no. 3, p. 2-23.

Dion, N.P., 1969, Hydrologic reconnaissance of the Bear River Basin in southeastern Idaho: Idaho Department of Reclamation, Water Information Bulletin 13, 66 p.

Dixon, J.S., 1982, Regional structural synthesis, Wyoming salient of Western Overthrust Belt, American Association of Petroleum Geologists Bulletin, v. 66, no. 10, p. 1560-1580.

Downing, Glenn Ray, 1991, Days out of Doors: A Portneuf Valley Chronicle: Pocatello, Idaho, Glenn Ray Downing 960 Wayne Ave, Pocatello, Id. 83201, 295 p.

Dykes, Fred W., 1985, A view of Idaho history as seen from Big Butte: unpublished, Fred. W. Dykes, Box 4414, Pocatello Id 83205-4414, 17 p.

Dykes, Fred W., 1989, Jeffrey's Cutoff; Idaho's forgotten Oregon Trail route: Fred. W. Dykes, Box 4414, Pocatello Idaho 83205-4414.

Eliason, Carol, and Hubbard, Mary, 1987, Holbrook and surrounding areas history book 1878-1987: Holbrook, Idaho, 491 p.

Etulain, R.W., and Marley, B.W., editors, 1974 (3rd printing, 1984), The Idaho Heritage: A collection of historical essays: Pocatello, Idaho, Idaho State University Press, 230 p.

Evans, J.H., 1936, Charles Coulson Rich: Pioneer Builder of the West: New York, Macmillan Co., 400 p.

Evenson, E.B., Cotter, J.F.P., and Clinch, J.M., 1982, Glaciation of the Pioneer Mountains: A proposed model for Idaho: in Bonnichsen, Bill, and Breckenridge, R.M., editors, Cenozoic Geology of Idaho, Idaho Bureau of Mines and Geology Bulletin 26, p. 653-665.

Evenson, E.B., Breckenridge, R.M., and Stephens, G.C., 1988, Field Guides to the Quaternary Geology of Central Idaho: in Link, P.K., and Hackett, W.R., editors, Guidebook to the Geology of Central and Southern Idaho: Idaho Geological Survey Bulletin 27, p. 201-244.

Farnworth, Jo Ann, 1993, Montpelier and the Oregon Short Line: Montpelier, Idaho, 85 p.

Fiesinger, D.W., Perkins, W.D. and Puchy, B.J., 1982, Mineralogy and Petrology of Tertiary-Quaternary Volcanic Rocks in Caribou County, Idaho, in Bonnichsen, Bill, and Breckenridge, R.M., editors, Cenozoic Geology of Idaho: Idaho Bureau of Mines and Geology Bulletin 26, p. 465-488.

Fisher, F.S., and Johnson, K.M., editors, 1995, Geology and Mineral Resource Assessment of the Challis 1° x 2° Quadrangle, Idaho: U.S. Geological Survey Professional Paper 1525, 204 p.

Foote, Mary Hallock, 1972, A Victorian Gentlewoman in the Far West, edited by Rodman W. Paul: San Marino, California, The Huntington Library, 416 p.

Gittins, H. Leigh, 1976, Idaho's Gold Road: Moscow Idaho, The University Press of Idaho, 165 p.

Gittins, H. Leigh, 1983, Pocatello Portrait: The Early Years, 1878 to 1928: Moscow, Idaho, The University Press of Idaho, 224 p.

Green, Roberta H., 1992, They Passed This Way: Summerhouse Press, P.O. Box 770, Challis, Idaho 83226, 56 p.

Greenwood, Annie Pike, 1934, reprinted 1988, We Sagebrush Folks: Moscow, Idaho, University of Idaho Press, 489p.

Hackett, W.R., Pelton, J., and Brockway, C., 1986, Geohydrologic story of the eastern Snake River Plain and the Idaho National Engineering Laboratory: Idaho Falls, Idaho: U.S. Department of Energy, Idaho Operations Office, Idaho National Engineering Laboratory, 32 p.

Hackett, William R., and Smith, Richard P., 1992, Quaternary volcanism, tectonics, and sedimentation in the Idaho National Engineering Laboratory area: in Wilson, J.R., editor, Field guide to geologic excursions in Utah and adjacent areas of Nevada, Idaho, and Wyoming: Utah Geological Survey Miscellaneous Publication 92-3, p. 1-18.

Haines, A.L., ed., 1965, Osborne Russell's Journal of a Trapper: University of Nebraska Press, 191 p.

Hale, L.A., editor, 1967, Anatomy of the Western Phosphate Field: Salt Lake City, Intermountain Association of Geologists, 15th Annual Field Conference Guidebook, 287 p.

Hansen, Sam, and others, 1984, Hard times in Iaho between the great wars: Pocatello, Idaho, Idaho State University Press (reprinted from Rendezvous, Idaho State University Journal of Arts and Letters, volume XX, no. 1), 90 p.

Harder, E. B. and Harder, H. K. (compilers), 1982, Seventy-five years at Aberdeen: A History of the First Mennonite Church, Aberdeen, Idaho: First Mennonite Church, P. O. Box 246, Aberdeen, Idaho, 83210, 383 p.

Harstad, P.T., 1972, Reminiscences of Oscar Sonnenkalb, Idaho Surveyor and Pioneer: Pocatello, Idaho, Idaho State University Press, 66 p.

Hart, Newell, 1973 (reprinted 1986), Hometown Album: Preston, Idaho, Cache Valley Newsletter Publishing Co.

Hatzenbuehler, Ron, 1994, Idaho migration and settlement: in Idaho and the American West, Boise, Idaho Humanities Council, p. 14-15.

Hayden, F.V., 1883, Twelfth Annual Report of the U.S. Geological and Geographical Survey of the Territories—Wyoming & Idaho, for the year 1878: Washington, Government Printing Office.

Hearst, Jonena, M., 1990, Paleontology and depositional setting of the Duck Point local fauna (Late Pleistocene, Rancholabrean) Power County, Southeastern Idaho: M.S. Thesis, Pocatello, Idaho, Idaho State University, 275 p.

Hladky, F.R., Kellogg, K.S., Oriel, S.S., Link, P.K., Nielson, J.W., and Amerman, R.E., 1992, Geologic map of the eastern part of the Fort Hall Indian Reservation, Bannock, Bingham, and Caribou Counties, Idaho: U.S. Geological Survey Miscellaneous Investigations Series Map I-2006, scale 1:50,000.

Hope, A.C., 1990, Hudspeth Cutoff, Idaho's legacy of Wheels: Idaho Falls, Idaho, Bookshelf Bindery and Press, P.O. Box 2204, Idaho Falls, Idaho, 222 p.

Howard, Minnie F., 1928, Early life and times of the First Congregational Church of Pocatello: Pocatello, Idaho, The Tribune Co. 65 p.

Howell, Glade F., 1960, Early history of Malad Valley: M.A. Thesis, Department of History, Brigham Young University, 130 p.

Huerta, Audrey D., 1992, Lake Creek Fault: Evidence of Pre-Challis shear within south-central Idaho: M.S. Thesis, Pocatello, Idaho, Idaho State University, 57 p.

Idaho State Historical Society, 1976, Idaho: An Illustrated History: Boise, Idaho, Idaho State Historical Society, 250 p.

Idaho Humanities Council, 1994, Idaho and the American West, Boise, Idaho, 36p.

Idaho Yesterdays, 1986, Special Issue: Irrigation in Idaho, v. 30, no. 1-2, 76 p.

Jarrett, R. D., and Malde, H. E., 1987, Paleodischarge of the late Pleistocene Bonneville Flood, Snake River Idaho, computed from new evidence: Geological Society of America Bulletin v. 99, p. 127-134.

Johnson, Elaine S. and Carney, Ellen, The Mountain: Carriboo and other Gold Camps in Idaho, 1990, Maverick Publications, Inc. P.O. Box 5007, Bend Oregon, 97708, 245 p.

Kerns, G.L., and Kerns, R.L., Jr., editors, 1985, Orogenic patterns and stratigraphy of north-central Utah and Southeastern Idaho: Utah Geological Association Publication 14, 329.

King, P.B., 1977, The Evoution of North America, revised dition, Princeton, New Jersey, Princeton University Press, 197 p.

Kissane, Leedice, 1983, Pocatello Memories, Pocatello, Idaho: The Idaho State University Press, 129 p.

Kuntz, M.A., and twelve others, 1992, Geologic map of the Idaho National Engineering Laboratory and adjoining areas, eastern Idaho: U.S. Geological Survey Miscellaneous Investigations Series Map I-2320, scale 1:100,000.

Kuntz, M.A., Champion, D.E., and Lefebvre, R.H., 1987, Geology of the Craters of the Moon lava field, Idaho: in Beus, S.S., editor, Rocky Mountain Section of the Geological Society of America: Boulder, Colorado, Geological Society of America Centennial Field Guide, Volume 2, p. 123-126.

Kuntz, M.A., Champion, D.E., Lefebvre, R.H., and Covington, H.R., 1988, Geologic map of the Craters of the Moon, Kings Bowl, and Wapi lava fields and the Great Rift volcanic rift zone, south-central Idaho: U.S. Geological Survey Miscellaneous Investigations Series Map I-1632, scale 1:24,000.

Kuntz, M.A., Lefebvre, R.H., and Champion, D.E., 1989, Geologic map of the Watchman quadrangle, Butte County, Idaho: U.S. Geological Survey Geologic Quadrangle Map GQ-1633, scale 1:24,000.

Kuntz, M.A., Champion, D.E., and Lefebvre, R.H., 1990, Geologic map of the Fissure Butte quadrangle, Blaine and Butte Counties, Idaho: U.S. Geological Survey Geologic Quadrangle Map GQ-1635, scale 1:24,000.

Lavender, David S., 1965, The Great West: New York, N.Y., American Heritage Publishing Co.

Liljeblad, Sven, 1959, Indian People of Idaho, in S. Beal and M. Wells, eds., History of Idaho: Pocatello, Lewis Historical Publishing, p. 29-59.

Liljeblad, Sven, 1960, The Indians of Idaho: Idaho Yesterdays, v. 4, no. 3, p. 22-28.

Link, P.K., 1982, Geology of the Pocatello Formation (Upper Proterozoic) and geologic mapping in the Bannock Range, southeastern Idaho [Ph.D. Thesis]: Santa Barbara, University of California, 131 p.

Link, P.K., 1987, The Late Proterozoic Pocatello Formation: A record of continental rifting and glacial marine sedimentation, Portneuf Narrows, southeastern Idaho: in Beus, S.S., editor, Rocky Mountain Section of the Geological Society of America, Centennial Field Guide volume 2, p. 139-143.

Link, P.K., ed., 1994, Hydrogeology, Waste Disposal, Science and Politics: Proceedings of the 30th Symposium on Engineering Geology and Geotechnical Engineering: Pocatello, Idaho, College of Engineering, Idaho State University, 652 p.

Link, P.K., and Hackett, W.R., editors, 1988, Guidebook to the geology of central and southern Idaho: Idaho Geological Survey Bulletin 27, 318 p.

Link, P.K., and Smith, L.H., 1992, Late Proterozoic and Early Cambrian stratigraphy, paleobiology, and tectonics: Northern Utah and southeastern Idaho: in Wilson, J.R., editor, Field Guide to Geologic Excursions in Utah and Adjacent Areas of Nevada, Idaho, and Wyoming: Utah Geological Survey Miscellaneous Publication 92-3, p. 461-481.

Link, P.K., Jansen, S.T., Halimdihardja, P., Lande. and Zahn, P., 1987, Stratigraphy of the Brigham Group (Late Proterozoic-Cambrian), Bannock, Portneuf, and Bear River Ranges, southeastern Idaho: in Miller, W.R., editor, The thrust belt revisited: Wyoming Geological Association, 38th annual field conference guidebook, p. 133-148.

Link, P.K., Mahoney, J.B., McCalpin, J, Henkelman, J.J., and Smith, B.L., 1987, Field trip roadlog for the Bear River Landslide Complex: in Robinson, Lee, editor, Proceedings of the 23rd Symposium on Engineering Geology and Soils Engineering, Logan, Utah, 334-352 p.

Link, P.K., Nielson, J.W., McDonald, C., and Smith, J.L., 1990, History and geology of the J.R. Simplot Company Gay Mine, Bingham County, Idaho: in Robinson, Lee, editor, 1990 Symposium on Engineering Geology and Geotechnical Engineering, Pocatello, Idaho, p. 24-1 to 24-12.

Link, P.K., Kuntz, M.A., and Platt, L.B., editors, 1992, Regional Geology of Eastern Idaho and Western Wyoming: Geological Society of America Memoir 179, 310 p.

Link, P.K., Warren, Ian, Preacher, J.M., and Skipp, Betty, 1996, Stratigraphic analysis and interpretation of the Mississippian Copper Basin Group, McGowan Creek Formation, and White Knob Limestone, south-central Idaho: in Longman, M.W., and Sonnenfeld, M.D. eds., 1996, Paleozoic Systems of the Rocky Mountain Region: Rocky Mountain Section SEPM (Society for Sedimentary Geology), Denver, p. 117-144.

Lohse, E.S., and Holmer, R.N., editors, 1990 (2nd printing 1992), Fort Hall and the Shoshone-Bannock: Pocatello, Idaho, The Idaho State University Press, 60 p.

Lovin, Hugh T., 1985, Free Enterprise and large-scale reclamation on the Twin Falls-North Side Tract, 1907-1930, Idaho Yesterdays, v. 29, no. 1, p. 2-14.

Mabey, Don, 1979, The Bend of Bear River. Bountiful, Utah, Horizon Publishers and Distributors, 136 p.

Madsen, B.D., 1958, The Bannock of Idaho: Caldwell, Idaho, The Caxton Printers Ltd., 382 p.

Madsen, B.D., 1980, The Northern Shoshoni: Caldwell, Idaho, The Caxton Printers, Ltd., 259 p.

Madsen, B. D., 1985, The Shoshoni Frontier and the Bear River Massacre: Salt Lake City, University of Utah Press.

Madsen, B.D., 1986, Chief Pocatello: The "White Plume": Salt Lake City, University of Utah Press, 142 p.

Madsen, B. D., 1993, The "Almo Massacre" revisited: Idaho Yesterdays, v. 37, no. 3, p. 54-64.

Mahoney, J.B., Link, P.K., Henkelman, J.J., McCalpin, J., and Smith, B.L., 1987, The Bear River Landslide Complex, Preston, Idaho: Geologic considerations and historical perspectives: in McCalpin, J., editor, Proceedings of the 23rd Symposium on engineering geology and soils engineering: Boise, Idaho, Idaho Department of Transportation, p. 306-353.

Mahoney, J.B., Link, P.K., Burton, B.R., Geslin, J.K., and O'Brien, J.P., 1991, Pennsylvanian and Permian Sun Valley Group, Wood River Basin, South-Central Idaho: in Cooper, J.D., and Stevens, C.H., eds., Paleozoic Paleogeography of the Western United States—II: Pacific Section, Society of Economic Paleontologists and Mineralogists Publication 67, p. 551-579.

Malde, H.E., 1968, The catastrophic late Pleistocene Bonneville Flood in the Snake River Plain, Idaho: U.S. Geological Survey Professional Paper 596, 52 p.

Malde, H.E., 1987, Shoshone Falls, Idaho; A Pleistocene relic of the catastrophic Bonneville Flood: in Beus, S.S., editor, Rocky Mountain Section of the Geological Society of America: Boulder, Colorado, Geological Society of America Centennial Field Guide, Volume 2, p. 135-138.

Malde, H.,E., 1991, Quaternary geology and structural history of the Snake River Plain, Idaho and Oregon: in Morrison, R.B., editor, Quaternary Nonglacial Geology: Conterminous U.S., Boulder, Colorado, Geological Society of America, The Geology of North America, volume K-2, p. 251-281.

Malde, H.E., and Powers, H.A., 1972, Geologic map of the Glenns Ferry—Hagerman area, west-central Snake River Plain, Idaho: U.S. Geological Survey Miscellaneous Geologic Investigations Map I-696, scale 1:48,000.

Maley, Terry, 1987, Exploring Idaho Geology: Mineral Land Publications, P.O. Box 1186, Boise, Idaho, 83701, 232 p.

Mansfield, G.R., 1927, Geography, geology and mineral resources of part of southeastern Idaho, with descriptions of Carboniferous and Triassic fossils, by G.H. Girty: U.S. Geological Survey Professional Paper 152, 453 p.

Maughan, Ralph W., 1992, Anatomy of the Snake River Plain: An Amateur's View: Pocatello, Idaho, The Idaho State University Press, 69 p.

McCarthy, Max R., 1987, The Last Chance Canal Company: Provo, Utah, Brigham Young University Charles Redd Center for Western Studies, Monograph no. 16, 131p.

McCoy, W.D., 1987, Quaternary aminostratigraphy of the Bonneville Basin, western United States: Geological Society of America Bulletin, v. 98, p. 99-112.

McCurry, M., Estes, M., Fromm, J., Welhan, J., and Barrash, Warren, 1994, Three-dimensional chemical structure of the INEL aquifer system near the Idaho Chemical Processing Plant: in Link, P.K., ed., Hydrogeology, Waste Disposal, Science and Politics, Proceedings 30th Symposium, Engineering Geology and Geotechnical Engineering, College of Engineering, Idaho State University, p. 207-219.

Miller, W.R., ed., The thrust belt revisited: Wyoming Geological Association, Casper, 38TH Annual Field Conference Guidebook.

Merkley, Anne, 1994, Cultural Contrast and Material Change: The Wrensted-Garvey Photographs of Northern Shoshone and Bannock Indians: M.A. Thesis, Department of Anthropology, Idaho State University, 296 p.

Merrill, I. R., 1990, Tim Goodale and his cutoff: A major trail segment during and after the fourth emigration wave: Overland Journal, v. 8, no. 3, p. 9-16.

Miller, D.M., Armstrong, R.L., Compton, R.R., and Todd, V.R., 1983, Geology of the Albion-Raft River-Grouse Creek Mountains area, northwestern Utah and southern Idaho: in Gurgel, K.D., editor, Geologic excursions in the Overthrust Belt and Metamorphic Core Complexes of the Intermountain Region: Utah Geological and Mineral Survey, Special Studies 59, p. 1-62.

Morgan, D.L., 1987, The State of Deseret: Logan, Utah, Utah State University Press, 201p.

Mytton, James, W., Williams, Paul L., and Morgan, William A., 1990, Geologic map of the Stricker 4 Quadrangle, Cassia County, Idaho: U.S. Geological Survey Miscellaneous Investigations Series, Map I-2052, scale 1:48,000.

Norvich, R.F., and Larson, A.L., 1970, A reconnaissance of the water resources in the Portneuf River Basin, Idaho: Idaho Department of Reclamation, Water Information Bulletin 16, 58 p.

O'Connor, J.E., 1990, Hydrology, hydraulics, and sediment transport of Pleistocene Lake Bonneville flooding on the Snake River, Idaho:(PhD. thesis): Tucson, Arizona, University of Arizona, 192 p.

O'Connor, J.E., 1993, Hydrology, hydraulics, and geomorphology of the Bonneville flood: Geological Society of America Special Paper 274, 83p.

O'Connor, J.E. and Baker, V.R., 1992, Magnitudes and implications of peak discharges from Glacial Lake Missoula: Geological Society of America Bulletin, v. 104, p. 267-279.

Olinger, J.C., 1991, A Place of Conscience: Camp Downey, Pocatello, Idaho, Idaho State University Press, 61p.

Oriel, S.S., and Platt, L. B., 1980, Geologic map of the Preston 1° x 2° quadrangle, southeastern Idaho and western Wyoming: U.S. Geological Survey Miscellaneous Investigations Map I-1127, scale 1:250,000.

Oriel, S.S., and Armstrong, F.C., 1986, Tectonic development of Idaho-Wyoming thrust belt: Authors' commentary, in Peterson, J.A., editor, Paleotectonics and sedimentation: American Association of Petroleum Geologists Memoir 41, p. 267-279.

Palmer, Tim, 1991, The Snake River: Window to the West: Washington D.C., Island Press, 320 p.

Paul, Rodman W., 1975, When culture came to Boise: Mary Hallock Foote in Idaho: Idaho Yesterdays, v. 20, no. 2, p. 2-12.

Peterson, F.Ross, 1976, Idaho: A Bicentennial History: New York, Norton.

Peterson, F. Ross, 1994, Water and Agriculture: The Idaho Story: *in* Idaho and the American West, Boise,Idaho, Idaho Humanities Council, p. 21-26.

Pierce, K.L., and Morgan, L.A., 1992, The track of the Yellowstone hot spot: Volcanism, faulting, and uplift, *in* Link, P.K., Kuntz, M.A., and Platt, L.B., editors, Regional Geology of Eastern Idaho and Western Wyoming: Geological Society of America Memoir 179, p. 1-53.

Poulsen, E.J., 1962, Robert Price: Salt Lake City, Granite Publishing Company, 179p. .

Ralston, D.R., and six others, 1980, Interactions of mining and water resource systems in the southeastern Idaho Phosphate Field: Idaho Water Resources Research Institute Research Technical Completion Report, Project C-7651, Moscow, Idaho, University of Idaho, 214 p.

Ralston, D.R., and six others, 1983, Thermal Ground Water Flow Systems in the Thrust Zone in southeastern Idaho: Idaho Water and Energy Resources Research Institute, Research Technical Completion Report, Moscow, Idaho, University of Idaho, 336 p.

Rathbun, Sara L., 1993, Pleistocene cataclysmic flooding along the Big Lost River, east central Idaho: Geomorphology, v. 8, p. 305-319.

Reisner, Marc, 1986, Cadillac Desert: New York, New York,Penguin Books, 582 p.

Reitzes, L.B., 1981, Paris: A Look at Idaho Architecture: Boise, Idaho State Historical Preservation Office, 104 p.

Ricks, J.E., ed., 1956, The History of a Valley: Cache Valley, Utah-Idaho: Logan, Utah, Cache Valley Centennial Commission, 504 p.

Rodenbaugh,E.F., 1953, Sketches of Idaho Geology, Caldwll, Idaho, Caxton Printers, Ltd., 267p.

Rodgers, D.W., Hackett, W.R., and Ore, H.T., 1990, Extension of the Yellowstone Plateau, eastern Snake River Plain, and Owyhee Plateau: Geology, v. 18, p. 1138-1141.

Saltzer, S.D., and Hodges, K.V., 1988, The Middle Mountain shear zone, southern Idaho: Kinematic analysis of an early Tertiary high-temperature detachment: Geological Society of American Bulletin, v. 100, p. 96-103.

Schwantes, Carlos, 1991, In Mountain Shadows: A History of Idaho: Lincoln, Nebraska, University of Nebraska Press.

Schwarze, D.M., 1960, Geology of the Lava Hot Springs area, Idaho: Occasional Papers of the Idaho State College Museum, Pocatello, Number 4, 51 p.

Scott, W.E., 1982, Surficial geologic map of the eastern Snake River Plain and adjacent areas, 111° to 115° W., Idaho and Wyoming: U.S. Geological Survey Miscellaneous Investigations Series Map I-1372, scale 1:250,000.

Scott, W.E., Pierce, K.L., Bradbury, J.P., and Forester, R.M., 1982, Revised Quaternary stratigraphy and chronology in the American Falls area, southeastern Idaho, *in* Bonnichsen, Bill, and Breckenridge, R.M., editors, Cenozoic Geology of Idaho, Idaho Bureau of Mines and Geology Bulletin 26, p. 581-595.

Simmonds, A.J., 1980, Southeast Idaho as a Pioneer Mormon Safety Valve: Idaho Yesterdays, v. 23, no. 4, p. 20-30.

Simmonds, A.J., 1988, Idaho's Last Colony: Northern Cache Valley under the Test Oath, 1972-1896: Idaho Yesterdays, v. 32, no. 2, p. 2-14.

South Bannock Historical Center, 1990, A Century of Transition, 1890-1990, Pocatello, Idaho State University Press, 32 p.

Stearns, H.T., Crandall, L., and Steward, W.G., 1938, Geology and groundwater resources of the Snake River Plain in southeastern Idaho: U.S. Geological Survey Water Supply Paper 774, 268 p.

Stegner, Wallace, 1964 (reprinted 1971) The gathering of Zion: The story of the Mormon Trail: New York, McGraw Hill Book Company, 331 p.

Stegner, Wallace, 1971 (reprinted 1992), Angle of Repose: New York, Penguin Books, 569 p.

Swanson, Earl H., 1972, Birch Creek: Human Ecology in the Cool Desert of the Northern Rocky Mountains, 9000 B.C.-A.D. 1850: Pocatello, Idaho, The Idaho State University Press.

Swanson, Earl, 1957, "Since time immemorial . . . " The Problem of Shoshone Chronology: Idaho Yesterdays, v. 1, no. 4, p. 21-26.

Swetnam, Susan Hendricks, 1991, Lives of the Saints in southeast Idaho: An Introduction to Mormon Pioneer Life Story Writing: Moscow, Idaho, University of Idaho Press, 188 p.

Taylor, Dorice, 1980, Sun Valley: Sun Valley, Idaho, ExLibris, Sun Valley, Idaho 83353, 264 p.

The Chesterfield Foundation, Inc. 1982, Chesterfield: Mormon outpost in Idaho: The Chesterfield Foundation Inc, Rural Route, Bancroft Idaho, 83217.

Trimble, D.E., 1976, Geology of the Michaud and Pocatello quadrangles, Bannock and Power Counties, Idaho: U.S. Geological Survey Bulletin 1400, 88 p.

van Dandt, F.K., 1966, Boundaries of the United States and the several states: U.S. Geological Survey Bulletin 1212, 291 p.

Ward, Laurie, 1982, Bannock Valley: Keith W. Watkins and Sons, Inc., Providence UT 84332, 322 p.

Weeks., F.B., and Heikes, V.C., 1908, Notes on the Fort Hall mining district, Idaho: U.S. Geological Survey Bulletin 340, p. 175-183.

Wells, M.W., 1966, Walla Walla's Vision of a Greater Washington: Idaho Yesterdays, v. 10, no. 3, p. 20-31.

Wells, M.W., 1978, Anti-Mormonism in Idaho, 1872-92: Provo, Utah, Brigham Young University Press, 197 p.

Wells, Merle W., 1983, Gold Camps and Silver Cities; Nineteenth century mining in central and southern Idaho (2nd edition): Idaho Bureau of Mines and Geology Bulletin 22, 165 p.

Whitehead, R.L., 1986, Geohydrologic framework of the Snake River Plain, Idaho and eastern Oregon: U.S. Geological Survey Hydrologic Investigations Atlas HA-681, scale 1:1,000,000.

Whitehead, R.L., 1992, Geohydrologic Framework of the Snake River Plain Regional Aquifer System, Idaho and Eastern Oregon, U.S. Geological Survey Professional Paper 1408-B, 32 p.

Whitehead, R.L., and Covington, H.R., 1987, Thousand Springs area near Hagerman, Idaho, *in* Beus, S.S., editor, Rocky Mountain Section of the Geological Society of America: Boulder, (Colorado, Geological Society of America Centennial Field Guide, Volume 2, p.131-134.

Williams, P.L., Covington, H.R., and Pierce, K.L., 1982, Cenozoic stratigraphy and tectonic evolution of the Raft River Basin, Idaho: *in* Bonnichsen, B., and Breckenridge, R.M., eds., Cenozoic geology of Idaho: Idaho Bureau of Mines and Geology Bulletin 26, p. 491-504.

Williams, P.L., Mytton, J.W., and Covington, H.R., 1990, Geologic map of the Stricker 1 quadrangle, Cassia, Twin Falls, and Jerome Counties, Idaho: U.S. Geological Survey Miscellaneous Investigations Series Map I-2078, scale 1:24,000.

Worl, R.G., Kiilsgaard, T.H., Bennett, E.H., Link, P.K., Lewis, R.S., Mitchell, V.E., Johnson, K.M., and Snyder, L.D., 1991, Geologic map of the Hailey 1° x 2° quadrangle, Idaho: U.S. Geoical Survey Open-File report 91-340, scale 1:250,000.

Worl, R.G., Link, P.K., Winkler, G.R., and Johnson, K.M., editors, 1995, Geology and Mineral Resources of the Hailey 1° x 2° Quadrangle and the western part of the Idaho Falls 1° x 2° Quadrangle, Idaho: U.S. Geological Survey Bulletin 2064, Chapters A-R.

Wright, Bessie, M., Oakley, Idaho, Cassia County, Pioneer Town: 1987, Horizon Publishers, Bountiful, Utah, 211 p.

Wrigley, R.L., Jr., 1942, The Occupational Structure of Pocatello, Idaho [Ph.D. dissertation]: Chicago, Illinois,University of Chicago Libraries, 211 p.

Wrigley, R.L., Jr., 1943, The Early History of Pocatello, Idaho: Pacific Northwest Quarterly, v. 34, p. 353-365.

Wyndham, Harald, editor, 1986, Famous Potatoes, Southeast Idaho Poetry: Pocatello, Idaho, Blue Scarab Press, 243 S. 8th Avenue, Pocatello, Idaho 83201, 64 p.

Wyndham, Harald, editor, 1989, Things to do in Idaho: Pocatello, Idaho, Blue Scarab Press, 243 S. 8th Avenue, Pocatello, Idaho 83201, 40 p.

Pocatello High School looking west from Arthur Ave., 1920s. Bannock County Historical Society collection.

UNION PACIFIC SHOP EMPLOYEES — POCATELLO, IDAHO. 1936.

Index

26 Index

Preston 2, 22, 30, 32, 33, 48, 53, 54, 58, 62, 63, 78, 80, 87, 94-99, 112
Preston, Bishop Wm. B., 97
Preuss Range 76, 81
Promontory Point 51, 53
Protestants 122
Provo level 30, 94
Provo shoreline 27, 28, 30, 95, 96
Provo, Utah 49, 74, 78, 90, 99, 164
Pullman 172
Putnam Mountain 13, 43, 104

Q

Queen of the Hills (silver mine, Bellevue) 170
Queen's Crown 147, 169

R

rabbit 164
Raft Formation 150
Raft River 10, 17, 32, 43, 57, 72, 100, 101, 159, 160, 161
Raft River Mountains 17
Railroad YMCA 124
Rainey, Joe 141
Rainey Park 128
Ramsey Transfer 58, 59, 130
Rapid Creek 106
Raymond Canyon, Wyoming 15
Raymond Park 115
Red Hill 3, 2, 29, 113, 115, 125, 127, 132, 133, 135
red light district 131
Red Rock Butte 28
Red Rock Pass 27, 28, 30, 38, 54, 95, 97, 99, 108
Register Rock 44, 158
Rendezvous 39, 41, 138, 156
Reorganized LDS Church (Josephites) 102
Republican 48, 49, 118, 127, 128, 16
residence time 31, 32
Rexburg 47, 49, 58, 62, 63, 72, 73
rhyolite dome 22, 84, 144, 145, 146
Rich, Charles C., 47, 76, 78
right of way 54, 57, 58, 103, 105, 108, 109, 112, 116, 117, 130, 153
river hawthorne 105
Riverdale 54, 97, 98
Riverside Hotel 115
Roadside Geology of Idaho 21, 33
Robbers Roost Creek 51
Rock Creek 1, 20, 165
Rockland 100, 152, 160

Rockland Valley 152, 160
Rocky Mountains 10, 37, 40, 77, 171
Roosevelt, Theodore 117
Roosevelt, Franklin Delano 129, 147
Root Hog 43, 145
Ross Fork 85, 127, 141, 142
Ross Fork Agency 54
Ross Mountain 103
Ross Park 36, 107, 127, 128
roundhouse 55, 59, 61, 66, 77, 116, 130, 173
Rucker, Jack 85
Rupert 33, 47, 71
Russell, Osborne 76, 79, 95, 101, 103
RWMC (Radioactive Waste Management Complex) 146

S

Sacramento 53
Sagwich (Chief) 102
Saint Charles 76
Salmon City 47, 148
Salmon Falls Creek 72
Salmon River 12, 17, 36, 68, 69, 148
Salmon River arch 17
Salmon River Mountains 12
Salt Lake City 6, 11, 20, 22, 26-28, 30, 32-33, 37, 44, 47, 49, 50, 53, 62-63, 68, 71, 76, 78-80, 88, 95, 96, 101-102, 159
Salt Lake Formation 22
Salvucci, Mrs. Dominic 138
Samaria 101
Samaria Mountain 100, 101, 102
San Bernardino 47, 77
San Diego 46
St. Joseph's Catholic Church (Pocatello) 115, 121, 122, 124
St. Andrews Episcopal Church (Pocatello) 121
St. Anthony (town) 40
St. Anthony Catholic Church (Pocatello) 122
Sawtooth Mountains 25, 169
Scadden, W.A. 141
Schaffgotsch, Count Felix, 171
Scout Mountain 13, 30, 102, 103, 104, 127, 136
Seattle Ridge Lodge 168
Second Advent of Christ 79
Secretary of the Interior 59
Sevier orogeny 12
Shanghai Chinese Restaurant (Pocatello) 121
Shaw Building (Pocatello) 131
sheep 37, 70, 74, 85, 87, 100, 104, 122, 141, 151, 165,

171, 173
Sheep Rock 11, 43, 79, 80, 86
Sheepeater 37
Sheepskin Road 141
Shoshone (Indians) 36-38, 169-171
Shoshone (town) 11, 22, 58
Shoshone Falls 71, 162, 163, 165, 166, 173
Shoshoni 36, 37, 48, 57, 80, 96, 102, 156
Sierra Nevada 26, 43, 44, 6
Silent City of Rocks 18, 44, 45, 158, 159, 160, 161
silver 14, 17, 58, 82, 93, 168, 170, 172-173
Silver Bow, Montana 58
Simplot, J.R. (Company) 14, 32, 82, 116, 128, 130, 142, 143
Simplot Square 116, 130
Skaggs Brothers 152
slag 14
Slight Canyon 78
Smith, Arco 148
Smith, Joseph 46, 48, 49, 77, 102
Smoky Canyon 14, 82, 143
Smoky Mountains 17, 171
Snake River 28, 30, 40, 41, 43, 47, 49, 50, 55, 58, 68, 69, 72, 73, 87, 89, 95, 109, 128, 140-142, 151, 154, 159, 162, 165
Snake River Plain 1, 3-6, 10-12, 15, 17, 21, 22, 24, 27, 31, 32, 33, 36, 44, 53, 54, 70, 71, 74, 101, 103, 107, 112, 133, 138, 144-147, 149, 153, 156, 161, 163, 166
Snake River Plain Aquifer 4, 31, 32, 70, 144, 146, 147, 156, 166
Snake River Plain-Columbia Plateau Province 12
Snake River Plain-Yellowstone Hot Spot 4, 10, 12, 21-24, 27, 32, 107, 149
Snaky Canyon Formation 13
Soda Point Reservoir 79, 80, 81
Soda Springs 10, 11, 14, 15, 20, 22, 27, 43, 44, 53, 78-86, 95, 97, 99, 101, 143, 165
Soda Springs Cemetery 80, 85, 90
Sonnenkalb, Oscar 47-49, 63, 69, 74, 86, 88, 90, 99, 102, 117, 126, 138, 151
Sousa, John Philip 177
South Fork of Circle Creek (Silent City of Rocks) 159
South Lincoln St. (Pocatello) 126
South Pass 43, 44, 83
southeastern Idaho 1, 2, 11, 12, 15, 28, 32, 33, 47, 49, 78, 91, 92, 99, 101-103, 109, 132, 138, 156, 166
Southern Branch of the University of Idaho 132, 134
Southern Pacific 155
Spain 39, 40, 47
Spheroidal weathering 22

Hood Building, built 1893, at corner of North Main and West Lander, downtown Pocatello, looking north on Main, mid-1920s. The facade of this building was covered with plastic in the 1960s. After J.C. Penney moved to the Pine Ridge Mall, the building stood empty for over 10 years. In 1994 it was purchased by the City of Pocatello. After being condemned, the building was razed in May, 1996. The Chief Foundation plans to build a Theater and Convention Facility on the site. Bannock County Historical Society Collection.

Pocatello Tribune paper boys and staff, 1929 or 1930. Photo taken in front of Zwiegert Packing Co. meat market on West Center Street, across from the Bannock Hotel. Bannock County Historical Society Collection.

View of Bannock Hotel, Spring, late 1920's, taken from the Whitman Hotel building, downtown Pocatello. Kinport Peak is on the skyline in the center of the view. Note the bank of snow in the upper left part of photo that is shaped like the number 7. It is said that, in those years when there is enough snow for the "7" to form, you can plant your garden in Pocatello without fear of frost damage when the "7" becomes visible. The growing season is less than 90 days. Summer begins only when the snowbank melts away (in mid-May or early June). In the center of the view is the U.S. Court House, built in 1916, and enlarged in 1920. It is now home of Dudley's Sports Bar. To its left are the Telephone Building (light-colored, across street), the Kasiska Building (behind the chimney) and the Benson Hotel (in shadow in corner). To its right is the Bannock Hotel and, in front of it, the Valentine Building. Bannock County Historical Society Collection.

Hotel Bannock Employees 1936   75 Reasons Why Our Service Is Better

Bannock Hotel Employees, 1936. The Bannock was a first class hotel, in the grand style. Photo was taken in the old Elks Club Lodge Room, North Arthur, Pocatello. In the center of the front row is S.E. Brady, owner of the Bannock Hotel. Bannock County Historical Society Collection.

Flood of Portneuf River, mid-February 1962. Aerial view looks south at the north end of Pocatello. The flood was caused by heavy rain on snow-covered and frozen ground in the Gem Valley area. It led to the construction of the concrete channel through downtown Pocatello.

The straight road on the right is Gathe Drive, with the West Bench (Valleyview Dr. and Highland Blvd.) behind. The West Pocatello subdivision (between Oakwood Dr. and Foothill Blvd. is in the distance across the flooded ground near the river. In the middle center is where Main and Arthur come together. In the foreground, on the northeast side of the river, are the stockyards. Above them and closer to the river is the north end of the Pacific Fruit Express facility, and above that, on the far side of the railroad is a large metal building of Gate City Steel.

The curving road immediately left of the river and west of the track is the original route of U.S. Highway 30. The large white building with the peaked roof, surrounded by flood waters, is the old El Rio Club, which was a bar and gambling hall at a time when neither activity was legal. Photo courtesy of Doug Madden.